W9-AOP-360

# THE LAND AND THE PROMISE

# The Land and the Promise

## THE GREATEST STORIES FROM THE BIBLE

RETOLD BY

Frank G. Slaughter

CLEVELAND AND NEW YORK

THE WORLD PUBLISHING COMPANY

CHRIST METHODIST CHURCH LIBRARY
MEMPHIS, TENNESSEE
413

*Published by* The World Publishing Company

2231 West 110th Street, Cleveland 2, Ohio

Published simultaneously in Canada by

Nelson, Foster & Scott Ltd.


*Library of Congress Catalog Card Number:* 60-11455


FIRST EDITION

wp660

Copyright © 1960 by Frank G. Slaughter.
All rights reserved. No part of this book may be reproduced in
any form without written permission from the publisher, except for brief passages included in a review appearing in a news-
paper or magazine. Printed in the United States of America.

# Contents

# CONTENTS

# CONTENTS

# I. Land of Promise

*"Get thee out of thy country . . . unto a land that I will shew thee."*

GENESIS 12:1

# 1. Covenant in the Cloud

*"I do set my bow in the cloud, and it shall be for a token of a covenant between me and the earth."*

GENESIS 9:13

THE MAN called Adam was happy and unafraid.

Not only had God made him in his own image, but Adam had been placed in the fairest part of the new-made world, created by God in six days from the formless void of eternal darkness and warmed by the sun in the heavens. From Adam's own body God had created a mate for him called Eve, and the two dwelt peacefully with all other living things.

The whole earth was a pleasant place in the first days of its existence, with rippling streams and great rivers, tall trees and tiny flowers, great mountains and warm, pleasant valleys. Located at the headwaters of four great rivers, the garden called Eden was the fairest of all. In it Adam and his mate walked unafraid, for nothing threatened them there. Only one thing was forbidden to them, the fruit from the tree of knowledge growing in the center of the garden. Of this God had said, "On the day that you eat of it, you shall surely die."

From the beginning, God had given mankind a free choice between good and evil, evidenced by the presence of the tree of knowledge in the garden. When the serpent sought the downfall of the creatures God had set above all others, it offered Eve the fruit of the forbidden tree.

11

"Surely you shall not die," the tempter assured her when she hesitated. "For God knows that in the day you eat of it, your eyes shall be opened and you shall be as God." And thus reassured, Eve succumbed to the subtle temptation of the serpent and ate the fruit, giving some to her husband.

In the instant that the man and the woman chose evil over good by yielding to temptation, everything was changed. Conscious now of their nakedness, they were ashamed; when God came into the garden in the evening, they had already sewed leaves together to make aprons. Thus fear and shame came to the world because the first man and woman disobeyed God's commands, but even then the Lord had mercy upon them and did not kill them.

"Cursed is the ground for your sake," God told them sternly. "By the sweat of your face you shall eat bread until you return to the ground, for dust you are and unto dust you shall return."

Thus death, too, came where it had not been known before. For their sin, Adam and Eve were thrust out of the beautiful garden and forced to fend for themselves, hiding from the animals they had formerly trusted and from the fury of the storm and the lightning. Dwelling in caves, walking the forests carefully for fear of the serpent who had now become his enemy, Adam hunted animals for his family's meat and tilled the soil for their bread. In time Eve gave birth to a child and said, "I have gotten a man from the Lord." She named him Cain and when a second son was born, he was called Abel.

Life for the cave dwellers was a constant battle against the elements and the world around them. Cain grew up to be a powerful man of strong passions, quick-tempered and resentful when his father assigned to him the task of tilling the soil. Abel, on the other hand, was gentle and kind. He gladly kept the sheep they learned to tame and protect from other beasts, forming a source not only of meat but of wool for clothing.

Conscious of their sin, Adam and his family sought the favor of the Lord through gifts and offerings. Cain grudgingly brought the fruit of the ground, but Abel freely gave the first-born of his flock in gratitude for the way they had multiplied and had been protected from harm. God looked into Abel's heart and saw that he was good, but he recognized the anger and rebellion which characterized Cain's every action. When the Lord looked with favor upon Abel but did not respect the offering of Cain, the older brother was bitter. While Abel watched the sheep, Cain waylaid and killed him but could not hide from God the evil he had done.

"The voice of your brother's blood cries out to me from the ground," God told Cain sternly. "Now you are cursed from the earth, and shall be a fugitive and a vagabond."

Fleeing from the wrath of God, Cain left his family and, embittered and angry, found a cave for himself somewhat to the east of where they had been living.

Adam and Eve were saddened by the death of their gentle son and the expulsion of their violent one from the region where God had allowed them to dwell. In due time, Eve bore another son called Seth who possessed both the strength of Cain and the good qualities of Abel, but as the race of men descended from Adam and his sons grew upon the earth, the evil loosened by Eve's fall under temptation by the serpent increased. When finally the wickedness of man became so great that his every thought was evil, God regretted making Adam in his image and said: "I will destroy man whom I created upon the face of the earth, both man and beast, and the creeping things, and the fowls of the air."

One man found grace in the eyes of the Lord, however, a descendant of Seth called Noah. The Lord directed Noah to build a great boat called an ark against the time when flood waters would cover the earth, and to take into the vessel two of everything that grew upon the earth, both flesh and fowl, and the food which these must eat. Noah obeyed the commandments of God without question and when the great ark was finished, gathered into it the animals, the fowl, the grain, and other foods. With Noah and his wife into the ark went also his sons Shem, Ham, and Japheth with their wives.

Soon rain started to fall in torrents and as the water rose, the ark began to float. In time even the hills were covered; no land was visible and everything living upon the earth where the flood extended was destroyed—except those in the ark. Sturdily built according to the instructions God had given Noah, the great vessel floated safely upon the raging waters.

At last the rains ceased, the waters began to recede, and on the seventeenth day of the seventh month the ark came to rest upon a mountain called Ararat. Noah sent out a dove in search of land, and the bird flew about looking for a resting place but finding none, returned. When a second dove came back with an olive leaf in its beak, Noah and those in the ark rejoiced, for they knew that the waters had begun to abate. At the end of another seven days, the dove was set free again; this time it did not return, so they began to make preparations to leave the ark.

"Be fruitful, multiply and replenish the earth," God instructed Noah before the ark was opened. "Behold, I establish my covenant with you and with your seed after you. I set my bow in the cloud and it shall be the token of a covenant between me and the earth. When I send a cloud over the earth, the bow shall be seen in the cloud that I may remember the everlasting covenant between God and every living creature of all flesh that is upon the earth."

Thus because one man, Noah, and his family, did not share the sinful ways of the world, God spared him and spared mankind through him. Since that day, the rainbow in the clouds after the storm has been a token of the eternal covenant or promise of God to man.

# 2. Journey to Canaan

*"Fear not, Abram: I am thy shield,
and thy exceeding great reward."*

GENESIS 15:1

T HE SONS of Noah multiplied rapidly, as God had promised, and spread over the face of the earth. Some came
finally to a land called Shinar or Chaldea and there
decided to make brick and mortar and build a city and a tower.
Because they were vain, they wished the top of the tower to
reach into heaven so that all men might look upon it and
remember them, but God was watching. Recognizing the vanity
in their hearts, the Lord confounded their speech so that they
could not understand one another and were scattered abroad,
leaving the tower forever unfinished. Its name was called Babel
because there God first confounded the language of men; upon
the site eventually grew up a great city called Babylon.

Nowhere on the earth were the people more thickly con-
centrated than in the fertile valley of the Tigris and Euphrates
rivers which, according to ancient tradition, had their origin in
the Garden of Eden itself. Recurrent floods covered the lowlands with fertile soil, replenishing the fields. Crops grew easily,
for water was lifted from the rivers to irrigate them during dry
seasons. Flocks pastured upon the rich grasslands grew fat and
increased. It was easy to wrest food and the means of pur-
chasing clothing and other needed articles from the soil, so men

15

soon began to congregate in cities. One of the largest and most magnificent of these was Ur in Chaldea, near the mouth of the two great rivers.

As always happens where men have leisure, they began to spend it in frivolous pursuits and the worship of many gods. The priests and other learned men in the cities of Chaldea had already begun to write, scratching pictures and symbols upon tablets of clay which were then baked to preserve them. During the great flood which had covered all that men knew of the world then, the whole valley of the Tigris and Euphrates rivers, including the cities, had been buried under deep layers of mud, but new cities had soon been built. The greatest of all was Ur.

Lying upon an island formed by the river and a great irrigation canal, Ur was a veritable warren of narrow streets lined with square, flat-roofed houses built of mud bricks dried in the sun. Artisans had their shops at ground level and lived above, sleeping most of the year upon the roof-tops where it was cool at night. The city was surrounded by a broad outer wall inside which almost a quarter-million people made their homes.

In Ur the rich lived luxuriously; they wore daggers of gold and helmets of the same precious metal, ornaments of alabaster and silver, necklaces and bracelets made from carnelian, agate, and lapis lazuli. They drank from golden cups, ate from golden plates, and the women plucked their eyebrows with golden tweezers. Skilled artists carved stone and ivory into ornaments and images of the gods, while many thousands of workmen labored daily building tombs for kings and their consorts and for rich noblemen. Yet in Ur there was also grinding poverty and misery and a large part of its population were slaves.

Ships moved up and down the great rivers, carrying to other cities the products from the furnaces and hammers of the artisans. Travelers journeyed even as far as Egypt to the southwest, returning to tell wondrous stories of the great civilizations beside the river called the Nile which, like the Tigris and Euphrates, periodically covered the fields and fertilized them with the spring floods.

As the people of Ur grew more luxurious in their tastes, they constructed taller buildings, particularly a magnificent temple called the "House of the Great Light." The tower or *ziggurat* of the temple overlooked a section of the city set aside for the worship of the moon god, Nannar—the principal deity of Ur— and the area called the Temenos, where stood a great platform from which the king spoke to the people on state occasions.

For the most part Ur's inhabitants had long since forgotten the covenant of the rainbow that God had made with Noah after the flood. They worshipped all manner of gods, often with licentious and lustful rites, thinking that if they praised these creatures of their imaginings highly enough, they would be favored by them. Not so, however, a man named Terah. As he was a shepherd and a herdsman rather than an artisan, he did not live within the walls of Ur, but on the outskirts or suburbs of the city. With him were his sons Abraham (originally Abram) and Nahor, and his grandson Lot, whose father, Haran, had died some time before.

Terah was a pious man, worshipping the God of his fore-fathers. When he saw how the people of Ur ran after many deities and how lust and riotous living were corrupting them, he made plans to leave the wicked city. With his family, he started northwestward along the Tigris-Euphrates valley, fol-lowing the great caravan road leading to Canaan and Egypt, known even then as the "Way of the Sea."

Abraham took his barren wife Sarah with him and Nahor his wife Milcah. Lot also traveled in the long caravan which included Terah's flocks, his belongings, his herdsmen, and the servants of his household. Near the city of Haran, an important caravan junction far to the northwest near the border between the country of the Amorites and Hittites, the tribe pitched their tents and pastured their flocks. When Terah died, Abra-ham became chief or sheikh of his family or tribe. Convinced that Sarah would never be able to bear him a child, but loving her much too deeply to put another in her place, he took the step of adopting his servant and steward Eliezer so that his line might be continued.

God had a far greater purpose for Abraham, however, than simply to tend his flocks in Haran. "Get you out of your country

and from your kindred and from your father's house to a land
I will show you," God commanded. "I will make of you a great
nation and will bless you and make your name great."

Obeying without question the voice of God, Abraham made
preparations for the long journey southwestward into Canaan.
Bidding Nahor and his family good-bye, he and his tribe, with
their flocks, herds, and other possessions, moved southward along
the bank of the river Balikh, a tributary of the mighty Euphrates. Here they were in the territory of the kings of Mari, a
great city some two hundred miles to the southeast and about an
equal distance upstream from Babylon. Crossing the Euphrates
near its junction with the Balikh, they continued southward and
a little to the west until they saw against the skyline ahead the
delicate green feather dusters of palms marking the oasis of
Tadmor. There they paused awhile to graze the flocks and revel
in an endless supply of fresh water while enjoying their fill of
dates and other fruits.

From Tadmor the road led in a more westerly direction to
Damascus, already one of the oldest cities in the world. To the
weary travelers, Damascus, set in the midst of green fields
watered by a broad river and with flowering trees everywhere,
must have seemed a paradise. Pausing only to refresh themselves
and their flocks, however, the caravan of Abraham moved on
southwestward toward its goal, the land of Canaan.

As the road began to skirt the foothills of snow-capped Mount
Hermon to the north, the green fields of the flatlands around
Damascus gave way to the gray and brown of the desert, relieved
occasionally by irregular ranges of low-lying hills in the same
shades of color. Winding through the foothills of Mount Hermon, the road was hardly more than a rough track, and only occasionally did they see a village or meet other travelers. But
there were caves in which to sleep at night safe from robbers,
their sturdy men on guard outside, enclosed valleys where the
flocks could be pastured for a few days before moving on, and
tumbling streams where man and beast alike could drink pure
cold water.

Climbing steadily through the hills many days later, Abraham's caravan rounded a rocky shoulder and saw, stretching

before them, the heavily forested and well-watered hills of northern Galilee. Hurrying on, they crossed a stream whose icy waters tumbled through thickets of reeds and groves of oleander and myrtle, fanlike papyrus and balsam trees growing along the banks. This was the Jordan, a stream that burst from a cave on the slopes of Mount Hermon, to plunge downward—they were told—through a great rift that split the land here into two parts, ending finally at an enclosed sea so salt that it knew no life.

Moving between tumbled black basalt rocks that betrayed the volcanic origin of the land, Abraham and his people rounded another corner and the blue jewel of a lovely lake shone before their eyes. Cries of excitement went up, for this was the Sea of Chinnereth, of which they had heard even in far distant Ur, and one of the brightest jewels in all the treasures of Canaan.

The word Canaan meant "land of purple," so named because of the bright purple dye obtained from the shellfish or murex gathered upon its seacoast, still invisible beyond the mountain range to the west. The dye was already well known to the women of Abraham's tribe, for it was carried great distances and sold by caravan drivers who visited Canaan. With their love for bright-colored garments and stripes of blue and red, the women looked forward eagerly to being able to buy purple and other dyes here. On the hillsides to the northwest, they could see forests of cedar, a wood much prized by the Egyptians for building great ships, for fine furniture, and many things which these land-dwellers had heard of but never seen.

Had they known the whole truth about this teeming land to which they had come, Abraham and his followers might have been even more awed and perhaps afraid. Egyptian vessels as long as fifty paces and manned by dark-skinned Phoenician seamen brought spices and gold from the country of the blacks, copper and jewels from the rugged mountain region of Sinai separating Egypt from Canaan except along the coast, and fine cloth and ivory to the seaports of Canaan and Crete. On the return voyage to the cities of the Nile, the great ships bore silver and painted vases, the white paste called stibium, much prized for the cosmetic boxes of Egyptian nobles, blue dye for staining eyelids, bronze and copper for tools and utensils, precious jewels and exciting trinkets carved from seashells, besides many other valuable things.

Being shepherds, the tribe of Abraham did not turn to the teeming and rich seacoast centers of the new land. Central Canaan, they were told, was hill country, with caves where they could fortify themselves against invaders, and valleys where their flocks could graze and grow fat. Instinctively seeking a land like that in the region of Haran from which they had come, they moved southward through the passes west of the Sea of Chinnereth into the beautiful central valley of Jezreel and the Plain of Esdraelon. Directly ahead as they looked across the valley were the towering battlements of the Canaanite fortress cities of Jokneam, Ibleam, Taanach, and Megiddo, barring to invaders the populous cities off the seacoast. But having no wish to go farther west, they turned southward to explore the central ridge.

Abraham and his followers quickly decided that here was a country where they would be content to spend their lives like the other wandering tribes called "Apiru" by the Canaanites and "Hebrews" by the Egyptians. Moving to fresh pastures as the old were grazed over, the Apiru lived in caves or in nine-poled tents woven of goat's hair by the women. An occasional sale of hides to travelers passing along the caravan trails provided them with the few things they could not grow or make, such items as spears, arrows and axes, dye for clothing woven by the women on the looms they carried with them, and occasionally gold and silver for bracelets and other ornaments. At a high place called Shechem overlooking the broad valley of Jezreel, the Lord spoke to Abraham again, saying: "To your seed, I will give this land."

Abraham's heart was full and content as he looked about him. From the top of Mount Ebal, upon whose slope they were camped, he could see all the vastness and beauty of the country to which the Lord had led him. To the north, the foothills rose steadily to meet the snow-capped peak of Mount Hermon, while to the west lay the Great Sea—today's Mediterranean—glimpsed occasionally through the mountain passes as a patch of brilliant blue. To the east stretched a pattern of peaks and depressions leading to the deep cleft of the Jordan valley where there was summer even in the midst of winter. The elevation upon which he stood was already much favored by the Canaanites as a place for worshipping the tribal deities called Baals, and there Abraham gave thanks to his God.

# 3. A Visit to Egypt

*"And Abram went down into Egypt."*
GENESIS 12:10

OVING SLOWLY southward from pasture to pasture and spring to spring, Abraham and his people came finally to an area between the Canaanite city of Luz and the ruins of a center called Ai. It was a pleasant region in which grew almost everything they needed: vines, figs, pomegranates, olives, grain for food, cedars, cypresses, and many other trees for lumber and wood, as well as an adequate supply of water and grass for the flocks and herds. Once again, as at Shechem when he first entered Canaan, Abraham thanked the God who had guided him there, and made an offering of sacrifice upon a high hill.

The tribe now numbered several hundred, governed absolutely by Abraham as patriarch. With so many tough fighting men skilled with spear, bow and arrow, and the sling used to protect the cattle against prowling animals, they had little to fear from the robber bands which so often infested the caves overlooking the central highway leading through Canaan toward Egypt to the south. Hides and cloth were sold for grain to be ground in small portable mills made from a hollowed-out stone in which a second one was turned by means of a handle projecting from its surface. Kneaded into cakes with the addition of

22

the leaven which the women carefully preserved, the bread was cooked in stone ovens that were quickly built when a new camp was set up.

Butter was churned from milk by partially filling a skin and hanging it from a tripod of sticks, setting a girl or an old woman to shake it. Honey was easily found in hollow trees; fruits and berries could be gathered in the brush; and melons, lentils, cucumbers, and other vegetables could be purchased from the more agriculturally minded Canaanites. Although the tribe of Abraham were technically strangers in this land, the Canaanites were accustomed to the frequent appearances of these Wandering People, the "Apiru," and since Abraham's people were peaceful, there was no conflict.

When famine struck in Canaan, as it often did, the inhabitants suffered greatly unless they could afford to purchase grain in Egypt. There the Nile delta with its many river mouths formed an ideal spot for farming by irrigation, which the Egyptians had already been practising for thousands of years. The Hebrews had only to strike their tents and head the flocks and herds southward toward the delta region where there was grass aplenty. And since the Egyptians could profit from trade with the nomad herdsmen, the newcomers were welcomed, except when—as sometimes happened—they came as invaders.

When some time after their arrival in Canaan the pastures began to dry up, Abraham and his tribe confidently took the road southward from Mamre and Hebron through the parched desert wastes called the Negev. There they crossed the so-called "River of Egypt," a stream that was dry now but which swelled annually with the spring rains or *moreh* to become a raging torrent. Beyond the dry watercourse they were already in Egypt, but the Pharaohs did not maintain a border station north of the Prince's Wall, a string of fortresses a short distance to the south garrisoned with Egyptian soldiers. Man of peace that he was, Abraham was allowed to cross the border and, with his tribe, settled in a section, called Goshen, that encompassed the eastern portion of the Nile delta.

The Wandering People did not resemble the Egyptians in either features or dress. Much lighter-complexioned and with the sharply chiseled profiles characteristic of the Hittite tribes to the north, they were far more colorful. Abraham at the head of the column led a tame goat upon whose horns was affixed the bent stick of a shepherd. In fact, so characteristic of the nomadic people was this shepherd's crook that in Egyptian hieroglyphic writing it had already come to be the symbol for them. Blankets of wool were wrapped around their bodies and caught over one shoulder as a cloak, extending to the knees of the men and the ankles of the women. The bright colors and stripes of many shades favored by the Hebrews contrasted sharply with the plain white garments of the Egyptians.

Hebrew men had pointed beards. The women gathered their hair around the forehead with a ribbon and allowed it to fall upon their shoulders. They wore short boots, the men sandals. The men were well armed with spears, bows, arrows, and heavy throwing-sticks which, if they failed to strike the target, returned to the thrower. And always in a group of any size, there was at least one minstrel carrying the eight-stringed lyre with which he led his people in singing the melodic chants they loved.

The Canaanites had warned Abraham that the nobles of Egypt were given to licentiousness and lusting after the wives of other men, even killing the husbands of lovely visitors and taking the women for themselves. Though barren, Sarah was very beautiful and, mindful of the warnings, Abraham decided upon a stratagem by which he sought to outwit any who might desire her.

"Say you are my sister," he instructed her as soon as they crossed over into Egypt, hoping to keep her with the other women, unnoticed by the Egyptians.

The ruling Pharaoh—as the kings of Egypt were called—also lived in the delta region, however. And since Hebrew women were much prized by the Egyptians because of their beauty and their fiery nature, the customs officials at the Prince's Wall reported to the king immediately that an extraordinarily beautiful woman was in the retinue of the latest band of the Wandering People to cross the border. And shortly the king ordered Sarah brought into his household, intending to make her one of his many wives.

Abraham was showered with costly gifts by the Egyptian ruler, but these could not make up for the loss of the beautiful Sarah, whom he loved deeply in spite of her barrenness. Caught in a trap of his own making, however, Abraham could not protest, for in taking his alleged sister for a wife, Pharaoh had done him a great honor. Besides, if he tried to take Sarah back by force, Abraham knew he would run the risk of seeing his entire tribe destroyed. In his dilemma, he could only turn to God, admit his error in telling the lie, and beg for help. And—as always with those who trust him—the Lord did not desert the man whom he had brought from Ur to Egypt. Plague after plague descended upon the house of Pharaoh, and when the king learned the cause, he sent Sarah back to Abraham with more gifts, seeking to placate the anger of the Hebrews' powerful God. Thus Sarah was restored to her home, and the tribe, richer and more numerous than when they had come into Egypt, journeyed back to Canaan when the famine there ended.

Before they chose new pasture lands, Abraham's nephew Lot decided to settle in a different area. To the east lay the fertile plain of the lower Jordan with the rich and populous cities of Sodom and Gomorrah at the southern end of the Salt Sea. Eager to enjoy the pleasures of the cities, Lot chose to live there, while Abraham settled for a time in the neighborhood of Bethel where, before going into Egypt, he had erected an altar to the Lord.

A much-traveled caravan road ran along the eastern edge of the Jordan valley, connecting Egypt and the great copper mines in the region of Sinai to the south with Damascus, Mari, Babylon, and the other important population centers of the Euphrates basin. Naturally such an important trade route brought prosperity to the "Cities of the Plain," but it also afforded an easy route for invaders. For twelve years the rulers of Sodom, Gomorrah, Admar, Zeboam, and Zoar had paid tribute to one of these conquerors, Chedorlaomer, king of Elam. Finally, however, they rebelled against their absentee landlord, but in the battle that followed they were defeated and Lot was taken prisoner.

Abraham lived some distance to the east of Sodom and

CHRIST UNITED METHODIST CHURCH
4488 POPLAR AVENUE
MEMPHIS, TENNESSEE 38117

Gomorrah, but he did not hesitate to answer Lot's call for help. With several of the neighboring tribal chieftains, he gathered an army and defeated the troops of King Chedorlaomer in the foothills of Mount Hermon near where the Jordan has its origin. Much booty was captured in the battle, but when the King of Sodom insisted that Abraham take the major share, he refused.

"I will not take anything that is yours, lest you should say, 'I have made Abraham rich,' " he said, accepting only the portion allotted to those who had gone into battle with him.

Freed from oppression and the burden of tribute, the people of Sodom and Gomorrah became even more profligate and lustful than before. Finally God's patience was exhausted and he told Abraham of his intention to destroy the Cities of the Plain. Hoping to save Lot, Abraham begged God to spare Sodom if as many as ten good men could be found there, and to this the Lord agreed, sending to Lot's house two angels disguised as ordinary men.

Lot welcomed the strangers courteously and took them into his house, but the men of Sodom soon gathered outside, demanding that the visitors be turned over to them, as was the custom in this perverted city. This Lot refused to do, for among his people and Abraham's, a stranger was inviolate while in one's household and must be protected with one's life. When the men of Sodom insisted on having their way with the strangers—whom Lot still did not know were angels—he even offered to turn over to them instead his most precious possession, his two unmarried daughters, lest he be guilty of breaking the law of his people concerning hospitality. The attackers would not be appeased, however, and tried to break down the door of Lot's house, stopping only when the angels struck them blind.

"If you have sons-in-law, sons and daughters in the city, bring them out," the angels warned Lot. "The Lord has sent us to destroy it."

Lot went immediately to his older daughters' husbands, begging them and their families to leave Sodom with him, but they merely mocked him. When morning came he took only his wife and two youngest daughters with him and left the city at once.

"Do not look behind you or stay in the Plain," the angels had warned Lot and his family. "Escape to the mountains lest you be consumed." Even as they were fleeing into the hills from the lowland around the Salt Sea, the earth had already begun to rumble and shake beneath their feet as if in torment. Great fissures appeared, sending the walls and houses of the cities crashing down, and allowing the waters of the sea and the molten rocks that erupted through cracks in the earth to flow in so that a vast area at the southern end of the Salt Sea was buried beneath the surface.

Lot's wife had loved the luxury she had known in Sodom and dared to look back in spite of the strict order of the angel who had brought them out. Doing so, she stumbled and was swept into the torrent deluging the Plain. When the waters receded, her body was left covered with salt.

Lot and his two daughters escaped by hiding in a cave high upon the hillside; there they watched with fearful eyes the horrors taking place in the valley as the Lord kept his promise to Abraham, destroying everything in Sodom and Gomorrah except Lot, the one man who had proved himself righteous there.

From that day onward the lake that knew no life because of the salt was called the Sea of Judgment.

# 4. Isaac and Ishmael

> *"Thou shalt be a father of many nations."*
>
> GENESIS 17:4

"LIFT UP YOUR EYES and look northward and southward and eastward and westward," God said to Abraham one day while he and his people were living in the region around Bethel. "All the land you see I will give to you and your seed forever."

The scene was a familiar one to Abraham, for he had stood many times on the mountain peaks and looked across the vast panorama of this prosperous and fruitful land which God was giving to him and his people. To the north in the hills lay Shechem where he had made his first sacrifice upon arriving in Canaan. Beyond the Valley of Jezreel, in the cool, clear air before sunset, the top of Mount Tabor loomed above the lower hills, with the snow-capped peaks of Mount Hermon little more than a shadowy silhouette upon the horizon. To the northwest the range of Mount Carmel rose steadily, hiding the Great Sea into which it jutted as a projecting headland.

Eastward lay the deep cleft of the Jordan valley, a vast rift in the earth looking as if God had taken it between his hands and cracked it open, setting the river in the depths of the crevice. The valley of the Jordan nowhere extended more than ten miles from the river, but the whole area was heavily cultivated

28

CHRIST METHODIST CHURCH LIBRARY
MEMPHIS, TENNESSEE

by the Canaanites. There it was warm even in mid-winter, and flowers and trees bloomed months earlier than in the hill country where Abraham lived. But the hilly area was better suited for pasturing flocks and herds, and besides, it was more like the region of Padan-Aram from which the Hebrews had come to Canaan, a region where they could escape pursuit in their infrequent brushes with their neighbors by hiding in the caves and then falling swiftly upon their pursuers from ambush.

The place Abraham finally chose as his permanent habitation, the Plain of Mamre, lay to the south in an area called Hebron. This region was not densely populated, as were some areas to the north, and sloped gently in ranges of hills to the desert wastes of the Negev. The pastures around Hebron were green most of the year, and there was ample water from many springs for the needs of the Hebrew encampment.

Only one thing troubled Abraham and sometimes tried his faith in God, the fact that he had no sons to populate and hold this land in his name. God had promised him that his seed would multiply to cover the earth and that he would be the father of many nations, but Sarah still remained childless and time seemed to have passed them by. Abraham's love for Sarah did not falter because of her barrenness, however; nor did he take another wife, as easily he could without even asking her permission.

"How beautiful the look of her face," the minstrels sang of Sarah. "How fine is the hair of her head, how fair indeed are her eyes, and how pleasing her nose and all the radiance of her face! Above all women she is lovely and higher is her beauty than that of them all."

Nor did the singers exaggerate, for Sarah had once charmed the king of Egypt until the wrath of God had forced even Pharaoh to return her to Abraham.

"With all her beauty, there is much wisdom in her," the minstrels added, and in the end Sarah's wisdom overcame her natural reluctance to share her husband with another woman.

Among the Hebrews it was common practice where a wife was barren for the husband to have children by women servants. If during the birth of such a male child, the wife held the mother on her lap—"upon her knees" was the phrase—the child was considered to have been born of the wife's own body and ever after would be known as her own. This custom Sarah now invoked in order that Abraham might have an heir.

The maidservant chosen was an Egyptian named Hagar. She proved to have a bad disposition, however, and as soon as she was carrying Abraham's child, began to taunt Sarah with her barrenness. When Sarah complained to Abraham, he left the punishment up to her and she banished Hagar from the camp.

God was watching over the maidservant, though, for she, too, was part of his great purpose under the covenant he had made with Noah and with Abraham. "You shall bear a son and shall call his name Ishmael," the angel who brought help to Hagar in the wilderness told her. Obeying his command, she returned to the camp and there her son was born. But Sarah did not take the boy as her own, although she did let Hagar and Ishmael live in the camp unharmed.

To Abraham, now an old man, God spoke once again: "I am Almighty God; walk before me and be perfect. I will bless Sarah and give you a son also of her. You shall call his name Isaac, and I will establish an everlasting covenant with him and his seed after him."

Abraham was overjoyed when, miraculously it seemed, Sarah bore him a son. He was called Isaac as God had instructed, and at the boy's weaning a great feast of celebration was held. But the Egyptian woman, Hagar, mother of Abraham's other son, mocked Sarah because Ishmael was already strong and active while Isaac was still only a baby. And smarting under Hagar's taunts, Sarah went to Abraham.

"Cast out this bondwoman and her son!" she demanded angrily. "The son of Hagar shall not be the heir with Isaac!"

It was natural that Sarah should fight for her own son to inherit all that Abraham possessed as well as the title of chief. Under tribal law, Abraham had no choice except to order Hagar expelled with Ishmael, since the child was not legally the son of his wife, Sarah. But God comforted the sorrowing father. "In Isaac shall your seed be called," he assured Abraham. "But of the son of the bondwoman, I will also make a nation because he is your seed."

True to his promise, God led Hagar and Ishmael to safety in the wilderness of Paran between Canaan and Egypt. There the boy grew up to become an archer and a mighty warrior. In time his mother took a wife for him from the near-by land of Egypt, and a mighty people was eventually descended from him.

# 5. The Tempting of Abraham

*"And it came to pass after these things,*
*that God did tempt Abraham."*

GENESIS 22:1

ABRAHAM had obeyed God in all things and had been rewarded for his faith. He was a rich man, patriarch of a
powerful tribe, and possessor of a large area of valuable
land. In Isaac he had a son who was literally the center of his
existence, a strong, intelligent lad who was already an excellent
hunter and showed every sign of becoming a natural leader of
his people. But when Abraham became complacent, God put
him to a final test of his faith.

"Take your son, Isaac, whom you love," the Lord directed.
"Go into the land of Moriah and offer him there for a burnt
offering upon one of the mountains of which I will tell
you."

Though his heart was heavy, Abraham did not falter. Early
in the morning he ordered a mule saddled and started northward with Isaac and two of the young men, along with wood
for the burnt offering.

Isaac did not know the purpose of the trip and, like any
youth, enjoyed it. The way led through the hill country, taking
possibly three days, as Abraham was an old man and could not
travel fast. They were retracing a fairly heavily traveled road
that led southward from the Jebusite city of Urusalim, or

Jerusalem, past the village of Bethlehem to the Plain of Mamre and southward to the border of Egypt.

Bethlehem lay almost atop a broad ridge which extended in a somewhat north-south direction along the road to Hebron. From the top of the ridge, Abraham glimpsed occasionally the dull, slate-colored surface of the Sea of Judgment and, depressed as he was, could hardly repress a shiver of dread as he remembered the terrible day when the earth had writhed in torment and the Cities of the Plain had been destroyed. The tremblings of the earth which had produced the great rifts and fissures into which the doomed cities fell had extended even as far as Mamre, and for days afterward sulphurous mists rising from the boiling waters of the lake had drifted across the country.

North of Bethlehem, Abraham's little caravan turned off the main road and began to toil up the foothills of the mountain called Moriah overlooking the Jebusite city of Jerusalem, with its walls surrounding a hilltop visible across a fairly deep valley. Here Abraham brought the caravan to a halt and, leaving behind the two young men who had come with them, ordered Isaac to carry the wood for the sacrifice. Abraham himself bore a knife and a torch with which to kindle the burnt offering. As he began the sorrowful climb to the mountain top, he could hardly have been blamed for doubting God's justice, for, though finally given an heir in his old age, he was now, upon God's orders, having to destroy him, his own son.

Abraham never faltered, however. When they reached the mountain top, he directed Isaac to build an altar of stones and place the wood upon it. The boy had seen his father make sacrifices to the God of the Hebrews many times before and was familiar with the ritual. First a lamb or kid was killed swiftly with a bronze knife, and the blood drained into a bowl to be dashed upon the altar when the burning was completed. Then the dressed flesh was put aside to be roasted for a ceremonial meal, while the rest was tossed into the fire upon the altar.

"Here is fire and wood," Isaac said to his father in perplexity. "But where is the lamb for a burnt offering?"

Abraham's face was drawn with pain and his voice, when he spoke, was hoarse. "God will provide a lamb for a burnt offering," he assured the boy and, taking a cord from his robe, began to bind Isaac's wrists. His hands were trembling but with age, not with faltering in this final test of his faith. Isaac could not believe his father intended to kill him; he judged this to be merely some sort of ceremonial which he had never seen before. So when Abraham directed him to lie down upon the wood that covered the stones of the altar, he obeyed unhesitatingly.

With a groan of anguish, Abraham raised the carefully sharpened bronze knife and started to slash swiftly across Isaac's throat with the merciful stroke used to kill animals during the sacrifice. Only at the last moment did a familiar voice stay his hand.

"Abraham! Abraham!" the Lord called. "Do not lay your hand upon the lad nor do anything to him. Now I know that you fear God, since you did not withhold your only son from me."

His heart singing with joy, Abraham turned the blade of the knife upon the ropes binding Isaac and freed the boy. For the first time now he noticed a ram caught in the thicket near-by and, freeing the animal, he and Isaac quickly killed it and dressed out the flesh, kindling the fire upon the altar and tossing the remainder into it. As the black smoke and the odor of burning flesh rose skyward, they made the tender meat into a pack which Isaac carried down the mountain for a joyous meal of thanksgiving that night.

"Because you have done this thing and have not withheld your son, I will bless you and will multiply your seed as the stars of the heaven and as the sand which is upon the shore," God promised Abraham there on Mount Moriah overlooking the city of Jerusalem where, one day, a descendant of the Hebrew patriarch would build a great golden temple to his glory. "In your seed shall all the nations of the earth be blessed, because you have obeyed my voice."

Not for nearly two thousands years was that promise to be

fulfilled when God gave his own son as a sacrifice upon a rocky hillside just outside Jerusalem, showing the world the way to eternal life. But the covenant had been made as surely as God had placed his rainbow in the clouds, fulfilling the promise to Noah that mankind would never again be destroyed by flood.

# 6. A Wife for Isaac

*"He shall send his angel before thee,*
*and thou shalt take a wife unto my*
*son."*                          GENESIS 24:7

EBEKAH'S THOUGHTS were far away as she walked to the
well with the empty water jar upon her shoulder. She
knew she was beautiful, the spring from which she often
drank when gathering berries and fruits on the hillside assured
her of that. And she could be certain—in ways women know—
that more than one young man of Haran was considering sending
the matchmaker to her father, Bethuel, to dicker on the amount
of the *mohar* or bride price that would be paid for her. It would
be high; that went without question, for her father was
moderately well-off, as was her grandfather Nahor, who had
been brought from the great city of Ur to this beautiful rolling
region near the banks of the River Balikh by his father Terah
when little more than a youth.

In her fancies, Rebekah sometimes longed to see Ur, or even
Mari, which was much nearer downstream by way of the
Balikh and the Euphrates. Had she been a boy, she might have
joined one of the rafts supported by inflated skins that floated
down the river, carrying cloth, hides, and other goods to be
sold in the markets of the cities. Bethuel did not remember
much about Ur, but Nahor had described to Rebekah the beautiful temple of Ishtar with the statues of the royal worshippers

and the mosaic pattern of multicolored shells set into the walls, the broad streets and the great funeral processions when the body of a nobleman, with his retainers and his favorite possessions, made the final journey before they were all sealed in the tomb.

A friend of Rebekah's father had been to Mari and reported that the palace of the king was so large that one could hardly walk around it without stopping to rest. There were even rooms for bathing alone, Rebekah had been told—though this seemed almost incredible—and hundreds of slaves to wait upon the wives of the kings and rich noblemen.

These were but dreams, Rebekah knew, flights of a young girl's fancy in the years before she entered her husband's household and became—as being bought with the *mohar* implied— his slave. And as she walked along to the well, her ire at being treated thus as a chattel began for the hundredth time to rise. Unless she married a rich man—and where were there such in the country here outside Haran except old ones whose touch would make her shiver?—she could expect to live a life of toil and child-bearing such as left the women of her people hags before they were thirty, the age when a man was considered just old enough to sit in the councils of the elders.

They would all have been better off if Nahor had gone with his brother Abraham to Canaan, Rebekah thought resentfully. Travelers brought rumors of Abraham's great wealth: how he had led a confederation of kings and defeated King Chedorlaomer in battle, and how the herds and flocks of his tribe covered many hillsides in one of the richest parts of Canaan. Nahor had been afraid to make the long journey, preferring the safety of their pasture lands in Haran, but safety was not what a spirited young woman such as Rebekah desired. Deep inside her she was convinced that she had been intended for a better purpose than to become the wife of a herdsman, and each night she prayed in secret to the household god they had brought with them out of Ur to give her something more.

Bemused, as she often was, Rebekah did not notice, until she was a few paces from him, the man who was standing beside the well. His clothes were dusty and he looked tired, for he was old and gray of beard, but the girl's quick glance did not miss the fact that the mules standing patiently a little to one side were heavily laden and powdered with dust. From this she judged the visitor to be a traveler from far away and her eyes began to sparkle at the thought of the stories he might tell of distant lands. Carchemish, the Hittite capital, lay only about a hundred miles to the west, and traders often came to Haran to buy hides and the tough cloth woven from goat's-hair by the Hebrew women. But this man, she knew instinctively, had come from much farther away.

Rebekah did not speak to the stranger, since it was not seemly for a young woman to address a strange man. But as she swung the heavy earthenware pitcher down from her shoulder with a lithe movement of her strong young body, the man spoke courteously, like a servant addressing one above his station.

"Let me, I pray you, drink a little water from your pitcher," he begged.

Rebekah hurried to let the pitcher down into the shallow well and draw up the water. "Drink, my lord," she said, and when he had finished, added, "I will draw water for your animals also until they have finished drinking."

The stranger smiled, but she took it only as a tribute to her beauty; when he spoke again there was an odd intentness in his voice. "Whose daughter are you?" he asked. "Is there room in your father's house for me to lodge?"

"I am the daughter of Bethuel, the son of Milcah and Nahor," Rebekah replied. "We have straw and grain enough, and a room where you may lodge."

"Blessed is the Lord God of my master Abraham!" the man cried. "The Lord has led me to the house of my master's brethren!"

Rebekah was startled both by his manner and by his speech. Incredibly, he seemed to mean that he had come from Abraham, the almost legendary brother of her grandfather Nahor. She drew back instinctively, but stopped when she saw Eliezer open the pack of one of the mule's and take from it a gold earring

and a pair of golden bracelets. He gave these to her, telling her
that he was Eliezer, chief servant in Abraham's household, and
that his master had sent him from far-off Canaan to seek a
wife for his son Isaac among his own people rather than among
the women of Canaan. He went on to tell how he had prayed to
the Lord that when he came into the country of Abraham's
kinsmen, the girl selected by God to become Isaac's bride
would offer him water from a well, and it did seem to Rebekah
it must have been God who had led Eliezer to her.

When Rebekah's brother Laban heard the exciting news she
brought, he went to meet Eliezer, stabling and feeding the
mules while the traveler went inside to refresh himself. But
when they offered him food, Eliezer demurred.

"I will not eat until I have told my errand," he insisted and,
while they listened attentively, explained how Abraham had
sent him to Haran saying, "The Lord before whom I walk will
send his angel before you, and you shall take a wife for my son
from among my kinsmen and from my father's house."

Laban and Bethuel were as awed by the story of how God had
guided Eliezer to Rebekah as the girl herself had been. "This
comes from the Lord," they said. "Take Rebekah and let her be
your master's son's wife, as the Lord has spoken."

Rebekah had been listening, and when her father and brother
asked her consent—little more than a formality, it was true—
she gave it freely. Eliezer gave Bethuel and his family the
presents he had brought from Abraham—a far greater bride
price than had ever been given in that region—and with Rebekah and her nurse, the caravan started back the next morning
for Canaan. Following the route by which Abraham and his
tribe had come into the land God had promised them, they
came finally to a well in the Plain of Mamre where Isaac was
overseeing the pasturing of the family flocks and herds.

Rebekah was a spirited young woman, eager to see the wonders of the storied land of Canaan that would be her home.
She had put off the veil women usually wore while traveling,
for it was hot and only the servants were with her. When she
saw a tall, vigorous-looking man walking across a field toward

them in the evening as they approached Abraham's camp, her heart quickened suddenly.

"Who is it that walks across the field to meet us?" she asked.

"It is my master, Isaac," Eliezer replied.

Quickly Rebekah got down from the mule she had been riding and began to rearrange the veil of fine cloth over her shining hair, pulling it across her face to hide her features below the eyes. A woman's sure instinct told her that with her slender, lovely body and proud carriage she was far more attractive while walking than while riding upon the dust-covered mule. When Isaac came up to the caravan, the servants bowed before him and so did Rebekah, as befitted a properly brought-up maiden. But her eyes were studying him above the veil, and she could not help being thrilled by what she saw. This was the sort of husband she had dreamed of in Haran, tall, strong, handsome, a leader of men in his own right besides his heritage from Abraham.

Nor did Isaac miss the girl's beauty, the grace with which she made obeisance before him, the loveliness of her eyes when she finally raised them. All the while that Eliezer was telling how he had been guided to Rebekah beside the well in her father's country, Isaac's eyes did not leave the girl. He accompanied the caravan into the camp of the Hebrews and to the tent of Abraham and Sarah, who took Rebekah to their hearts. And with the final act of parental approval there was no further barrier to the marriage.

A wedding amongst persons of such importance in the camp of the Hebrews was always a festive occasion. On the day of the ceremony, a joyous procession gathered at one end of the camp. Those who were to participate, including the bridegroom, wore crowns of bright-colored blossoms. And since the garments of the Hebrews were always richly colored in this region where they had free access to the purple and other dyes of the Phoenicians, it was a colorful procession indeed that began to march through the camp toward the tent where Rebekah awaited the coming of the bridegroom. The young people danced and sang, played upon the eight-stringed lyre, and beat cymbals and tambours so that everyone—particularly the ever-present demons —would realize that this was a wedding instead of a funeral. And to frighten away any evil spirits that might try to approach and cause trouble, some of the young men walked alongside the procession brandishing their weapons.

Before the richly caparisoned tent where Rebekah awaited the coming of Isaac, preparations for the great feast had been going on since the day before. Ranged under tasseled canopies on either side of the tent were tables loaded with viands of all sorts and jars of wine, diluted with water, for the refreshment of the guests. Some of the musicians had harps formed by stretching the strings across a piece of sandalwood and orna-menting this with two horns which also served for carrying the instrument. The shepherds, who kept the sheep quiet upon the hillsides by playing upon flutes and reed pipes, had brought their instruments, and to furnish a rhythm for the dancing, the girls shook sistrums as a background to the high-pitched trilling of the flutes and reeds. Others banged upon timbrels, as the drums were called, and while the dancers shuffled and sprang about, they sang songs of praise for the lovely bride:

"*Turn, turn, Rebekah the beautiful,*
*Turn, turn, that we may gaze upon thee.*
*Ah, gaze on the beautiful one!*
*How beautiful are her steps and sandals,*
*How beautiful are her feet, the rapturous maiden!*"

As tradition prescribed, the celebration lasted far into the night until finally, around midnight, the bridegroom lifted his bride in his arms and carried her over the threshold of his tent to the nuptial couch.

Isaac and Rebekah had loved each other from the first mo-ment of their meeting, as God had intended by bringing them together so that the line of Abraham might be kept pure for the high purpose to which it was called by divine will. And as the years passed, their love deepened, though for many years Rebekah was barren.

Sarah died before Abraham and at his death the two were

buried together in a cave Abraham had purchased as a resting place in nearby Machpelah. Isaac, with Rebekah at his side, proved a wise patriarch, busying himself with the task of governing his steadily increasing people and administering wisely the possessions and riches which they gradually accumulated.

# 7. Jacob and Esau

*"And Jacob said, Sell me this day thy
birthright."*   GENESIS 25:31

IT WOULD HAVE BEEN hard to find two more different brothers
than Jacob and Esau, although they were twins. Conceived
by Rebekah after many years of barrenness, only a few
moments actually separated them, but Esau, the firstborn, was
legally entitled to be the heir and patriarch of the tribe. Jacob,
on the other hand, could look forward only to the lesser role of
the second son, obedient in all things to the eldest, and accepting
whatever his brother chose to give him.

Physically, Esau was large and red-haired, with much hair on
his body; he grew up to love hunting, fighting, feasting, and
other pleasures of the flesh. Jacob, however, was slender, quick,
and shrewd. While Esau hunted, Jacob remained with the flocks
and soon learned the secrets of breeding known to expert herdsmen—how to mate strong animals with good traits to produce
finer offspring, how to match color to color and produce cattle
with almost any coat desired.

Practical, thrifty Rebekah favored Jacob because he remained
at home and looked after his father's affairs when Isaac grew
old and became almost blind. But the father favored the lusty
Esau who brought him savory game and told him exciting stories
of the hunt and of the occasional skirmishes between the He-

brews and the Canaanite people. Instead of fighting the Canaanites, however, Jacob studied their agricultural practices, for
he realized that if the Hebrews grew their own vegetables and
grain, they would not have to buy from the Canaanites and
could keep for other uses more of the money derived from the
sale of hides and cloth. Esau was contemptuous when Jacob
had fields dug and planted with lentils and other vegetables,
but he did not disdain to eat the savory dishes prepared from
them, for in the matter of satisfying his appetites, the older
brother rarely exhibited much self-restraint.

One thing rankled in the soul of Jacob, the fact that solely
because Esau was the oldest by a few moments, he would
inherit at Isaac's death all that the younger son was working so
hard to build up and maintain. And being a shrewd trader, he
soon found a way to remedy what he considered the unfairness
of the situation.

Esau had been hunting one day and came into the tent
where Jacob was supervising the preparation of a pot full of
lentils cooked in a savory stew or pottage. The fragrance of it
had spread through the camp, drawing Esau to Jacob's tent.
Looking eagerly into the pot, he sniffed its contents.

"Feed me that pottage," he begged his brother, "for I am
hungry!"

Jacob's eyes brightened, but he was careful not to let Esau
notice it. "Sell me your birthright," he said shrewdly, knowing that Esau rarely looked any farther than the gratification of
his immediate desires.

Esau laughed, thinking Jacob was joking. "I am about to die.
What profit will this birthright be to me?"

"Swear to it," Jacob cannily insisted, and Esau laughingly
swore and then picked up a bowl and filled it with the savory
stew.

While Esau gorged himself, Jacob's mind was busy. He knew
that Esau's agreement to sell the birthright, especially when
made jokingly, need not be final. The right to say who should
inherit his property and the title of leader of the tribe still
rested with Isaac, now almost blind. Somehow Jacob must find a
way to make Isaac give him the parental blessing that would

name him the heir, a position to which he felt, with considerable reason, that he had the greater right. Unable to think of a way, he took the problem to his mother.

Rebekah had decided long ago that her Jacob with his sturdy virtues was much better fitted to be leader of the tribe than impulsive Esau, and she was quite willing to abet her favorite son in deceiving his father. Besides, she could not forget a dream she had had while carrying the twins in her body.

"Two nations are in your womb and two manners of people," the Lord had said to her in the dream. "The one people shall be stronger than the other people and the elder shall serve the younger." This she understood to mean that it was God's will for Esau to serve Jacob, a condition which could only come about if Jacob received the birthright and his father's blessing.

A few days later Esau went to kill venison for his father, giving Rebekah an opportunity to carry out the plan she had decided upon. "Bring me two fat kids from among the goats," she directed Jacob. "I will make savory meat for your father and you shall bring it to him, so that he will eat and bless you."

Jacob obeyed his mother, but he was doubtful that she would succeed. Isaac loved the game Esau brought in from the hunt and the older brother always carried the roast flesh to his father with his own hands, so that the moment Isaac touched Jacob, the old man, even though blind, would realize he was not Esau and the plan would fail.

Rebekah had thought of a way to get around this stumbling block, however. When the stew was ready, she helped Jacob put over his hands and across the back of his neck the skins of the goats he had killed. Thus prepared, he took the dish in to his father and said, "Arise and eat my venison that your soul may bless me."

Though Jacob had sought to imitate his brother's more hearty tones, Isaac realized that the voice did not sound quite like Esau's. "How is it that you have found it so quickly?" he demanded suspiciously.

"Because the Lord brought it to me," Jacob answered—truthfully enough considering his mother's conviction that it was God's will for him to inherit the birthright.

Isaac was still doubtful. "Come nearer that I may feel you, my son," he insisted, and Jacob confidently moved close to his father, knowing that the old man could not see well enough to realize that he was not Esau. And when Isaac smelled the blood upon the skins Jacob wore, and felt the hair on his hands and his neck, he was convinced—as Rebekah had intended—that it was indeed Esau.

"The smell of my son is as the smell of the field which the Lord has blessed," the old man said. "Be lord over your brethren and let your mother's sons bow down to you. Cursed be everyone that curses you and blessed be he that blesses you."

Jacob was content; with both the birthright and the blessing of his father, he was now the rightful heir and patriarch of the tribe. And even though Esau would undoubtedly be angry when he came from the hunt, Jacob knew that by tribal law there was nothing that the older brother could do about it.

Esau was not one to accept adversity without fighting back, however. Secretly he began to plot against Jacob, planning to kill him and, since many of the young men of the tribe—especially the hunters and the warriors—would follow the older son's leadership, Esau could be fairly certain of succeeding. In the end it seemed as if Jacob had outsmarted himself. Forced to flee from the camp to save his life, he had no place to go until Rebekah sent him to find shelter in Haran with her brother Laban.

Discouraged, with everything he had worked and schemed for seemingly lost, Jacob set out on the long journey to the River Balikh. He had not been able even to bring a tent and pack animals with him, and at night was forced to find shelter in the public khans or caravanseries that stood by the road. Usually little more than thatched shelters, these were poor protection indeed from the elements in time of storm, and Jacob could hardly be blamed for feeling that God had forsaken him.

That this was not true he learned one night in a dream when he saw a ladder leading up to heaven, with angels ascending and descending. In his depression and discouragement, he longed to ascend the ladder and enjoy the security and happiness to which it led, but God's words opened a different vista before him.

"I am the God of Abraham, your father, and of Isaac," the quiet voice assured him. "I will give the land where you lie to you and to your seed. You shall spread abroad to the east and to the north and to the south. In you and in your seed shall all the families of the earth be blessed."

Jacob awakened with a new sense of purpose and a new strength. Toiling up to the hilltop where the vision had come to him, he erected an altar and called it Bethel. There he made a vow to God:

"If the Lord will be with me and will keep me in this way that I go and will give me bread to eat and raiment to put on, so that I come again to my father's house in peace, then shall the Lord be my God. And this stone which I have set for a monument shall be God's house, and of all that you give me, I will surely give the tenth to you."

Thus it came about that Bethel ever afterward was a holy place for the descendants of Jacob. And the covenant he made there to give to the Lord a tenth of everything that he and his people produced has been kept by his descendants since that day.

# 8. The Plain Sister

> *"Leah was tender eyed, but Rachel was beautiful and well favoured."*
>
> GENESIS 29:17

LEAH WAS the plain daughter, while her sister Rachel was vivacious and beautiful. Leaving Leah to attend to the household duties when her father Laban grew old, Rachel took upon herself the care of the sheep, leading them each day to the spring where the shepherds gathered. When the stone that guarded the mouth of the spring was rolled away, Rachel let her flock drink while she stood near-by, conscious of the gaze of the young men upon her but giving them no encouragement.

There was a reason for Rachel's presence at this well each day, a reason that had little to do with attracting the attention of the shepherds. In the household of Laban, the story had often been told how the servant of Abraham had come to that very well, seeking a bride for Abraham's son Isaac, and how Rebekah—Leah's and Rachel's aunt—had been selected. Rachel naturally hoped for the good luck that her aunt had had in marrying a leader of his tribe like Isaac, but then many rich merchants also passed along these trails. Sometimes one of them paused to water his animals and drink, and the slender girl with the dark hair knew well what a lovely picture she made as she tended the sheep near-by.

The fact that her sister Leah was unmarried rankled particularly in Rachel's heart. According to custom, the marriage-maker could not approach Laban for the hand of Rachel until Leah had found a husband. And though Leah was gentle, kind, and far more skilled in household affairs than Rachel, she was not beautiful—except to those who knew her well enough to see the deep, inner loveliness of spirit that was her finest characteristic.

Gentle Leah was troubled that no one offered the bride price for her; when it came to marriage, however, young men did not set much store by the fact that she was skilled at the oven and able, from the grain she ground each morning in the small stone mill, to make crisp loaves that fairly melted in one's mouth. Nor did they notice that her fingers were skilled at spinning wool into thread, weaving it into rich cloth on the loom, and dyeing it with the bright colors favored by the Hebrews. They did not pause to note with what tender and loving care Leah looked after her father Laban in his old age, or how in time of sickness it was Leah who was sent to nurse the afflicted one back to health, using the healing herbs she gathered on the hillsides and carefully preserved. Leah's heart beat as quickly as Rachel's when she heard the story of Rebekah and Isaac, and she would gladly have become the wife of an industrious shepherd, caring for his household and bearing him strong sons, but she had long ago resigned herself to becoming at best an old man's bride.

When finally Jacob came into the region of his mother's people, it was naturally Rachel who saw him first, for he was thirsty and stopped at the well to drink. Three flocks of sheep were lying beside the well in the shadow of the trees, but the man had not yet rolled away the stone that guarded the well's mouth.

"Do you know Laban, the son of Nahor?" Jacob asked the shepherds, thinking that the well was closed to strangers.

"We know him," one of the shepherds answered noncommittally, for it was not wise to volunteer information to a stranger.

"Is he well?"

"He is well," the shepherd answered and nodded toward the

slope of the hill down which Rachel was coming with her father's flock. "Look, there is Rachel, his daughter, coming with the sheep."

Jacob frowned. It was late morning and his every instinct as a husbandman rebelled against keeping the sheep together by the well when they should have been watered long ago and scattered on the grassy hillsides to fatten themselves. He could not know, of course, that since the spring was on her father's land, the shepherds had no choice except to wait until after Rachel had watered his flocks.

Jacob's frown vanished when he saw Rachel. Putting his shoulder to the stone guarding the mouth of the spring, he pushed it away and, while Rachel's flock was drinking, went over to where she stood with the shepherd's crook in her hand. Rachel's eyes had not missed the presence of the tall stranger by the spring, nor the fact that he was handsome and that his clothing, though travel-worn and dust-stained, was of rich material. Her heart had begun to beat quickly even before he greeted her courteously.

"Shalom," he said in the formula of greeting. "The men tell me that you are the daughter of my kinsman, Laban."

"Your kinsman?" She caught her breath. Could this handsome stranger possibly be from the land of Abraham to which her aunt, Rebekah, had gone?

"Rebekah, Laban's sister, is my mother," Jacob replied.

"I am Rachel, daughter of Laban!" the girl cried.

"And I am Jacob, grandson of Abraham who came to Canaan from this very land!"

Canaan! How many times Rachel had repeated the magic name of the Land of Promise to which Abraham had gone and become rich, until his tribe—so travelers said—was like the sands of the sea. Perhaps this handsome grandson of Abraham had come to Haran seeking a bride, as had the servant of Abraham years ago when he had found Rebekah. The thought fairly took Rachel's breath away and so did the newcomer's action when he stepped forward and kissed her upon the forehead.

"I will go and tell my father," she cried breathlessly. Leaving the flock—in fact forgetting it entirely—she turned and ran toward her home. Jacob followed, driving the flock before him, lest they become scattered and another shepherd claim some of them for his own, or a wild animal find them unprotected and attack. He was barely halfway to the house, however, when Laban came hobbling to meet him, embracing him and giving him the kiss of welcome.

At the house Jacob met Leah, but with the vivacious Rachel beside him, listening with shining eyes and parted lips as he told of his journey, his dream, and the covenant he had made upon the hill called Bethel, he hardly noticed the older daughter. There were questions by the hundreds to be answered; Laban wished for news about his beloved sister Rebekah, and Rachel was eager to know everything about Canaan and its fabulous cities as well as the almost legendary land of Egypt to the south.

Occupied as he was, Jacob could not fail to note the delicious food served so unobtrusively by Leah, the cleanness of the house, the dried herbs for flavoring hanging from the rafters, and the spotless pots and pans beside the oven. Nor could he help perceiving that it was Leah who served them and afterwards cleaned up the remains of the feast of welcome for the traveler before coming to sit quietly with some mending in the corner of the room, listening to his tales—the narrative embellished a little, it was true, for what young man would not want to impress the eager and beautiful Rachel!

So pleasant was it in the house of Laban, and so bemused was Jacob with the beauty of the younger sister, that he remained a month. He did not fail to earn his keep, however, but went out each day to assist Rachel with the flock, though she needed little help. Before a week had passed he was thoroughly in love with the vivacious Rachel, but quite at a loss for money with which to pay the *mohar*, since he owned nothing except the clothes he stood in.

Laban was happy to have Jacob in his house, but he was a just man and could not let even a kinsman work without wages. Besides he was afraid that if he did not make it attractive for Jacob, the young man might go away. "Surely you are my bone and my flesh," he told Jacob when a month had passed. "Should you therefore serve me for nothing? What will your wages be?"

Jacob's eyes swept the household where he had found safety and happiness, a roof over his head, a comfortable cushion upon which to sleep, and delicious food to warm his stomach. His eyes passed over Leah with the other familiar objects of the house; self-effacing always, she seemed only a part of it. But they glowed when they fell upon the dark-haired Rachel and she, knowing his thoughts, lowered her own eyes demurely. Jacob took a deep breath and voiced a thought that had been much in his mind since the first day he had come to the household of Laban. "I will serve you seven years for Rachel, your younger daughter," he said.

Laban's shrewd gaze went from Rachel, whose eyes were still lowered, to Leah. He had noticed the way Leah's eyes sought out Jacob when the young man was not looking, nor did he miss the pain in them now and her sudden gasp before she stumbled blindly from the room. When his gaze returned to Jacob, Laban had made a decision. Knowing Leah's virtues and Rachel's faults but loving them equally, he thought he saw a way to please both daughters—while at the same time taking advantage of Jacob's obvious genius as a herdsman. And best of all, if his plan worked, he need not lose either his daughters or the riches that Jacob could bring him.

"It is better that I give her to you than to another man," Laban said. "Stay with me."

Jacob settled down happily in the household of Laban and took charge of Laban's flock. He saw Rachel every day and the years went rapidly by while his skill in breeding cattle and sheep and his zeal in looking after them caused the herds to increase mightily. Soon Laban was a rich man and could assign parts of his herds to his sons. To Jacob went nothing yet he worked patiently, for having made a bargain, he would not swerve from it. He did not lose track of the time, however, and when the seven years were finished, he came to Laban to claim his reward.

"Give me my wife, for my days are fulfilled," he said and

Laban at once ordered a great marriage feast to be held. All this time Laban had not raised the question that, according to tribal law, the younger girl could not be married until the older one was wed. Nor did he raise it now, for the plan he'd made seven years before took care of that.

During the years that he had been in Laban's household, Jacob had come to accept Leah as he accepted the food she prepared and the comfortable home in which he lived. He was fond of her but, compared to Rachel, she was like the shadow against the sunlight—he did not stop to remember that shadow gave a man rest and comfort but the sun's heat could destroy him.

Leah's heart was heavy as she went about readying the marriage feast, but she did not stint the preparations. Jacob's wedding must be a happy occasion for him, though her own heart was breaking; she loved him enough for that. She even pretended to enter into the merriment, feasting, and wine-drinking that accompanied such a happy occasion lest he see her unhappiness and pity her. As for Jacob, after seven years of work this was indeed a time of rejoicing; if he drank somewhat too heavily of the wine, it was a fitting time for it and there was Laban urging him on.

When Laban told Leah what she must do, her first impulse was to refuse, though she could not quell the sudden furious tumult of her senses at the thought. But when her father sternly ordered her to obey, she had no choice.

Finally, at midnight, the guests departed and it was time for the bridegroom to go into the dark chamber where—he naturally supposed—his wife awaited him. It never occurred to Jacob to doubt that the soft arms embracing him or the lips that kissed his were those of Rachel—how could he know that Rachel was weeping in another part of the house where her father had shut her up? Only when morning dawned did he discover that it was another than his beloved who lay in his arms—Leah the older daughter. Then it was too late, for she was his wife and to divorce her meant he could never have Rachel for whom he had served so many years. Besides, Jacob was fond of Leah and did not want to hurt her.

# 9. Jacob and Laban

*"The* LORD *watch between me and
thee, when we are absent one from another."* GENESIS 31:49

JACOB WAS justifiably indignant at Laban's deception in sub-
stituting Leah for Rachel, the bride for whom he had served
seven years. "What is this you have done to me?" he demanded angrily of his father-in-law. "Did I not serve with
you for Rachel? Why then have you deceived me?"

The wily Laban knew Jacob well by now. He knew the depth
of his passion for the beautiful daughter, and he had included in
his plan a way to insure retaining Jacob's services for many
more years. He was ready now to put the second part of the
plan into action. "It cannot be done so in our country," he
protested, "to give the younger daughter before the firstborn."

Jacob was a shrewd enough trader to recognize that he had
been outwitted and might as well make the best bargain he
could. When Laban suggested that he live with Leah for a
week—so that she might be spared the shame of being rejected
by her husband on the day after the wedding—and then serve
another seven years for Rachel, he agreed. This time, however,
he demanded his reward at the beginning, not the end, of the
service. Rachel became Jacob's second wife, and his favorite,
while Leah took up in his household much the same position
of second-best she had occupied in that of her father.

54

But God favored Leah over the sharper-witted Rachel. While the younger daughter remained barren, Leah gave Jacob a son who was named Reuben and, in the succeeding years, three more—Simeon, Levi, and Judah. As the years passed, Jacob turned more and more to the fruitful Leah and away from the barren Rachel who, in turn, upbraided him for her own lack. "Give me children or else I die!" she begged.

"Am I in the place of God who withholds the fruit of the womb from you?" Jacob demanded, tired of her nagging.

Recognizing that Leah had won over her again, Rachel resorted to a common practice. To Jacob she sent her maid Bilhah and when the child of that union was being born, took the mother upon her knees and thus claimed it as her own. "God has judged me and has heard my voice and given me a son," Rachel said happily and called the child Dan. A second son by Bilhah was called Naphtali.

Now it was Leah who chose to give birth vicariously; by her maid, Zilpah, were born Gad and Asher, following which Leah herself gave birth to Isaachar, Zebulun, and a daughter called Dinah. Finally God favored Rachel with a child of her own whom she called Joseph. And because Rachel had been his first love, Jacob loved Joseph above all others, keeping him always beside him.

Years thus passing, Jacob decided to leave the region of Padan-Aram and return to Canaan. The land was large enough for both him and his brother Esau, even if the older son of Isaac was still angry at the deception Jacob had practiced upon him—a deception which in the end had cost Jacob the inheritance of his father.

"Send me away that I may go to my own place and my own country," Jacob told Laban. "And give me my wives and children for whom I have served you."

Laban did not wish to lose the benefits of Jacob's skill as herdsman and breeder. "I pray you stay, if I have found favor in your eyes," he begged. "The Lord has blessed me for your sake, so tell me your wages and I will give it."

Jacob was now far from being the naïve young man who had been deceived by Laban in the matter of Leah and Rachel.

He had no possessions of his own, for all the cattle belonged to Laban; now he saw a way to turn to his own benefit Laban's selfishness in wanting him to stay. He drove a bargain with his father-in-law that thenceforth all brown, spotted, or ringstraked cattle born in the herd should be his, and to this Laban quickly agreed, thinking that Jacob had outsmarted himself. Jacob had learned much of cattle-breeding over the years, however, and by cleverly breeding together the stronger among the spotted animals, he stayed strictly within his bargain with Laban while managing to get the greater part of the cattle for himself.

As Jacob grew richer, Laban and his sons saw themselves losing cattle that they regarded as their own and they grew angry with Jacob for having cleverly—though legally—outwitted them. Word of their murmurings came to Jacob and, fearing that they might attack him, he secretly made preparations to go back to Canaan. Warning his wives not to tell their father or their brothers of his intention, he got his herds and possessions ready for the journey. And when Laban went into the hills to shear his own flocks where his sons were pasturing them, Jacob and his household—now a considerable number, for he was a rich man, both in sons, servants, and possessions—left Padan-Aram and started for Canaan. Crossing the Euphrates west of its junction with the River Balikh, he set his face southwest toward Damascus and the route into Canaan.

As he was shearing his flocks in the hills beyond Haran, word reached Laban three days after Jacob's departure that his son-in-law had left with all his belongings. Taking his sons and the fighting men of his family with him, Laban went immediately in pursuit. Driving the herds and carrying his numerous possessions, Jacob of necessity made much slower progress than did the angry Laban, yet with three days' start, it was a full week before Laban caught up with him. Meanwhile Jacob had turned southward after leaving Damascus and was following the old route called the King's Highway running east of the Sea of Chinnereth and the Jordan River through the hill country of Bashan and Gilead where there was ample pasturage for the cattle, sheep, and goats.

Along the way, Laban had a dream, possibly brought on by

his experience of Jacob's cleverness in the past. The dream was a warning to handle his son-in-law carefully, if he did not want to be bested again.

When Terah had brought his family out of Ur many years before, he had carried with him the images of the household god, the same who had guided Abraham and had cared for Jacob on the Mount of Bethel. The sons and grandsons of Abraham no longer worshipped the image of their god for, as when Abraham had been instructed to leave Haran and journey into Canaan, the Lord now spoke directly to them in dreams and visions. Laban still preserved the images, however, and these Rachel, without telling Jacob, had stolen when they left her father's household. Laban was naturally incensed, not only at losing the possessions which he considered Jacob to have taken by deceit, but at his taking the household god, presumably to earn the favor of the deity for himself.

Jacob, knowing nothing of Rachel's theft, was indignant. "With whomever you find your gods, let him not live," he said when Laban accused him of taking the images. "Discover anything of yours in what I have and take it."

Laban immediately searched the camp, but Rachel cleverly hid the images so that they were not discovered. As the search progressed, so did Jacob's anger at Laban. Finally he could contain himself no longer.

"What is my trespass and what is my sin that you have pursued so hotly after me?" he demanded. "You have searched all my stuff yet what have you found of yours? Set it here before my brethren and yours that they may judge between us."

Laban could not answer, for he had found nothing. "This twenty years have I been with you," Jacob continued angrily. "In the day the drought consumed me and the frost by night, and sleep departed from my eyes. I served you fourteen years for your two daughters and six years for your cattle, and you have changed my wages ten times. If the God of my father, the God of Abraham, and of Isaac had not been with me, you would have sent me away empty. Now God has seen my affliction and the labor of my hands, and has rebuked you."

Laban, fearing that God would punish him, was afraid to push his angry son-in-law any farther. "Come let us make a covenant," he suggested, and Jacob, as he had everything to lose in a fight with Laban and his men, agreed. A pile of stones was quickly erected as a pillar and an altar.

"Let this pillar be witness that I will not pass over this heap of stones to you, and you will not pass over this heap and this pillar to do me harm," Laban suggested. "The God of Abraham, and the God of Nahor, and the God of their father judge between us. The Lord watch between me and you when we are absent one from another."

The covenant was made and Jacob swore to it by the God of his father Isaac, sealing the compact with a sacrifice and the customary ceremonial meal. The following morning Laban and his men departed for the journey back home, leaving Jacob to keep all he had taken out of Padan-Aram.

Jacob realized that only fear of God's wrath had kept Laban from attacking him, but he could not know then that with this step the family of Abraham—known in Canaan as the Hebrews—had broken with the people and the land of their forefathers. From henceforth, they would be a nation to themselves.

# 10. The Wrestlers

*"Jacob was left alone; and there wrestled a man with him."*

GENESIS 32:24

WITH THE THREAT of Laban's anger no longer following them, Jacob and his train moved slowly southward through Bashan and Gilead east of the Jordan, letting the animals graze upon the lush grass and trading with the inhabitants, as did the Wandering People everywhere. Finally they came to the banks of the river Jabbok, a swift stream tumbling from rock to rock and pool to pool as it descended from the mountain ranges paralleling the east bank of the Jordan where it ran swiftly in its deep cleft toward the Sea of Judgment. There Jacob paused while his flocks and herds grazed and grew fat; and considered the problem of what sort of reception he could expect from his brother Esau.

Word had come to Jacob that Esau was now dwelling in the region of Mount Seir in the country of Edom, almost due south of his present location and a little over a week's journey away. Jacob still had no inkling of Esau's feeling for him after some twenty years of separation, however, so he decided to send messengers ahead to feel out his brother's sentiments.

"Thus you shall speak to my lord Esau," he instructed the emissary. "Your servant Jacob says, 'I have lived with Laban until now and I have oxen and asses, menservants and women-

59

servants. I have sent to tell my lord of my coming that I may find grace in your sight.' "

"We came to your brother Esau and he comes to meet you," the messengers reported upon their return. It was happy news, until they added, "And four hundred men with him."

This news troubled Jacob even more than had the pursuit by Laban. Esau was a mighty warrior and he already knew the temper of his brother's wrath which years ago had forced him to leave home. In his quandary Jacob could think only of his possessions; should Esau decide to attack him, he must somehow save part of what he had. And since half was better than none at all, he called his followers together and ordered everything divided then and there. When there were protests, he explained that if Esau conquered one half, the other half could escape by crossing the Jordan at the mouth of the Jabbok and entering Canaan. Having thus protected his possessions, Jacob turned to God.

"O God of my father Abraham and my father Isaac," he prayed, "the Lord who said to me, 'Return to your country and to your kindred and I will deal well with you,' I am not worthy of the least of all the mercies and of all the truth that you have showed to your servant. Deliver me, I pray you, from the hand of my brother Esau, lest he come and smite me and the mother with the children." Then he added, almost as a reminder to the Lord, "And you said, 'I will surely do good to you and make your seed as the sand of the sea, which cannot be numbered for multitude.' "

For hours Jacob waited for an answer but it did not come. Finally he arose and sadly ordered that one of the two halves into which his possessions had been divided be separated into several droves and sent ahead as presents to Esau to appease his anger. "Put a space between drove and drove," he commanded the servants in charge of them. "When Esau my brother meets you, say, 'They are your servant Jacob's. It is a present sent to my lord Esau and he is behind us.' "

Drove by drove, Jacob sent half of his possessions across the Jabbok southward toward where Esau and the four hundred men were advancing—for what purpose he did not yet know.

Finally, at the end of the long train of his belongings, he sent his wives, his womenservants, and his sons across the river until only he remained on the other side.

Jacob could take no pleasure in the measures to preserve his possessions and his life which God's apparent desertion had forced him to take. His was a peaceful people with no knowledge of war; nor was he a fighter himself, having spent his life in the study of husbandry and trading rather than in warlike pursuits. If his brother was not appeased by the several droves sent ahead as gifts, he knew that he would undoubtedly fall upon the women and children and all Jacob's family might be destroyed. Still there was no hope of opposing his brother and, as he crouched in the shadows with only the turbulent little stream as a barrier between himself and Esau, Jacob tasted the bitter gall of knowing that he was a coward willing to sacrifice even his loved ones to save his own life.

Darkness fell, and the shouts of the men driving the cattle southward, the voices of the women, the calls of the children died away in the distance. Alone with only his fear and his shame as companions, Jacob knew the bitterest loneliness he had ever experienced. He did not pray again, sensing that somehow he must have offended God—probably by his cowardice—else his prayer that afternoon would have been answered in some way. And having no person now to whom he could turn, he could only wait for death—or salvation through the mercy of God.

Jacob did not hear the footsteps of the man who appeared suddenly beside him, and the stranger's face, shadowed in the darkness, was unrecognizable. That he was tall and strong was apparent, and when Jacob greeted him fearfully but courteously, the man did not answer. Instead he seized Jacob with strong arms as if to crush him.

At long last the courage of desperation drove the paralysis of fear from Jacob's muscles. And as he fought back, wrestling silently there on the bank of the brawling stream, he felt a new strength and a new courage flowing into his sinews. His mysterious opponent was strong but Jacob knew a fierce joy at the realization that he was equally strong, that they were well-matched, and that, perhaps for the first time in his life, he could defend himself by his strength instead of by cunning and deception. He hardly felt fatigue as the hours passed while they wrestled there, still silently, under the trees.

Sometimes it was the stranger, at others it was Jacob who had the advantage in the fierce struggle which, it seemed, could have no ending. And yet something was happening, for amidst the panting and straining of physical combat, a new Jacob was being born, a Jacob who had courage and a new strength, who, though facing an adversary to whom he might lose his life, yet knew that even if he did lose it he still would have given a good account of himself. And somehow that knowledge brought Jacob a fiercer pride than he had ever experienced through besting another in a trade or even in outwitting the wily Laban.

Though here deep in the cleft near the river it was still semi-darkness, dawn was already beginning to gild the mountain heights overlooking the mountain valley when finally the stranger spoke. "Let me go, for the day breaks," he said.

Suddenly Jacob knew who his adversary was, for to an ordinary man the day would make no difference from the night in a contest such as this. "I will not let you go unless you bless me," he said firmly.

"What is your name?"

"Jacob."

"Your name shall no more be called Jacob but Israel," the deep voice said. "For as a prince you have power with God and with men and have prevailed."

Jacob did not loose his hold upon the stranger yet. "Tell me your name, I pray," he begged.

"Why is it that you ask my name?" the man said. "You have my blessing."

No sooner were the words of the blessing spoken than Jacob found himself alone, with only the trampled earth where they had striven together to show that he had not spent the night in solitude—or that the whole thing was not a dream. "This place shall be called Penuel," Jacob said in a tone of awe as he knelt to wash the sweat of combat from his body. "I have seen God face to face and my life has been preserved."

The sun was rising as Jacob crossed over the Jabbok and

hurried after his people. When he reached them he did not slink behind the women and children as he had last night, but forged on until he was at the head of the column and could see his brother Esau and the four hundred advancing to meet them.

The brothers came together in the open space between their people and embraced. "What do you mean by all this drove that I met?" Esau asked.

"They were sent to find grace in the sight of my lord."

"I have enough, my brother," said Esau. "Keep what you have for yourself."

Yesterday Jacob would have seized eagerly the chance to retain his cherished belongings, but not today. "Take, I pray, my blessing because God has dealt graciously with me and I have enough," he said.

A man called Israel was speaking, a man who had been born in night-long combat on the bank of the river Jabbok and had learned that he who would serve God and win divine favor must first put away covetousness and think of his fellow man before himself.

# 11. Joseph and His Brothers

*"They . . . sold Joseph to the Ishme-*
*elites for twenty pieces of silver."*

GENESIS 37:28

JOSEPH WAS HAPPY and not a little smug at his own good
fortune as he strode along the winding track from Shechem
to Dothan. As the firstborn of Rachel—whose barrenness
God had finally relieved after Jacob had crossed into Canaan
following his meeting with Esau—he was his father's favorite.
Rachel had given birth to a second son, Benjamin, but she
had died in childbirth and Jacob—called Israel since that
night when he had wrestled with the stranger on the banks of
the river Jabbok—had taken no more wives. Of his twelve sons
by Leah, Rachel, and the two maids, Zilpah and Bilhah, the
old man loved Joseph best of all. As a token of that love, he
had given the youth a magnificent coat dyed in many colors,
a garment far richer than any possessed by the other brothers.
Joseph wore it proudly wherever he went; it was wrapped about
his body today even though the warmth of spring was already
in the air.

Jacob's favoritism to Joseph had angered the other brothers,
and Joseph had done nothing to endear himself to them.
Because he was cleverer than they, his father had come to lean
more and more upon him, even though he was yet a youth
and far below the thirty years of age considered necessary in

order for a young man to sit in the councils of his people. While his brothers drove the flocks and herds from pasture to pasture, sometimes remaining away from the encampment at the old home of Abraham and Isaac at Mamre for several months, as shepherds of their race had been doing since time without memory, Joseph remained at home with his father, enjoying the fat of the land. And remembering how Jacob himself had stolen the birthright of his brother Esau, the brothers were naturally suspicious that Joseph might be scheming to get everything for himself.

None of this troubled Joseph particularly as he followed the winding caravan trail late one afternoon in spring, for he was busy with his own thoughts. The Canaanite village of Dothan where he expected to find his brothers pasturing their cattle, sheep, and goats lay to the north along the great central highway. He had already met several caravans from far-off Damascus and the lands along the Tigris and Euphrates basins of which he had often heard his father speak but which only the oldest among his brothers remembered now. Once he'd hidden in the underbrush to watch a band of Ishmaelites from across the Jordan to the east go by; hawk-faced, dark-skinned men, they were known better as thieves than as merchants, and the line of wretched humanity stumbling in chains at the end of the column named them slave dealers as well.

The road circled westward along the foothills of Mount Ebal for a short distance before turning northward through the hill country of the central highlands to Dothan, situated upon an elevation overlooking the fertile valleys where Joseph's brothers had taken the flocks and herds to graze upon the spring grass. The youth did not envy his brothers the chance to travel, however, for shepherding was not an easy occupation. Often they slept in the open with watchmen posted to protect the herd against marauding animals and, in this region, thieving Canaanites and Ishmaelites. The long nights, cold in winter here in the highlands, were whiled away with songs, playing upon the shepherd's flute and the eight-stringed harp, or with stories in which the adventures of tribal heroes were recounted in detail. One saga, told for centuries by shepherds, recounted the adventures of a legendary hero called Gilgamesh who had fought with the giant Enkidu and, when neither could conquer the other, had become friends. In the endless variations of this popular tale, the two then wandered the earth, righting wrongs and searching for the secret of life over death.

As he walked along, Joseph's thoughts were not on the caravans he met; Mamre was near the Way of the Sea and they were old sights to him. Instead, he was thinking—as he did much of the time—of two dreams he'd had not so long ago, dreams which had stirred his own imagination but had not endeared him to his brothers to whom he'd described them the next morning. In the first dream, Joseph had seen himself binding sheaves in the field during the harvest. As he watched, a strange thing had happened: the sheaf he had just bound with a wisp of cut grain wrapped about the stalks and tucked snugly under the band suddenly stood upright, while those bound by his brothers bowed before it.

"Shall you indeed reign over us?" the brothers had demanded caustically when Joseph told them of his dream. Nor did they feel any better toward him when he described a second dream, for in it the sun, the moon, and stars made obeisance to him.

This time Jacob, too, had rebuked Joseph. "What is this dream?" the old man demanded indignantly, thinking that he was only boasting. "Shall I and your mother and your brethren bow down to you?"

Joseph had not been intimidated by the laughter of his brothers, for the dreams merely confirmed what he knew in his heart already, that his was to be a far greater future than that of a shepherd like the rest of his people. Being next to the youngest, it was out of the question that he should succeed his father as patriarch, although he had the example of Jacob always before him showing how such things could be accomplished by a clever man, but his confidence never waned.

When he saw Dothan on the hill before him and the flocks and herds of his father grazing in the valley near-by, Joseph did not expect a warm welcome from his brothers. His mission was to count the animals and bring back a report to his father; he planned to spend no longer with his brothers than was necessary to accomplish this task.

By the bright colors of his robe, the brothers recognized Joseph while he was still some distance away. "Behold, the dreamer comes!" one of them said contemptuously.

"Let us kill him and throw him into a pit, pretending a wild animal has devoured him," another added. "Then we shall see what comes of his dreams!"

The others agreed, except Reuben. Knowing how much his father loved Joseph and how angry Jacob would be at him, the oldest, if anything happened to the younger brother, he tried to save Joseph from the anger of the others.

"Throw him into the pit in the wilderness," he suggested, planning to return later and release Joseph. "But lay no hand upon him."

The brothers grudgingly agreed; when Joseph reached them, they seized him, tore off his bright-colored robe, and tossed him into a dry well whose sides were too steep to be climbed. Paying no attention to his cries, they sat down to eat while Reuben went out to tend the flocks. The others still planned to kill Joseph while the older brother was away, but while they were eating, a caravan of Ishmaelites came into view on the highway.

"What profit is it if we kill our brother and hide his blood?" Judah suggested. "Let us sell him to the Ishmaelites."

The idea pleased them, for not only did it allow them to be rid of Joseph without having his blood on their hands, but at the same time gave them a chance to profit. So several of them went to accost the Ishmaelites while the others hauled Joseph from the well and dragged him over to the leader of the caravan. There was little time for haggling, as the transaction had to be completed before Reuben returned, so they got only a poor price—twenty pieces of silver instead of the thirty that was the established price for a male slave of even the meanest sort.

By the time Reuben came back, the transaction was completed and Joseph was on his way to the slave markets of Egypt. To complete the deception, the brothers killed a goat and, dipping Joseph's coat into the blood, sent it back to their father as proof that Joseph had been killed by a wild animal.

# 12. Joseph in Egypt

*"And Pharaoh said unto Joseph, See, I have set thee over all the land of Egypt."* GENESIS 41:41

NEFERA, wife of Potiphar, who was captain in the armies of Pharaoh, had everything she could wish—except the love of the Hebrew slave in her own household. And being a greedy woman, she would not be content until she either had him or had destroyed him.

It had been a stroke of good fortune for Joseph when he was sold to the Egyptian captain in the slave market of Avaris, the delta city which the Pharaohs of that period used as their capital. Potiphar was an upright man and a great warrior; he had been rewarded with considerable riches, had a fine house, many possessions, and a beautiful wife. But as he was often away from home on his military duties, he needed someone he could trust to oversee his household as a steward. And when he saw how clever and intelligent Joseph, the young slave, was, he put him in charge.

Nor did Joseph, even though only a slave, fail his master. The years during which he grew to be a man—a process hastened considerably by his brothers' rough treatment of him—had brought him a quick maturity and even greater wisdom. He served Potiphar well, superintending his servants and increasing the possessions of the Egyptian captain. One thing in Potiphar's

68

household Joseph did not try to remedy, however, was the discontent of Potiphar's beautiful wife.

Nefera interpreted Joseph's avoidance as evidence that her beauty had no effect upon him and, being passionate, shallow, and vicious, she did not hesitate to use all her wiles in an attempt to break down the reserve of the handsome Hebrew slave.

But all around as he went through the streets of Avaris, Joseph could see other slaves building tombs for their masters, hewing stone and hauling it across the country, or making bricks in the hot Egyptian sun. He realized fully how fortunate he had been in getting such a good master—a man who had evinced his trust in Joseph by placing everything in his care —and he had no intention of betraying Potiphar. Thus, the more insistent Nefera became in her attempts to seduce him, the more Joseph avoided her. Naturally this only angered the woman more and made her determined to have her way.

It was Joseph's custom during Potiphar's frequent absences to visit the apartment of his owner's wife each morning in order to report to her on the household activities and ask after her needs. The day came when the woman slave who always before had attended Nefera was no longer present, and Joseph entered the perfumed apartment to find his master's wife, alone, lying upon a cushioned couch, her body covered merely with the sheerest of the transparent fabrics woven by the Phoenicians of Byblus. He started to withdraw immediately, but Nefera ordered him to come closer. And being a slave, he could not refuse.

Joseph had not been entirely insensitive to the lure of the woman; indeed, he would have had to be made of stone not to have felt it. But he also knew Nefera for what she was, an abandoned creature who lived only for her own pleasure and was frequently unfaithful to Potiphar during his many absences. Still the truth of her intentions did not occur to him until suddenly she put her arms around him and tried to draw him down beside her. Too late Joseph realized that the servants had been sent away and the stage deliberately set for just this —Nefera's arms were tight about him and when he tried to pull away, her hand fastened on the waistband of the short white skirt or tunic that all slaves wore, tearing it from his body and leaving him wearing only his loincloth as he fled from the boudoir.

Joseph had counted himself well out of a dangerous situation —until he heard Nefera scream for the soldiers that her husband always left on guard. Instantly the whole household was in turmoil as the guards and the other servants hurried to her chamber. Joseph felt an almost irresistible impulse to escape before the guards could seize him, but he knew that his running now would be taken as an admission of guilt, removing any chance he might have of explaining to Potiphar what had really happened. He therefore made no resistance when the guards seized him and dragged him once more before Nefera, but stood proudly erect while she accused him of trying to seduce her and ordered him bound until her husband could punish him properly.

In the evening Nefera poured her own version of the story into the ears of Potiphar, accusing Joseph of trying to attack her and leaving his garment when she had resisted him and forced him to flee. Under ordinary circumstances, Potiphar would have been fully justified in striking Joseph down then and there for such a crime, but the Captain knew his wife and more than half suspected what had really happened. He would have been disgraced if he had taken the word of a slave over his wife in an affair such as this, however, so he ordered for Joseph the lightest punishment he could give—prison. There, with others awaiting the pleasure of Pharaoh, the young Hebrew spent many months with no inkling of what his fate would be.

God had a greater purpose for Joseph, however, than to die in prison or under the sword of the executioner, and that purpose was not long in being revealed. Recognizing Joseph's intelligence and his capacity for leadership, the jailer had placed him in charge of all the prisoners, including Pharaoh's baker and butler who had been locked up on the orders of the king, While there each of the men had a dream which he described to Joseph.

"In my dream a vine was before me," the chief butler said. "On the vine were three branches and it was as though it budded and blossoms shot forth and clusters brought forth rich grapes. Pharaoh's cup was in my hand, and I took the grapes and pressed them into the cup, and gave the cup into his hand."

"The three branches are three days," Joseph told him. "Within three days Pharaoh will lift up your head and restore you to your place, and you shall deliver his cup into his hand as you did before. When it is well with you," he added, "make mention of me to Pharaoh and bring me out of this house, for I was stolen out of the land of the Hebrews and have done nothing for which they should put me in the dungeon."

The chief baker also told Joseph his dream. "I saw three white baskets on my head," he said. "In the uppermost basket was all manner of baked meats for Pharaoh, and the birds ate them out of the basket on my head."

"This is the interpretation of your dream," Joseph told him. "The three baskets are three days before Pharaoh will lift your head from off you. He will hang it upon a tree and the birds shall eat your flesh."

Everything happened exactly as Joseph had said, but when the chief butler was restored to his place, he forgot all about the young slave.

Two years passed and Pharaoh had two dreams that troubled him very much. In the first, he stood by a river and saw seven well-favored cattle come up out of the water and feed in a meadow, but seven other ill-favored and lean-fleshed cattle also came up out of the river and ate up the seven fat cattle. In another dream that same night, Pharaoh saw seven fat ears of corn upon one stalk, but seven thin ears came up after them and destroyed the seven full ears.

The magicians and soothsayers of the court were not able to explain the dreams, but finally the chief butler remembered how the Hebrew slave had correctly interpreted his dream while in prison. He sent for Joseph at once and had him brought before Pharaoh.

"What God is about to do he shows to Pharaoh," Joseph

told the king and the court in explanation of the dreams. "Seven years of great plenty shall come throughout all the land of Egypt and after them years of famine. All the plenty shall be forgotten then and the famine shall consume the land."

Pharaoh was much impressed by Joseph's ready understanding of the dream. "What shall I do that my people shall not be destroyed by the years of famine?" he asked.

"Let Pharaoh seek out a man discreet and wise and set him over the land of Egypt," Joseph advised. "Let him appoint officers to take up the fifth part of all the food of those seven plenteous years, and keep it in the cities as a store against the seven years of famine."

"Since God had showed you all this, there is none so discreet and wise as you are," Pharaoh told Joseph. "You shall be over my house and all my people shall be ruled according to your word. Only in the throne will I be greater than you, and I have set you over all the land of Egypt."

With Joseph as viceroy, or grand vizier, answerable only to Pharaoh himself, the task of storing grain against the coming years of famine went forward rapidly. Even with the replenishment of fertile soil through the yearly floods, however, the rich delta region was not able to produce enough grain to sustain the whole land through seven years of famine. A way was needed to bring water to even larger areas of the Nile valley than were then under cultivation, and this Joseph soon discovered. Farther up the Nile where the floods were not so plenteous, he put thousands of men to work digging a great canal through which water was directed into a hitherto barren region. Irrigated by what the people quickly came to call Joseph's Canal, this area soon became a rich garden where grew lush crops of grain along with oranges, peaches, pomegranates, olives and, of course, grapes, for even the poorest Egyptian loved his wine.

As Joseph rode over the land superintending the activities of his overseers and the building of new granaries, the farmers at work paused to watch his chariot and bow down before this man who—though a Hebrew—was next in importance below the king. In summer the floods kept them out of the fields, but in the autumn the land was alive with people planting the crops.

The manner of planting was different from anything Joseph had seen before he came into Egypt, however. Here, so as to take advantage of all possible moisture, the seeds were sown while water still covered the land. Sowers scattered them from shallow-bottomed boats built from stalks of papyrus, the reeds that grew in vast swamps beside the rivers. (Split, beaten out, and soaked in water, papyrus reeds were also used for making rolls upon which records were written down by the scribes and messages sent from one place to another.)

After being sown, the seeds were trampled into the soft mud by herds of cattle either driven over the fields or following calves led by men in boats. After sprouting, the plants were cultivated with short-handled hoes of wood or bronze. The crops grew rapidly during each of the seven rich years, but with the subsiding of the flood in autumn they still had to be irrigated by water drawn from the river or from canals either by men carrying two buckets on a yoke across their shoulders, or by long wooden sweeps with buckets at the end.

Reaping was done with a hand sickle. In the mountains, backward people still used sickles made from a row of flint chips set in line as teeth, but in Egypt they were made of bronze. South of the Sea of Judgment there were great copper mines, and men had long since learned to melt down the soft red metal with smaller amounts of a darker one to produce the far harder alloy called bronze.

Threshing was still done as it had been since the oldest times. First the grain was piled upon a circle of hard-packed earth and then animals were driven across it. The chaff was winnowed by tossing the threshed grain into the wind with shovels made of wood. At the final threshing and stacking of the grain, overseers appointed at Joseph's order stood by to see that the fifth part was put into Pharaoh's granaries against the coming famine.

During these busy and prosperous years, Joseph married Asenath who gave him two sons, Manasseh and Ephraim. When the time of plenty ended and the period of famine began as he had predicted, he opened the storehouses and sold grain to the people so that they might not lack for bread. Through his period of great good fortune, Joseph did not fail to give thanks to God, recognizing himself as only an agent in working out the plan of divine will—including even the evil done him by the wife of Potiphar—whereby the Egyptian people and, as it turned out, his own family as well were saved from destruction.

The famine that attacked Egypt was not limited to the land along the Nile but also involved Canaan; soon Jacob—now called Israel—and his family began to suffer. When caravan drivers passing near Mamre and Hebron brought word that grain could be had in the cities of the delta, Jacob sent Joseph's ten brothers to buy corn, keeping only Benjamin, the youngest, with him. When the brothers came into Egypt, they did not recognize the magnificent prince to whom they made application to buy grain as the brother they had sold into slavery many years before. But Joseph remembered his brothers, as well as the dreams for which they had hated him.

"You are spies," he accused them when they were first brought before him.

"No, my lord, we came to buy food," the brothers protested. "We are all one man's sons, twelve brothers. The youngest is with our father, and one is not."

Joseph kept Simeon in prison as a hostage but sold corn to the others and let them go—after ordering them to bring Benjamin upon their next journey into Egypt. Secretly he put every man's money in his sack, however, and when Jacob's sons reached home and found the money, they were very much afraid.

"Joseph and Simeon are gone and now you will take Benjamin away," Jacob said sadly when they told him of the Egyptian viceroy's demand that they bring Benjamin to Egypt. "All these things are against me."

"Kill my sons if I do not bring him to you," Judah offered, so Jacob sent the brothers back to Egypt with Benjamin, carrying, as a gift to the Egyptian nobleman, the best fruits of the land—some balm, a little honey, spices, myrrh, nuts, and almonds. He also made them take double money so that they could return what had been put into their sacks and pay for the grain they would buy on this journey.

When Joseph saw Benjamin, he ordered his steward to make ready a great feast while the sacks of his brothers were filled with grain. Once again the purchase money was placed in the mouth of each sack, but into Benjamin's Joseph also put his own silver cup. Then when the sons of Jacob were some distance away from the city, he sent his steward to follow them and find the cup, choosing this way to punish them for what they had done to him.

"God forbid that your servants should do this thing," the brothers protested when the steward accused them of stealing. "The money we found in our sacks' mouths we brought again out of the land of Canaan. How then should we steal silver or gold from your lord's house? With whomever of your servants it is found, let him die and we also will be your lord's bondsmen."

"Let it be according to your words," the steward agreed. "He with whom it is found shall be my servant and you shall be blameless."

When the cup was found in Benjamin's sack, all the brothers returned to Joseph's house and prostrated themselves before him. Judah, the oldest, offered to remain as Joseph's bondsman so that Benjamin might be returned to his father, but Joseph punished them no longer.

"I am Joseph your brother whom you sold into Egypt," he told them. "Do not be grieved or angry with yourselves that you sold me, for God sent me before you to preserve life. Hurry to my father and say, 'Thus says your son Joseph, God has made me lord of all Egypt. Come dwell in the land of Goshen and be near me, you and your children and your children's children and your flocks and your herds and all that you have. There I will nourish you, for there are yet five years of famine.' "

"I will go down with you into Egypt and I will surely bring you up again," God promised Jacob when he prayed for guidance and, ever obedient to the Lord's will, he and all his people came and lived in the land of Goshen in the fertile Nile delta.

When Jacob died, his body was embalmed with rich spices, as were the bodies of the noblemen of Egypt. And after the forty days necessary for the process of embalming and the days of mourning were completed, a great funeral procession journeyed into the land of Canaan as far as the cave of Machpelah where Abraham and Sarah were buried. Jacob's body was placed with them but his people remained in Egypt.

# 13. A Great Nation

> "*Fear not to go down into Egypt; for I will there make of thee a great nation.*" GENESIS 46.3

PRINCE AHMOSE stood upon the balcony outside his mother's apartment and looked over the teeming city of Raamses below. He was a handsome young man with a prominent nose and with the somewhat lighter color of the northern people from Canaan and Aram rather than the more delicately cut features of the Egyptians. But then so many kings' daughters had been sent to Pharaoh as wives to cement treaties made with distant rulers that many princes of the royal household had the same appearance and coloring as Ahmose.

As the son of Pharaoh's daughter rather than of Pharaoh himself, Ahmose had no hope of succeeding to the throne, but many opportunities were open to a nobleman of intelligence, courage, and loyalty. There was the superintendency of the king's mines in the mountainous regions of Sinai, where copper, gold, and turquoises were dug from the depths of the earth; there was the ambassadorship to the kings of Mari and the other countries of the north. And, of course, a fortune could be made in trade with vessels fashioned from the famed Phoenician cedars, ships which regularly plied between the river ports of Egypt and the seaports of Crete, Canaan, and the shores of the Great Sea. Or, if he chose the intrigues of palace politics, Ahmose might even hope to rise to the position of Grand Vizier, second only to Pharaoh himself.

Altogether it was a pleasant life that lay before Prince Ahmose. He lacked nothing he really desired; his short skirt and loincloth were of the finest linen, and the gold chain he wore about his neck marked him as a member of the royal household. When he went abroad, he could ride if he wished in a chariot made of wood imported from the northern countries— ash, birch, stone-oak, or hornbeam. In the streets the people bowed before him as the son of Pharaoh, although some whispered the story that Ahmose was really the child of a Hebrew slave adopted by the king's daughter and raised up in the royal household.

Ahmose had never asked his mother about his birth but he, too, had heard how one day when the daughter of Pharaoh had been bathing in the Nile, a tiny ark woven of rushes and daubed with pitch to make it float had been found near the shore. In it was a baby boy, child of the Hebrew slaves, placed there by its mother because an edict had gone out from Pharaoh that every male born to a Hebrew woman should be destroyed lest the slaves grow so numerous that they become a threat to the Egyptians. Being gentle and kind, the princess had adopted the child—according to the story—taking as his nurse a Hebrew woman living near by who, the princess suspected, was the real mother, and raising him in her household as her son. At any rate, no one could have been loved more than Ahmose was, so he had asked no questions and had been happy—until lately when a vague unrest to which he could not give a name began to trouble him.

A long line of slaves was passing through the street below, staggering under the heavy loads they were carrying from the brickyards where they labored, molding clay and straw into bricks and baking them to the hardness needed for building. As the lash of the overseer fell upon one poor fellow's back, Ahmose felt a momentary stab of pity for those less fortunate than he. If it were true, he thought, that he was from these subject people whose coming into Egypt in a time when one of their number, a man named Joseph, had been Grand Vizier, was duly set down by the scribes in the papyrus rolls containing the history of Egypt, then he had every reason to be grateful for the good fortune that had put him in the palace of Pharaoh instead of in the clay pit. Why then was he unhappy?

Perhaps, Ahmose thought, he needed a change of scene, such as a long voyage up the Nile beyond the great cataracts into the mysterious region called the Mountains of the Moon from which the sacred river was said to take its origin. Or he might journey to the eastward, to the fabled cities on the banks of the Tigris and Euphrates where, travelers said, a civilization as great and as rich as that of Egypt existed. Or again he could push even farther east to visit the legendary countries of the brown men whose culture was said to be also very far advanced.

The more Ahmose thought about the idea of travel, the more it caught his fancy. Leaving the balcony, he descended the outer stairway leading to the enclosed garden of the palace and made his way to the street. There a cacophony of sound met his ears, slaves groaning under the whip, men and women laughing and talking as they walked along the streets or paused to look into the shops. Here a silversmith worked with delicate tools to fashion fine jewelry, and there a potter shaped a delicate vase on his wheel—turned by kicking a disk at the lower end of the shaft with his feet—before applying the colors that would be glazed into the surface by heat and perhaps one day delight the eye of a princess in some far-off land. In another shop, workers in glass were dipping vase-shaped bags of sand into the clear molten liquid again and again, letting it cool and harden before they washed out the sand to leave the vases hollow.

Ahmose paid little attention to these everyday wonders and continued on to the waterfront where, on one of the many branches of the Nile that spread like a fan to form the fertile delta, were the royal quays. There, among the merchants, vessels trading up and down the river, a sleek galley from the distant coast of Canaan was moored. Pausing to admire it, Ahmose remembered a story in the scribal records he had studied in the palace school where the princes of the royal household were taught, the story of how, long ago, a fleet of war galleys had made the final thrust which had driven out a hated invader.

Centuries before, the papyrus rolls recorded—about the time Abraham had come into Canaan from Haran—a great change had come over the Middle Kingdom, which included the delta. Like a whirlwind, a bold fighting nation called the Hyksos had swept into Egypt from Canaan and Syria. Semitic tribes whose forefathers had invaded Chaldea many centuries before—establishing the line of Terah from which had come Abraham, Isaac, and Jacob—had poured past the Princes' Wall to the north which the Pharaohs had erected to protect themselves from invasion, and overrun the low country. Driving hundreds of chariots drawn by swift horses, the Hyksos easily overcame the Egyptians and, taking the rich delta country for themselves, had put even the princes of the upper Nile under tribute.

For several centuries, Hyksos kings had ruled here, holding the Egyptians in subjection. Joseph had come to power under a Hyksos Pharaoh, but some time after his death a sharp change had taken place in Egypt. Beginning at Thebes farther up-river, a rebellion had begun and spread rapidly when the Egyptians rose against their hated conquerors. Some said the rebellion was touched off when the Hyksos Pharaoh of Avaris—now Pi-Raamses in the Nile delta—had objected to the roaring of hippopotami in the swamps outside a neighboring ruler's city. Actually, the pent-up hatred of the Egyptians for the invaders had needed only a spark to touch it off.

From Thebes Egyptian armies invaded the delta region, and a fleet of war galleys sailed northward—downstream on the Nile—to launch an attack by water. Fighting desperately, the Hyksos had been forced to retreat across the River of Egypt into Canaan and, constantly harried by the victorious Egyptians, to draw back still farther until all of Canaan, including the rich seaport cities of the Phoenician coast, fell under the hand of the victors. In a few years Egypt had become a world power with its dominion extending almost to the Euphrates far to the northeast where lived a strange brown-skinned people called the Mitanni. With them a common frontier and an uneasy peace had been made, but for more than a thousand years the area lying between Egypt to the south and the fierce fighting people to the north was a battleground. No more could the Wandering People, as the Hebrew tribes still were called, enter and live peacefully with the other inhabitants as in the days of Abraham.

Hating the Hyksos, the Egyptians naturally hated the descendants of Jacob, or Israel, who had found favor with the Hyksos kings. No sooner did they regain control of the country than they placed the Hebrews in subjection, and in the treasure cities of Pithom and Raamses in the Nile delta, the descendants of Abraham, Isaac, and Jacob—who had been promised the land of Canaan as their own by their God—labored for Pharaoh as slaves. Even in slavery they had multiplied rapidly, however, and soon began to rival in numbers the Egyptians of the area. It was then that Pharaoh had issued the order to destroy every male Hebrew child and, though the rule was evaded in many ways, it was a bitter burden to the oppressed Hebrews. To evade this order, Ahmose's mother had placed him in the rushes where Pharaoh's daughter would be sure to find him, but even she had hardly dared to hope that the son of an Israelite slave would grow up as a prince in the royal house of Egypt.

Even tied up at the quay, the long graceful lines of the sea-going ships were thrilling to a young man. The curved prows could be used to ram an opposing ship, and from the high sterns, shaped like the lotus blossom, bowmen could shoot down upon an attacker. In addition to the banks of oars and benches for the rowers, each galley had a tall mast just back of the center with a broad square sail swinging from a yard. Hanging from the steering post in the stern were two long sweeps manned while under way by several steersmen in order to hold the course before the wind. Such ships, Ahmose knew, could travel long distances over the Great Sea and even ride out storms if they were not able to find shelter in a protected port.

Yes, Ahmose decided, he would ask his mother right away to petition Pharaoh to let him travel as an ambassador to the people along the Euphrates and perhaps to the great Hittite empire extending across the northern arc above the eastern end of the Great Sea. Eager to put his plan into action, he took a short cut past the clay pits and the brickyards where the slaves worked.

Lost in excited planning for the voyage, Ahmose's thoughts were suddenly interrupted by the screams of a man and the sound of a heavy cudgel striking human flesh. He was at the edge of the brickyards and could not determine where the sounds came from until he rounded a pile of clay and saw an old slave kneeling in the bottom of a pit while a snarling Egyptian overseer wielded a cudgel upon him.

Had Ahmose stopped to think, he might have acted otherwise, for slaves died almost every day under the lash or club in Pi-Raamses. But the injustice of a strong man beating an old one to death stirred a deep anger within him and, leaping into the pit, he grappled with the overseer. As for the latter, had he noticed the gold chain around Ahmose's neck, he would not have resisted; taken by surprise, however, he tried to turn the cudgel upon the intruder. In the subsequent struggle, Ahmose finally managed to wrest the weapon from the overseer's hand and strike him down. Only when he bent over the limp body did he realize, to his horror, that the overseer was dead.

The slave who was being beaten had taken advantage of the distraction to escape, leaving Ahmose alone with the dead man. A panic seized the young prince then, for there was no witness to testify that he had not killed the overseer without provocation, and Egyptian justice was strict in matters of this sort. Looking about him quickly and noting that the place where the brief fight had occurred was hidden from view, Ahmose hurriedly scooped out a hole in the loose sand and, dumping the body of the dead overseer into it, covered it over, smoothing out the sand to hide any sign of the grave. This done, he quickly left the clay pit and returned to the palace.

That night Ahmose spent hours trying to understand the impulse which had made him go to the rescue of the slave without even stopping to ask the man's crime. Strange, too, was the fact that he felt no particular pangs of conscience at having killed the overseer and, as he lay awake in his chamber, a pattern began to take place in his mind, a pattern which included the

story he'd heard about his own birth and his adoption by
Pharaoh's daughter. Finally he went to the gentle woman he had
always called mother and heard from her own lips the true story
of how he had come to her. Only then did Ahmose understand
why he had gone to the aid of his kinsman, the slave, and
realize what was the source of the vague discontent which had
been troubling him these past months. Deep inside him, he
knew now, his instinctive loyalty to his own people had been
protesting against their state of enslavement; soon he must
choose to be either Hebrew or Egyptian.

As it happened, Ahmose never had a chance to make his
choice; in fact it seemed that the succeeding series of events
was part of some plan—as indeed it was. When he went to the
brickyards the next day, thinking to talk to some of the Hebrews
and learn about the conditions under which they existed and
how he might help them, Ahmose saw two of the men fighting
with each other. And since fighting could easily lead to a fatal
whipping for both, he tried to separate them.

"Who made you a prince and a judge over us?" one of the
Hebrews jeered. "Do you intend to kill me as you did the
Egyptian?"

It was obvious what had happened; the slave whose life he
had saved had seen Ahmose kill the overseer and had spread
the story abroad. Eventually, word of it must come to Pharaoh
and, once the truth of his origin was revealed in court testimony, he would be executed—like any Hebrew—for attacking
an overseer. Only one course of action was open; he must escape
before the soldiers came to arrest him.

To travel by the Way of the Sea, which passed through the
border stations of the Princes' Wall, was out of the question.
Even if Ahmose were not overtaken on the road, a swift courier
could reach the border ahead of him and order his arrest. Nor
could he travel by ship, for the master of the port accounted
for every man aboard the vessels leaving there. Only one route
lay open—the traditional one for escaping slaves—eastward
across a shallow lake called the Sea of Reeds where vast swamps
of papyrus spread into the forbidding mountain region of

Sinai. In that area Egyptian authority was at best only nominal and there was little chance of his being taken. So Ahmose did embark upon his journey after all—but under far different circumstances and to a different land from that which he had planned.

# 14. The Voice from the Fire

*"God called unto him out of the midst
of the bush, and said, Moses, Moses."*
EXODUS 3:4

WITH GENTLE HANDS Moses—he had given up his Egyptian name of Ahmose for the shorter version when he crossed the border of that land—freed the lamb from where it had been entangled in the brambles. As, bleating ecstatically, it went bounding down the hillside to where its mother waited, he thought with a smile that he had found a peace and a happiness here in this rough land of forbidding mountains and enclosed fertile valleys that he could never have known as a prince of Egypt. Sometimes he had pondered the fate which had brought him here and what it might mean, but he could see no farther than the immediate happiness of his work: his flocks and herds which increased every day, Zipporah, priest Jethro's lovely daughter who was his wife, and the strong son she had borne to him. No man could ask for more, he told himself, and yet there were times when he suffered the same feeling of unrest that he'd experienced back in Egypt.

Moses had talked it over with Jethro, his father-in-law, and the old priest had assured him that every man's life was lived according to God's plan if he but gave himself up to divine will. But, study the events which had brought him here as he would, Moses could still see no farther than the rough hills of Midian

85

and the great towering mountain of Horeb or Sinai upon whose slopes he stood. There was work to be done, however, another sheep having strayed from the flock he was tending. Leaving them under the watchful eye of Zipporah, he began to climb the steep, rocky slope, calling as he went. He could see his wife now, as slender and as lovely as when he'd first beheld her drawing water from the well near her father's house, and as he climbed, Moses found his thoughts going back to the day when he had first come into this land.

He had been exhausted when he'd staggered up to the well and gulped down the cool water, sloshing it over his face in his eagerness to appease his thirst. Though he'd seen no sign of pursuit, he had taken no chances of being captured and carried back to Egypt for execution. Hiding by day, first in the reeds along the wide morass of the Sea of Reeds and later, when the country grew more hilly, behind rocks and in caves, he'd made slow and painful progress. He'd been able to take neither weapons nor money with him in his flight from Egypt and so was forced to fend for himself, living upon roots and berries and an occasional small animal knocked down with a sling that he'd made from his leather girdle, or fish caught with his bare hands in the shallow mountain streams. As a prince of Egypt, he'd had no training in fending for himself and, though he was fairly skilled in arms, this last was of no account because he had no weapons.

When he could, Moses had traveled the rough mountain tracks by which metal was hauled from the mines to be smelted and turquoises dug from the earth were taken to Egypt to be polished and sold. Sometimes he'd been forced to cross patches of trackless desert with only what water he could carry in a small skin he'd stripped from an animal and cured by stretching it in the sun during the day. If it would have helped any, he might have cursed the fate that had made him a Hebrew. But he'd had no strength to waste, needing all of it to stay alive, and even living had begun to seem hardly worth the trouble— until he'd happened upon the spring of Jethro, a Midianite priest.

For a while after quenching his thirst, Moses had lain in the mud where the spring overflowed, reveling in the coolness while it restored strength to his body. When he heard the voices of women coming to the spring, he'd dragged himself into the underbrush near-by to hide. From that haven, he'd watched the seven daughters of Jethro draw water for their father's flock and, when a group of shepherds tried to drive them away, had summoned up enough strength to burst from the underbrush, swinging a club he'd used to protect himself from wild animals.

Surprised perhaps more than they were intimidated, the shepherds had run away and Moses had helped the women water their animals. He'd seen one of them, the oldest and the comeliest, run to a house near-by; soon she returned to beg him to share their food and their home. In the pleasant and happy family of Jethro, Moses had soon found in the love of the gentle girl who had become his wife a happiness he'd never known.

In Egypt during the trying years of their bondage, many of the descendants of Jacob—that is, of Israel—had drifted away from the worship of Yahweh, or Jehovah, who had made a covenant with their forefather Abraham to keep them always as his own. Jethro, however, was not only a devout man but a descendant of Abraham as well through the patriarch's second wife, Ketura, whom he had married after Sarah's death. Referred to as Kenites because many of them were metalsmiths, working with the copper mined in this area, Jethro's people devoutly followed the God whom so many of Abraham's other descendants had largely forgotten. Having grown up in the palace of Pharaoh, Moses knew little of Yahweh, but in the household of Jethro he learned anew the old story of the land promised to Abraham and his descendants and the covenant that God had made with them. Moses had no inkling that he had been selected for any special purpose, however, and except for this occasional strange unrest that seized him, he was content with his lot.

As he climbed the rough track followed by shepherds seeking lost sheep on the heights of Mount Horeb, Moses felt the air grow cooler and saw the sun dip lower in the west. He knew he should turn back soon, for to be caught on these peaks by nightfall with no way to make a fire could be perilous. But knowledge of the peril faced by the sheep and its terror at being lost drove him onward, until suddenly he rounded a craggy outcrop and saw before him something he could not believe, even with the evidence of his own eyes.

A bush standing beside the track was afire! Yet though the flames burned brightly, they did not consume the bush!

Moses hesitated but did not run away, as a less courageous man might have done. Instead, he moved closer, the better to see this strange phenomenon. It was then that someone he could not see spoke to him in a voice that seemed to come as much from inside himself as from either the mountainside or the bush.

"Moses! Moses!" the strange voice said.

"Here am I," he answered wonderingly.

"Do not come nearer," the voice warned. "But put off your shoes for you stand upon holy ground."

As Moses stooped to loosen his sandals, the voice continued: "I am the God of your father, the God of Abraham, the God of Isaac, and the God of Jacob."

At last Moses knew why the bush had burned without being consumed and how a voice could speak to him though he could see no one. And knowing, he hid his face, instinctively afraid to see God.

"I have seen the affliction of my people who are in Egypt," the voice continued. "I have heard their cry and have come down to bring them to a land flowing with milk and honey. Come now and I will send you to Pharaoh to bring forth my people, the Children of Israel, out of Egypt."

But Moses protested. "Who am I, Lord, that I should bring them out?"

"This shall be a token to you that I have sent you," the Lord assured him. "When you have brought the people out of Egypt, you shall serve God upon this mountain."

Moses looked up at the cloud-wrapped summit of Mount Sinai, with the wreath of smoke hovering always over it from the fires burning deep inside its rocky height. It was indeed a fitting dwelling place for a god, he thought, particularly the all-powerful God worshipped by the Hebrews. But when he thought of going back to Egypt where his own people had mocked him as the murderer of the Egyptian overseer, and where a sentence of death probably awaited him, his courage waned.

"When I come to the children of Israel and say to them, 'The God of your fathers has sent me,'" he protested, "they will say to me, 'What is his name?' What shall I say to them then?"

"Say to the children, 'I AM has sent you, the Lord God of your fathers, the God of Abraham, of Isaac, and of Jacob. This is my name forever and this is my memorial unto all generations.'"

When Moses still hesitated, God asked, "What is that in your hand?"

"A rod."

"Cast it on the ground."

Moses obeyed and drew back in alarm when the rod became a wriggling serpent whose strike could mean a horrible death. But when the Lord commanded him to pick up the serpent, he somehow found courage to seize it by the tail and immediately it became a harmless rod once again.

"O my Lord, I am not eloquent," Moses made a last protest. "I am slow of speech and have a slow tongue."

"Aaron your brother can speak well and will be your spokesman before the people," God assured him. "You shall take this rod in your hand and with it you shall do signs."

Moses protested no more but came down from the mountain and told Jethro and Zipporah what had happened. The priest recognized that at last God was using Moses in the purpose for which he had been selected, and encouraged him to go back to Egypt. The very next day Moses left the house of Jethro with his wife and his child, carrying as his protection for the long journey only the rod with which he hoped to free his people from oppression, and his faith in the God who had called him to his destiny at last.

# 15. Let My People Go

*"Thus saith the Lord God of Israel,*
*Let my people go."*  EXODUS 5:1

THE SPECTACLE of one they had known as an Egyptian
prince and a murderer returning with the news that a
God many of them had forgotten had chosen him as the
agent to lead them from subjection into the land promised to
Abraham centuries ago was too ludicrous for many of the
Hebrews to consider seriously. But when Moses spoke the words
of Yahweh through the eloquent voice of Aaron, and when he
performed miracles with the rod greater than any they had
ever seen done before—even by the soothsayers and magicians
of Pharaoh himself—many began to believe. And believing,
they began to hope at last for deliverance from this hated land
where they had been enslaved for so many centuries.

Pharaoh was even less impressed than the Hebrews when
Moses first appeared before him. The old king was dead, but
the new one, bearing the name of Rameses—after another before him—was even sterner and harsher than his father had
been. He gave Moses a hearing, but he obviously did not
listen seriously to this burning-eyed man in the ragged robe
and worn sandals, with the horny callouses of toil upon his
hands. No god, Pharaoh undoubtedly thought, would select
such a man as a priest or even a messenger. Besides, if the

Israelites really did have a god of their own, as this man called
Moses claimed, he would long since have freed them from
slavery.

"Thus says the Lord God of Israel," Moses told Pharaoh.
" 'Let my people go that they may hold a feast in the wilderness.' "

"Who is this lord that I should obey his orders and let
Israel go?" Rameses demanded contemptuously. Without waiting for an answer, he gave orders that the burdens of the Hebrews should be increased, and that they should not be furnished
straw for the bricks, but should be forced to gather it for themselves while still producing the regular quota.

When the people upbraided Moses for putting new burdens
upon them, he turned again to God. "Lord," Moses said reproachfully, "why have you so evilly treated these people?"

"Say to the Children of Israel, I am the Lord," God instructed
Moses. "I will bring you out from under the burden of the
Egyptians, and will take you to me for a people and I will be to
you a God. I will bring you into the land which I swore to give
to Abraham, to Isaac, and to Jacob and give it to you for a
heritage."

Moses and Aaron returned to Pharaoh and when Aaron threw
down his rod before the king and his servants, it became a serpent. But Pharaoh called his wise men and sorcerers, and their
rods, too, became serpents. And even though Aaron's rod swal-
lowed up the others, the king still refused to let the Israelites
go. Then the Lord instructed Moses and Aaron to perform
another miracle in order to show his power; in the sight of the
king and his court, they struck the surface of the Nile with
the rod and immediately the water turned red and the fish
died, making the river putrid so that the Egyptians could not
drink it. This feat the magicians of Egypt also equalled, so
Pharaoh was convinced that Moses was a charlatan and again
refused to free the Hebrews.

Moses next brought a plague of frogs from the brooks and
streams to cover the land, but the magicians of Pharaoh's court
did the same thing, so he turned dust into lice and sent swarms
of flies over the country.

"Go, sacrifice to your god," Pharaoh told him, but when the plague was removed, the king broke his word as he had broken it before. God then sent a pestilence that killed the cattle of the Egyptians while leaving unharmed those of the Israelites, and Moses sprinkled ashes into the air to become a plague of boils upon the unhappy Egyptians. When Pharaoh still would not give the Hebrews permission to leave, a pestilence of hailstones and fire descended upon the land, striking down men and cattle in the fields. Only in the land of Goshen, where the Israelites lived, was there no hail.

With each new pestilence, including a cloud of locusts so thick that it covered the whole land and a great darkness lasting for a period of three days, Pharaoh gave his promise to free the Hebrews. Yet no sooner was each pestilence removed than he refused to honor his promise. Finally God readied the greatest punishment of all and in preparation for it gave Moses explicit instructions which his people must follow.

On the tenth day of the month, which was in the beginning of spring, each Hebrew family was instructed to take a lamb and kill it, smearing the blood as a mark across the side and up the post of the doors of all the houses. Afterward the roasted flesh of the lamb was to be eaten ceremonially with bitter herbs and unleavened bread, the whole to be finished by midnight.

"I will pass through the land of Egypt this night and will smite all the first-born, both man and beast," God explained to Moses. "Against all the gods of Egypt will I execute judgment, but when I see the blood upon the houses, I will pass over you and the plague shall not be upon you to destroy you."

"This day shall be to you a memorial," the Lord cautioned Moses finally. "You shall keep it a feast to the Lord forever."

The Children of Israel were convinced now that Moses did indeed wield the power of the Lord and obeyed his instructions carefully. That night death struck in every Egyptian household, but wherever the blood of the lamb was smeared upon the doorway, death passed over and the first-born were spared.

Now at last Pharaoh bowed to the god of the Hebrews. "Rise up and get you forth from among my people," he ordered

Moses. "Go serve your Lord; take your flocks and herds and be gone."

The Israelites were ready and began to move out at once, taking with them everything they possessed—their flocks, herds, and cattle with the gold, silver, and other treasures they had managed to amass during the long centuries of their stay in Egypt. The shortest route to Canaan from the city of Pi-Raamses would have been the coastal route, but this was heavily fortified and would provide an easy path for the armies of Pharaoh, should he decide to follow them with chariots. Remembering his own experience when he had fled from Egypt, Moses led the Israelites southward from Raamses to Succoth, not far from the Sea of Reeds and the so-called bitter lakes. From there they traveled still southward for several days along the western border of the shallow-lake chain separating the land of Goshen from the Wilderness of Sin or Sinai, before making camp to rest.

Only the tragic death of the first-born had forced the Egyptian king to release the Hebrews. When word came that the Israelites had not yet crossed over the shallow lakes into the rugged mountain country of Sinai, Rameses decided to make a sortie by chariot and punish the straggling horde of former slaves who had no weapons or fighting men capable of defending themselves against the trained Egyptian cavalry. At the head of his own troops, Rameses began a lightning dash across the lowlands to attack the Hebrew camp.

Word of the approaching Egyptian army came to the Israelites in their camp by the shore of the shallow Reed Sea, throwing them into a panic. The Bible tells how they began to upbraid the very man who had freed them from slavery.

"It would have been better for us to serve the Egyptians than to die in the wilderness," they cried to Moses, but he was now far different from the man who had protested against his selection on Mount Sinai and had called doubtfully upon the Lord in Egypt when Pharaoh had not acceded to his first demand. With the freeing of his people, Moses' faith in God had become absolute; it did not waver now before the greatest danger that they had yet faced.

"Stand still and see the salvation of the Lord which he will show you," he told them. "The Egyptians you have seen today you shall see no more."

Taking heart from Moses' confidence, the Israelites followed his orders when he told them to prepare to march. And as he waded into the shallow lake with the rod held up before him, an east wind swept the water back until the bottom appeared in many places and the Israelites were able to cross over safely to the other side.

By this time Pharaoh and his chariots had reached the shore behind the fleeing Israelites and, seeing how shallow the water was, unhesitatingly plunged in to follow. Moses held his ground until the last of the Hebrews had struggled ashore on the opposite side, with the leading chariots of the Egyptians only a few paces behind them. Then he raised the rod once again and immediately the wind abated and the waters swept back to drown the hosts of Pharaoh and bury their chariots beneath the surface.

On the eastern shore, the Hebrews watched with wide-eyed wonder the destruction of their enemies. When the last chariot had disappeared beneath the water, they fell to their knees while Moses raised a prayer of thanksgiving to God who had delivered them as he had promised. With no more danger behind them, they could now look forward eagerly to the fulfillment of the second part of God's covenant: that the Land of Promise in Canaan should be theirs.

# 16. The Golden Calf

*"He . . . made . . . a molten calf: and
they said, These be thy gods, O Israel."*

EXODUS 32:4

"WHEN YOU have brought forth the people out of
Egypt, you shall serve God upon this mountain,"
the Lord had told Moses from the burning bush,
Now the Hebrews—having followed the cloud by day and the
pillar of fire by night which God had given them for a guide—
were encamped at the foot of Mount Sinai while Moses, upon
the heights, received the laws God had prepared to guide them
forever. This took many days and while they waited, longing
to be out of this rough and mountainous country and into the
land of plenty which had been promised them, the people grew
restive. Forgetting the bounty of the Lord who had provided
manna—a nutritious gum-like substance which they gathered
each morning beneath certain bushes—they soon drifted into
mischief.

"Make us gods which shall go before us," they begged Aaron,
for it was easier to worship a god made of a precious metal that
could be seen than a unseen deity whose edicts came through
the mouth of a man. "As for Moses, we do not know what has
become of him."

God had selected Aaron for a high purpose, to be chief among
the priests who served the ark of wood and the tabernacle with

ten curtains of fine linen which Moses had been instructed to build. As a symbol of their God it went always before the Israelites to remind them of the covenant which he had made with them and to which their forefathers had agreed. But now Aaron failed in his trust; when the people begged him to make them a golden calf like the idols worshipped by the people of Canaan, he yielded to them.

Their discontent forgotten now, the Israelites busied themselves gathering golden earrings and ornaments of all sorts to be used in making the image. A forge and bellows were set up and the metal was melted down and poured into a mold made from sand and clay. When it had cooled, Aaron trimmed it with a graving tool made from the flint-hard black obsidian that abounded in this volcanic region. Then he polished the golden idol until it shone like the sun and built an altar before it, while the people gathered food for a great feast of celebration and brought out all their stores of wine.

"Tomorrow is a feast to the Lord," Aaron proclaimed, forgetting that one of the first laws given to Moses by God forbade the worship of any graven image. On the morrow they gathered before the calf, to eat, drink, dance, and engage in the licentious practices that went with the worship of the corrupt gods of Canaan.

Upon the mountaintop Moses had paused to make a sacrifice to the Lord before coming down to the people with the tablets upon which were engraved the laws they were to obey. To him came the angry voice of God, saying, "Go down, for your people have corrupted themselves. Let me alone that I may consume them, and I will make of you a great nation."

Rebellious and ever ready to complain, the Israelites had tried Moses' patience more than once by their lack of faith. He knew they deserved to be destroyed for this final act of blasphemy; nor could he fail to be tempted by the promise that a new nation would be made from his own successors alone. Yet he did not yield to the temptation, but sought to appease the anger of the Lord and save his people.

"Why should the Egyptians say, 'For mischief did he bring them out into the mountains to slay them and consume them from the face of the earth?'" he protested. "Remember Abraham, Isaac, and Jacob, your servants to whom you swore, 'I will multiply your seed as the stars of heaven and they shall inherit all this land forever.'"

The Lord listened to Moses and spared the Israelites, even after their great sin. But Moses, when he saw the depth of their depravity, was horrified and in his anger threw down the tablets containing the Law and broke them. The golden calf he ground into dust and destroyed, as the terrified and now repentant people hid themselves from his wrath.

For two years the Hebrews lived in the shadow of Mount Sinai at Hazeroth; during this time God spoke often to Moses, setting down every detail of his law. At the end of two years, they moved into the Wilderness of Paran lying west of the Gulf of Aqabah and the country of the Edomites. Here they were on the southern border of Canaan, but before going into the land promised them by God, Moses sent spies to see what cities and strongholds lay ahead.

The spies visited Hebron, where Abraham had lived, and came as far as the brook of Eschol, well into southern Canaan. Some—like Joshua, the young military leader who had become Moses' chief lieutenant, and Caleb, one of the chief captains —reported it to be a land flowing, as God had said, with milk and honey. And although they saw large fortified cities, the two soldiers had faith that God would let the Israelites prevail. The majority of the spies, however, were afraid.

"We saw the children of Annok there," they said. "The Amalekites dwell in the land to the south. The Hittites, the Jebusites, and the Ammorites live in the mountains, and the Canaanites by the sea." When they went on to speak mysteriously of giants, many of the Israelites were terrified.

"Would God that we had died in the land of Egypt!" the timid cried. "Let us choose a captain and return to Egypt!" Many were swayed by fear and when Moses tried to reason with them, they even threw stones at him.

Once more God was angry with this faithless people, but again Moses pleaded for them until finally God relented—to a degree.

"Because all those men who have seen my glory and my miracles have not listened to my voice," the Lord said, "they shall none of them see the land wherein I swore to make you dwell, save only Caleb, the son of Jephunneh, and Joshua, the son of Nun. Your little ones—whom you said would be a prey—shall know the land you have despised, but your children shall wander in the wilderness for forty years."

Thus because of God's anger at their lack of faith, the Israelites were not allowed to take the direct route into Canaan from the south. At Kadesh, they turned eastward toward the mountains lying near the southern end of the Salt Sea and the desert called Zin. Through many vicissitudes they moved slowly northward, sustained by manna gathered each morning.

The years passed and they fought with many people while moving slowly through the lands lying east of the Sea of Judgment. In time they came to occupy Heshbon, the capital of Moab, and Joshua in command of the now toughened and skilled fighting men moved northward to defeat the men of Bashan and secure the northern flank. With this done, they were ready to cross over the Jordan and enter Canaan from the east.

Moses had grown old and frail during the long years of wandering, but he had persevered, sustained by his unwavering faith in God. Now the time had come for him to lay down his burdens. "Get you up into Mount Nebo and see the land I have given to the children of Israel," God told him. "When you have seen it, you shall be gathered to your people."

Even with death facing him, Moses thought not of himself but of those who so often had proved faithless. "Let the Lord set a man over the congregation so that they will not be as sheep who have no shepherd," he begged.

"Take Joshua the son of Nun and lay your hands upon him," God commanded. "Put some of your honor upon him that all the children of Israel may be obedient."

Always first in battle and a great natural leader, Joshua had well earned the honor of governing the people. He had led the Israelites against the kingdoms on the east side of Jordan and conquered an area extending as far north as Mount Hermon, including all of Gilead and Bashan.

"Your eyes have seen all that the Lord your God has done to these kings," Moses told Joshua now. "So shall the Lord do to all the kingdoms where you pass. You shall not fear them, for the Lord your God shall fight for you."

With Joshua consecrated as the leader of the Israelites, God led Moses from the plains of Moab up into the mountain of Nebo—also called Pisgah—overlooking Jericho a few miles away across the Jordan. There he showed to the dying man the whole vast expanse of the land which had been given to his people for their home.

"This is the land I swore to Abraham, to Isaac, and to Jacob saying, 'I will give it to your seed,'" the Lord told Moses. "I have caused you to see it with your eyes but you shall not go over there."

Moses did not protest. He had served God faithfully since that day when the voice had spoken to him from the bush on Mount Sinai. He had asked no reward—and he asked none now —except the satisfaction of knowing that he had brought his people safely to the borders of the Land of Promise.

# II. The Land Regained

"Go over this Jordan, thou, and all this people, unto the land which I do give to them."

JOSHUA 1:2

# 1. Rahab of Jericho

*"They went, and came into an harlot's house, named Rahab, and lodged there.* JOSHUA 2:1

SWIFT-RUNNING and often turbulent as it cut its way through the deep cleft marking its course southward to the Sea of Judgment, the Jordan was easily fordable between the cities of Canaan and Heshbon—the former capital of the Amorites—only at Bethany-beyond-Jordan, or Bethabara. Six miles to the west stood Jericho, one of the oldest cities in the world, a heavily fortified junction point guarding the most direct route into central Canaan.

Having secured the east bank of the Jordan preparatory to invading Canaan, Joshua and the Israelites were camped upon the Plains of Moab just east of Bethabara. First, however, they needed to know accurately the strength of fortress Jericho, which they must subdue before marching deeper into the Land of Promise. For that purpose two spies were sent into the city: Salmon, a young prince of Israel, and Caleb, the hard-bitten captain who had accompanied Joshua years before on a spying trip into Canaan from the south.

With many travelers passing to and fro on the busy trade route that touched the gates of Jericho, an inn—which traditionally served also as a brothel—was a profitable business. And in Jericho none was busier or more profitable than the establishment operated by a young woman called Rahab. As shrewd as she was beautiful, Rahab had listened carefully to the stories of travelers who had visited the camp of the Hebrews on the Plains of Moab. She knew almost to a man the strength of Joshua's forces and, more important, that the astounding victories of the Israelites had been accomplished largely through the favor of a god whose power, she was sure, was much greater than that of the local deities of Canaan, known as Baals. Therefore, when two strangers appeared at Rahab's establishment, she guessed their identity and saw in a flash of insight how she might turn their presence to her own account. As she moved across the room to welcome them, Rahab heard the older, sturdier one speak sharply to the younger, who had apparently been protesting against their coming to such a place.

"Where else could we learn more than in a brothel?" the short man said. His face was scarred from battle and as he stood, looking around him with a gaze that missed no detail, however small, he was like a solid rock.

"Are you travelers?" Rahab asked the two in greeting.

She saw the older man's eyes survey her with a quick, appraising glance, taking in the dancer's grace of body, the heavy cosmetics that could not hide the natural loveliness of her skin. "Why do you think that?" he demanded.

Rahab lowered her voice. "You are not of Jericho, and you have not called for wine or spoken of the Hebrews, whom everyone in Jericho fears."

"Caleb—" the younger man started to speak.

"Peace, Salmon," Caleb said under his breath. "This woman is clever. She can be of use to us."

Caleb turned back to Rahab. "Yes, we are travelers," he said in a somewhat louder voice in case any of the drinkers were listening. "From Urusalim on the way to Heshbon, to buy hides from the Hebrews. Can you let us have a sleeping place for the night and some food?"

"You shall have that and more," she said quickly, then lowered her voice. "I can give you the information you seek."

"What do we need to know?" Caleb asked, still watching her warily.

"That the people of Jericho are so afraid of the Hebrews that their courage has left them and their legs are like jelly."

Caleb shrugged, but Rahab saw that the younger man, the one called Salmon, was watching her closely—and suspiciously.

"If this is true, how does it concern us?" Caleb asked.

"You are not travelers but soldiers," Rahab said. "Perhaps spies would be the better word."

"Why did you not betray us to the soldiers of your king then?"

Rahab glanced around; night was approaching and the room was filling rapidly. "We can talk of that later. There is a stairway outside. Take the chamber on the north corner and wait there. I will come as soon as I can."

Just then there was a commotion at the doorway to the establishment. "Make way!" a loud voice shouted. "Make way, harlots, for the soldiers of the king!"

"You must have been seen entering Jericho," Rahab said quickly to Caleb. "Take the stairway to the roof. I have rushes drying there; hide yourself beneath them."

The two men were out the back door into the courtyard before she had finished speaking, and Rahab went to the front where the soldiers were already pushing their way inside. "Wine!" she called to the servants. "Wine for the brave soldiers who protect us from the Hebrews!"

"We have no time to drink wine tonight, Rahab," said the captain of the guard, a burly man with a bronze sword hanging from his belt and a spear in his hand. "Two men were seen entering this house just now."

Rahab gave him a warm smile. "But Hazor, strangers are always coming and going here. How else could we live?"

There was a burst of laughter from the drinkers at the sally, but the captain would not be put off. "These men are Israelites, sent to search out the country. Bring them out."

Rahab swung her arm in a wide inviting gesture, the heavy bracelets she wore jingling musically. "See for yourself, Hazor," she said. "Jab among the rushes drying on the roof, if you are so terrified by the Israelites."

Hazor cursed and ordered his men out into the courtyard

and up the stairway leading to the upper floor. As Rahab had shrewdly planned, he gave the roof only a cursory glance, lest he be laughed at by the others if he went poking among the rushes and found nothing. Besides, it hardly seemed likely that spies would hide in such an exposed place.

Downstairs the soldiers of the guard had already given up the search and were drinking the cup of wine Rahab ordered for each of them to show that she held no grudge against them for suspecting her of harboring traitors. But she did not hurry to the roof as soon as the guards left, lest someone among those drinking below should notice and follow her. Besides it was not yet dark and, if she were to save the two men who had trusted her—and whom she planned to use in saving her own life—she must wait until darkness had fallen.

Hearing the tramp of the guard marching out of the court-yard, Caleb and Salmon gingerly eased themselves from beneath the bundles of rushes piled upon the roof. They could thank Yahweh that Rahab had happened to have a fresh supply drying there, enough to hide them when they had flattened themselves out against the low parapet that ran around the rooftop so that no would inadvertently fall over it. Being trained observers sent to spy out the defenses of Jericho, they gave a careful scrutiny to the city still visible in the rapidly falling twilight.

What they saw verified reports already given Joshua by travel-ers who had used the caravan trail leading past Jericho and the customs station for the collection of tribute set up by its king. Already so old that none of its inhabitants knew its origin, Jeri-cho was one of the most heavily fortified cities in the entire region and guarded the passes which were the main entrance route into Canaan from the lands across the Jordan.

A great spring near the gates of the city not only furnished water for the people but irrigated the area around it. And since this region was within the vast cleft through which the Jordan flowed and only a few miles from the Sea of Judgment, the climate was mild and warm most of the year. Palms, fruit trees, flowering shrubs grew everywhere—Jericho looked like a small garden of Eden, with the towering battlements of the fortifica-tions rising from the elevation of a large knoll gleaming white against the cool green canopy of the palms and luxuriant lower growth.

Seen here at close view—for Rahab's house actually stood upon the walls—Jericho was a formidable fortress indeed. A continuous wall more than two paces in thickness constructed of stone and brick surrounded the entire city. Inside this outer rampart, separated by a space filled with stone and rubble, was a second wall not quite so thick as the outer one. Houses were often perched upon both walls with the windows of one side— as with Rahab's establishment—looking outside the city.

Salmon and Caleb had descended to the second-floor chamber and were comparing notes on the defenses of Jericho when Rahab came up the stairway carrying a strong cord. "The guards will come again when they do not find you in the city," she warned. "Before they do, you must leave."

"We have seen what we came to see," Caleb agreed. "But first tell us why you helped us. You are not of our people."

"I know the god you worship has given you this land and already the inhabitants are faint with terror," Rahab told him. "Since I have shown you kindness, swear to me by your lord that you will save all my household alive and deliver them from death."

"Our life for yours provided you do not speak of our business," Caleb promised. He picked up the heavy cord she had brought and saw that it was scarlet in color, a characteristic of the rope used to bind their packs by the dyers who traveled this way to and from the seacoast. "When we come into the land, place this cord in the window and the blood of whoever is with you in the house will be upon our heads if any hand is laid upon him."

"The guard will go after you when they find you are not in the city," Rahab warned as she tied the cord to a bench and dropped the other end through the window that opened outside the walls. "Hide in the mountains for three days until they come back. Then you can be on your way."

When Caleb and Salmon had disappeared into the darkness outside the walls, Rahab pulled up the cord. Before she piled it in a corner, however, she cut off a section and placed it inside her robe where it would be safe the day she needed it to mark the window.

Nor was that day long in coming. The task of Caleb and Salmon in Jericho had not so much been to spy out the defenses —which even from a distance could be seen to be formidable— but to determine the temper of the inhabitants. Joshua did not doubt for a moment that the Lord, who had brought his people out of the wilderness and had put under subjection to them the whole eastern bank of the Jordan—except for the kingdoms of Edom and Moab which had been bypassed—would breach the walls of Jericho when the final attack was made upon the city. What he did need to know was whether the inhabitants could be expected to fight fiercely, and this information Rahab had now given to Caleb and Salmon.

Other spies had brought similar facts about many of the cities of Canaan. Several centuries of Egyptian rule had depleted the wealth and strength of the entire country. Lately Egypt itself had grown weaker and was no longer able to maintain order in the land, limiting its activities almost entirely to the collection of taxes. Rarely had the kings in city-states of Canaan such as Jericho, Jerusalem, Gibeon, and Lachish been able to work together, since each hesitated to join forces with the other lest he be destroyed. The country was ripe, therefore, for a unified conquering force, just such a one as the Israelites had become under Joshua's inspired leadership.

To Rahab, waiting in Jericho for the Hebrew attack, word came that the Israelites were drawn up on the eastern bank of the Jordan as if preparing to ford it. This caused no little laughter and derision among the men who drank wine and made merry in her establishment in the evenings, for at this time of the year the river was so swollen by the spring rains that it was impassable at the ordinary fords east of Jericho. When a few days later the earth began to quiver in the warning tremors heralding a season of earthquakes, however, the people began to look at each other fearfully, wondering whether this could be the handiwork of the god in whom the Hebrews were said to believe so implicitly.

They had their answer a few days later when word came that

the earth cliffs at Adamah, a crossing point up river where the
swift stream always undermined its banks, had tumbled into the
Jordan, damming it temporarily and leaving the fords at Bethabara dry. Such things had happened before, according to the
storytellers, but the people of Jericho interpreted this particular
incident as the forewarning of doom. Nor were they reassured
when the fires of the Israelite camps appeared on the hills
across from Jericho, and travelers reported that the invaders had
easily crossed the now dry river bed with all their possessions.

Now a strange thing happened which even Rahab could not
understand. Instead of laying a siege train up to the spring to
cut off the water supply as was usually done, the Israelites made
no active move against Jericho. Instead, for an entire week their
army marched around the city without shooting an arrow toward
it, led by bearers carrying the strange structure called the Ark
in which they seemed to believe their god dwelt. Seven priests
marched at the head of the procession blowing upon the *shofar*,
a ram's-horn trumpet which they used in their worship and for
sounding the call to battle.

At first the people of Jericho were terrified, interpreting this
strange action as a ritual used by the Israelites in calling upon
their god. But when the days passed and nothing happened,
they began to laugh. Even Rahab, confident though she was that
the god of the Israelites would deliver the city into their hands,
began to wonder. She took no chances, however, but kept the
scarlet cord bound in her window as the signal agreed upon.

All that week the tremblings of the earth grew stronger while
the Hebrews marched around Jericho each day, blowing their
trumpets but committing no other warlike act. On the seventh
day the colorful procession did not return to the camp in the
hills after circling the city; instead it made round after round—
seven in all. When the seventh was finished, the priests blew a
loud blast on the trumpets and the people gave a great shout.

The inhabitants of Jericho had begun to take the daily circuit
of the city walls as a matter of course, but when word came
that the would-be invaders were circling it again and again, they
hurried to see this strange phenomenon. Thus it happened that
a considerable portion of the population was standing upon the

walls when, as the shouts of the Israelites died away, the earth began to rumble and quake and great fissures appeared in the fortifications. Too late—though indeed they could not have protected themselves from such a great earthquake in any event —the people of Jericho tried to run for safety. But the mound upon which the city stood was already being torn apart by a convulsion of the earth itself and, as the buildings began to fall, fires roared into being and the whole city quickly became a holocaust.

As if waiting for this very event, the Israelite soldiers had remained outside the walls. Now they rushed in to bring upon Jericho, the dreaded curse of *herem*, under which not even an animal of a doomed city or household was spared death. Salmon, the young captain who had come with Caleb, found Rahab crouching with her family in her miraculously intact house, praying to the Hebrew god whose name she did not even know. Guided by the scarlet cord in the window, Salmon was able to find the inn and lead her and her household to safety minutes before the walls of her house finally collapsed under the buffeting of the earthquake.

In all of Jericho, only the harlot Rahab and her family were spared, because she had saved the spies from death. Once again God had worked through the forces of nature to carry out his will, as when a strong wind had swept back the waters of the Reed—sometimes mistakenly called the Red—Sea and allowed the Israelites to cross unharmed, but had subsided to let the flood destroy the chariots of Egypt. And yet again had it been so when the manna kept God's people alive in the wilderness.

With Jericho destroyed, the way was open for Joshua to attack the other strongholds of Canaan that still barred entrance into the fruitful plains and valleys where Abraham had once pastured his flocks.

# 2. The Wise Men of Gibeon

*"We be come from a far country: now
therefore make ye a league with us."*
JOSHUA 9:6

JOSHUA WAS NOT only a great fighting man and military
leader, inspiring those he led to feats of unusual bravery; he
was also the ruler—with the council of the elders—of a
great people. In the latter capacity he was sometimes called
upon to make difficult decisions, as happened when a motley
procession approached the camp of the Hebrews at Gilgal near
Jericho late one afternoon.

Limping animals bore packs made up of old rags, and the
wineskins and water-containers of the visitors were cracked and
dry, showing that they had been exposed to the sun for a long
time. The men themselves were as bedraggled as their mounts;
they wore ragged and dusty clothes, and their worn sandals
barely hung on their feet. Even the bread they carried was dry
and moldy, as if it had been in their packs for a long time. In
fact, the whole picture had been shrewdly contrived to give the
appearance of men weakened by travel over a great distance.

To Joshua the emissaries said, "We have come from a far
country. Now make a treaty with us."

"You might live here among us," the captain objected. "Why
should we make a treaty with you?"

The men bowed their heads. "We are your servants. Do as you will with us."

No one could suspect these meek-appearing men of representing an enemy of any strength. Joshua's voice was less harsh when he asked, "Who are you? And where are you from?"

"We have come from a very far country because we heard the fame of the lord your god," the leader of the group told him. "We heard all that he did in Egypt and to the kings of the country beyond the Jordan, so our elders sent us to meet you and say, 'We are your servants, make a treaty with us.'" He took a hunk of moldy bread from the ragged pack on one of the mules and held it up for the Israelites to see. "This bread we took hot for our provisions out of our houses."

Another of the travelers squeezed one of the dry and cracked wine skins until it burst, letting the dregs flow upon the ground. "See how the wine skins are torn?" he said. "And how our clothing and sandals are worn from the journey?"

"Rest and eat," Joshua told them kindly. "We will consider what to do with you tomorrow."

Joshua's strategy in the campaign to regain the Land of Promise had never included capturing the area mile by mile. Instead he hoped to conquer most of the leading city-states in that region, rightly surmising that he who controlled the strongholds could also rule the rest of the country. A ring of fortified cities guarded the route by which he had chosen to enter the land. Jericho had been the key, but before he could unlock it completely, he had first to subdue a number of other strongholds, especially Bethel—close to the ruins of another city called Ai and often confused with it—Gibeon, Kirjath-Jearim, Beeroth, Lachish, and several others.

The attack upon Bethel-Ai had almost come to grief when the action of a man named Achan, in hiding some of the gold and silver from Jericho which the Hebrews had been forbidden to take, brought God's wrath down upon them. But Achan's sin had been discovered through the ceremony of casting lots, and he had been stoned to death with all his family by the angry people. Joshua had then attacked Bethel-Ai and, through a ruse, lured its inhabitants from the walls where the soldiers of Israel ambushed and destroyed them.

Word of the seemingly irresistible progress of the Israelites into Canaan had set the kings of many of the city-states trembling. Five of them had already formed a league for joint defense against attack, but four cities lying just ahead—Gibeon, Chephirah, Beeroth, and Kirjath-Jearim—chose another way, that of deception. As leader of this confederation, the elders who ruled Gibeon had decided to send a delegation to Joshua at Gilgal across from the ruins of Jericho, where the Israelite armies were resting after the destruction of Bethel-Ai. First, however, they had taken the precaution of making it seem that the emissaries had come from a great distance and that therefore their cities did not lie on the route which Joshua planned to follow into the heart of Canaan. These were the men who had appeared at the Israelite camp at Gilgal, asking that a treaty of peace be made with their people.

In the discussion that night among the elders of the congregation who, with Joshua, made up the governing body of Israel, he pointed out the advantage of having a treaty of peace with a people who might be at their backs as they moved deeper into Canaan. Obviously, by securing the rear they could concentrate all their forces upon the powerful confederation of kings being built up to oppose them, so it was quickly decided to give the emissaries the treaty they desired. The next morning Joshua and the elders of Israel swore a solemn covenant to let them and their people live and not attack them.

It was three days before the truth of the deception which the men of Gibeon had practiced became known. When it did, Joshua was furious but nothing could be done. The leaders of Israel had given their word and to go back on it would be to invoke the wrath of God. For half a day the matter was discussed, then Joshua issued to the deceivers the verdict of Israel's leaders.

"Because you said, 'We are very far away from you,' whereas you lived among us, you shall be cursed," he told them sternly. "Your people shall become bondsmen, hewers of wood and drawers of water for the house of my God."

The Gibeonites were willing to accept any menial role to escape the utter destruction which had been visited upon Jericho and Bethel-Ai, so they agreed meekly to the terms. Actually, there was a distinct advantage for Joshua in having the four cities disarmed and no longer a threat to him when he faced attack by the powerful forces of five kings led by Adonizedec of Jerusalem. In open battle, Adonizedec and his allies might have defeated the Hebrews, but he made the mistake of first attacking the cities of the Gibeonite confederation before launching their main attack upon the Israelites.

To Joshua and the army of Israel encamped at Gilgal came a desperate plea for help from his allies in Gibeon and the other cities of that group. It was a plea he could not ignore and, from the description the messengers gave of the way Adonizedec had carelessly arranged his forces around Gibeon, it actually seemed to afford the opportunity which Joshua needed badly, that of a surprise attack. Guided by the messengers, the Israelite army made a forced march at night by a secret road across the mountaintops and, as dawn broke, looked down upon the besieged city of Gibeon.

The king of Jerusalem had amassed a mighty army indeed. Joshua could even see the flash of the sun from the gold-crested helmets of Egyptian officers which could only mean that Egypt had sent forces to aid the five kings and that the coming battle would be a decisive one. A victory for the Israelites would leave many of the major strongholds in that area undefended and easily attacked. Defeat, on the other hand, meant a stricken and scattered people streaming back across the Jordan to lick their wounds in the mountainous country to the east of the river—if they were not destroyed by the kings of Edom and Moab, who eagerly awaited a suitable opportunity to attack.

Joshua did not hesitate; the Lord had promised him a victory and his faith was unshaken, even by the superior forces ranged against him. As the enemy went carelessly about preparations for what seemed an easy task, the destruction of Gibeon, the Israelite fighting men swept down upon them in the half-light of dawn. Thousands of the enemy were spitted upon the spears of the first line of the Hebrews before they could seize their weapons and armor. Others went down under a rain of arrows falling just ahead of the attackers, shot by bowmen of the second rank.

Somehow in the carnage that followed, Adonizedec managed to get a portion of his forces together and organize a retreat westward by way of Beth-Horon and the valley of Aijalon toward the shore of the Great Sea. They might have escaped to the protection of the mighty fortress of Gezer, but a great storm arose and huge hailstones rained down upon the luckless king of Jerusalem and his allies, battering many of them to the earth. Afterward the sun shone so bright and clear that many among the Israelites swore later that God had made the sun stand still in the heavens so that Joshua and his fighting men could see how to destroy the enemy utterly. The five kings were captured as they hid in a cave, and were killed by the victorious Hebrews.

In the first few years after the entry of the Hebrews into Canaan, Joshua secured, in a series of brilliantly executed military campaigns, the whole of the land which God had promised to the children of Israel, from Mount Hermon in the north to below Hebron in the south. A few Canaanite strongholds, like Uru-Salim, or Jerusalem, in the south and Megiddo in the north, were bypassed, but when the major campaigns were finished, Joshua was able to divide the land as an inheritance to Israel according to their organization by tribes as Moses had commanded. To Caleb, his lieutenant, Joshua gave the land of Hebron for an inheritance and, when the fighting was finished, called the soldiers from among the tribes of Reuben and Gad and the half-tribe of Manasseh.

"You have kept all that Moses, the servant of the Lord, commanded you and have obeyed my voice," Joshua told them. "Now return to your tents and to the land of your possession, which Moses gave you on the other side of the Jordan." Then he blessed them and sent them away with much of the spoils they had gained from the Canaanite cities.

Being a shepherd people, the Israelites lived mostly in the hills and had little to do with the Canaanites who still populated the valleys. There were sporadic outbreaks of fighting, but in general it was a time of peace under Joshua's firm leadership. As the years passed, however, some among the Israelites forgot their covenant with God, and began to worship idols according to the Canaanite custom. Joshua was old now, and one day, many years after the Lord had given Canaan into Israel's hands, he called the people, their elders, and their leaders together in Shechem.

"You are witnesses against yourselves that you have chosen the Lord to serve him," he reminded them.

"We are witnesses," the people replied in unison.

"Then put away the strange gods that are among you and incline your heart to the Lord God of Israel," he commanded sternly.

"The Lord our God we will serve and his voice we will obey," the people promised, so Joshua made a covenant with them that day and set up a great stone under an oak by the altar they had erected there.

"This stone has heard all the words of the Lord which he spoke to us," he warned the people. "It shall be a witness to you, lest you deny your God."

Not long afterward Joshua died and was buried in the region of his inheritance on Mount Ephraim. The bones of Joseph—which the Hebrews had brought up out of Egypt—were also buried in Shechem, for they considered themselves secure now in the Land of Promise.

# 3. Deborah and Jael

> *"Sisera gathered together all his chari-*
> *ots, even nine hundred chariots of*
> *iron."*                     JUDGES 4:13

SISERA HAD NOTHING but contempt for the Israelites.
As general commanding the cavalry of King Jabin, he did
not live at the capital city of Hazor near Lake Huleh, where
Joshua had won a great battle over a Canaanite army. Instead,
he kept the chariots at Harosheth in the foothills of Mount
Carmel, overlooking the fertile plains of Jezreel and Sharon and
the fortified cities of Megiddo, Ibleam, and Taanach. From there
Sisera could move swiftly into action to crush any resistance on
the part of the near-by Israelite tribes. And with his hundreds
of chariots made from iron, the new metal of the Hittites, just
now coming into use freely among the people of the coast and
the lowlands, he could prevent any sizable force from gathering
to resist the oppression he carried out in the name of his king.

"If you are a great people, get up into the hill country and
cut down for yourselves there," Joshua had told the tribe of
Joseph when they had protested the size of the district of Canaan
allotted them in the division of the land among the twelve tribes.
Many had taken his advice, not only in the territory of Joseph
but in other areas as well. Along the central mountain range
of Canaan where there were many narrow valleys and streams
for pasturing cattle, the Hebrews had forsaken tents and nomad
life to follow the example of the Canaanites. From the heavy

117

growth of cedar and other trees covering the hills, they had cut logs and hewed them into timbers to build rough houses, living together, in villages, though rarely ever in cities. Some had even begun to plant vineyards and till the soil of the fertile upland valleys.

By their very nature the Hebrews were an independent people, wary of centralized government. Living in a loose tribal organization, once Joshua had let the army disband after they settled in Canaan, they were united only by their common ancestry and the worship of their single God. As they had built the golden calf while Moses was communing with the Lord on Mount Sinai, now some forsook Yahweh for the more colorful and licentious practices attending the worship of the pagan gods of Canaan. For their sin they were punished by God with loss of freedom, and in one of the more drastic of these acts of punishment the northern tribes came under subjection to Jabin and his cruel captain, Sisera.

With Joshua dead, there was no single leader of all the tribes any more. But when conditions became intolerable and the people called upon God to save them, great natural leaders named *shophetim* or judges arose to free them from oppression. Since the district of Issachar, one of the smallest among the tribes, was near Sisera's stronghold at Harosheth, the hand of the oppressor was heaviest upon them and their cries for help the loudest. This time it was a woman who rallied the people to resist.

In the world of Sisera's day, which was not long after a woman named Helen had caused the Greeks to attack and subdue by stratagem the powerful fortress of Troy, Hebrew women were much admired for their beauty. Raids upon the Hebrew tribes were carried out frequently by their neighbors in order to capture slaves for the markets of Egypt where they brought higher prices than the women of any other nationality. Sarah, the wife of Abraham, had charmed a Pharaoh; Rebekah, though many hundreds of miles away, had been selected by God to become the bride of Isaac; and Jacob had been willing to labor fourteen years for the beautiful Rachel. They had given their husbands strong sons who had become leaders of their people. Now a woman was to play a new role in Israel; Deborah, the wife of Lapidoth and a prophetess in her own right, became one of the *shophetim* to whom the people looked for leadership in a time of trouble.

Deborah's beauty seemed more like the inner serenity of Leah than like the fiery loveliness of Rachel. At any rate, of her steadfastness and her wisdom, her ability to keep her head in times of grave peril there was no doubt. Trusting in her wisdom —evidenced by the justice and understanding in the decisions which she made in matters that came before her as judge—the people rallied to her when she organized an army of ten thousand men from among the tribes to fight against the unbearable oppressions of Sisera.

Israel already had a military leader in the person of Barak. He came from the town of Kedesh, north of Hazor in the territory of Naphtali, and was a practical fighter. He knew that without weapons of iron and chariots of their own, even the most inspired warriors would have little chance in battle against the trained chariot fighters of Sisera's army—unless the Lord fought at their side. When Deborah assured him that God would deliver the enemy into their hands, practical Barak agreed to take command of the forces—if Deborah would accompany them.

Since ancient times women often have gone with their men into battle, inspiring them to outdo themselves, and Deborah did not hesitate to undertake the risk to her own personal safety. But she added a cryptic and mysterious warning which Barak did not understand until the fighting itself was ended: "The journey will not be for your honor, for the Lord will sell Sisera into the hand of a woman."

Sisera was delighted when he learned that Barak and Deborah were gathering an army to fight against him. It would be a rare catch indeed to destroy not only the Israelite fighting men but their leader and the woman who had stirred them up. Heretofore Sisera's skirmishes with the Israelite guerrilla bands had always ended with the Hebrews withdrawing into the hills where his iron chariots could not follow. Now he hoped to cut off and trap Barak's army upon the plain where he would have an overwhelming advantage. In preparation for the campaign,

Sisera gathered all of Jabin's chariots, nine hundred in number, and moved eastward. Meanwhile Barak had withdrawn into the foothills in order to avoid an engagement with Sisera's forces upon the lowlands.

Briefly there was a stalemate, with Barak in the hills and Sisera with his chariots on the plain, until one man saw a way to profit from the dilemma of the Canaanite general. His name was Heber and as a Kenite—the family to which Jethro, the father-in-law of Moses, had belonged—he was a worshipper of Jehovah and supposedly loyal to Israel. Greed triumphed over loyalty in Heber's case, however, and despite the protests of his wife, Jael, he betrayed to Sisera the location of the Israelite forces. With this information, Sisera was able to isolate and surround Barak's army in the foothills, leaving him no choice except to descend into the plain and try to break through the ring of iron hemming him in.

Under such circumstances, Israelite forces on other occasions had lost heart and been cut to pieces in small battles, or had fled back through the mountain passes into the Jordan valley. This time, however, valiant Deborah inspired both Barak and his men with confidence that God was fighting on their side. And with that confidence, they did something no Israelite army had done before; they came down to the plain and confidently attacked Sisera's hosts in spite of the tremendous advantage the enemy's vast squadrons of chariots gave him.

It was a one-sided battle at first, but the tide turned when a violent rainstorm changed the flat, dry land into a sea of mud. In this situation, chariots were more of a handicap than an asset and the battle quickly developed into a wholesale slaughter of the Canaanite fighting men, who were accustomed to fighting under the protection of the iron vehicles. Assured by the timely rainstorm that the Lord was indeed fighting on their side as Deborah had promised, the Hebrews fell upon the fleeing Canaanites and destroyed them.

Separated from his own men and with his chariot bogged in the mud, Sisera was no longer the contemptuous general who had confidently surrounded the Israelite army on Mount Tabor by means of the information given him by the traitor, Heber.

Slogging through the mud on foot, he managed to reach the hills and make his way to the tent of the Kenite. There he was sure he could obtain shelter while the Hebrews searched the surrounding area for survivors to destroy them. And since the Kenites were worshippers of the same god, Sisera did not think the Israelites would look in the tent of Heber for survivors.

In spite of her husband's treachery, however, Heber's wife, Jael, was loyal to Israel. She had taken no part in the betrayal of Barak's whereabouts to Sisera and, when she saw the Canaanite general approaching, a plan formed quickly in her mind. Putting on a warm smile and a welcoming manner, she went out to meet him.

"Turn in, my lord. Turn in and fear not!" she called to Sisera. And sure that he had found a safe hiding place among friendly people, he went into the tent.

"Give me a little water to drink," he panted, for he was near exhaustion.

Jael gave him a drink from a skin of goat's milk and when he lay down upon a sleeping pallet, she covered him up.

"Stand in the door of the tent," Sisera directed her. "If any man comes and asks you if there is a man here, say no."

Jael pretended to do as Sisera bade her, but as soon as he was asleep she took a mallet and an iron tent peg—part of Sisera's payment to Heber for betraying Barak—and with firm strokes drove the peg through the skull of the Canaanite general and into the ground. Once or twice his body jerked convulsively, then was still.

Barak and his men, pursuing Sisera, would have passed the tent of Heber, but Jael went out to meet them. "Come and I will show you the man you seek," she said proudly.

Weapons in hand they approached the tent cautiously, but Sisera—he of the nine hundred chariots—was no longer a threat. The victory—brought about by the courage and faith of two women—was complete. That night, at the great feast of celebration, Deborah and Barak composed a song of praise to the Lord which was to be sung ever afterward around Israel's campfires whenever the exploits of its heroes were recounted.

# 4. The Camels of Midian

> *"Both they and their camels were*
> *without number: and they entered*
> *into the land to destroy it."*
>
> JUDGES 6:5

INSIDE THE CAVE there was barely room for Gideon to drive the cattle back and forth across the pile of wheat he was threshing. Sometimes they bumped into the wine press, which had occupied the cave alone until now. As far back as anyone could remember, wine had been pressed out underground where it could be kept cool and the process of fermentation controlled, rather than out in the sun where the heat would turn it quickly to vinegar. But surely in the history of Israel, Gideon thought resentfully as he carefully turned the animals within the narrow space, no one had ever threshed wheat in such a place as this—until the coming of the Midianites.

The great victory over Sisera had given the Hebrews new heart. In the months that followed they had overcome many strong points and driven out the Canaanite prince-kings from such fortified cities as Megiddo and Taanach. But as had happened over and over again, they had soon become complacent and, forgetting that God had sent the rain which had mired the chariots of Sisera, turned to the soft ways of the Canaanite cities and the pleasures attendant upon worshipping pagan gods. And once again, as on earlier occasions, God sent a new punishment upon them.

This time it was the Midianites, hordes of fierce warriors from the desert fastnesses between southern Canaan and Mount Sinai, and their allies, the Amalekites. With them they brought a new weapon, as effective in its way as were the iron chariots of the Canaanite general until the rain mired them. This was the camel. Domesticated for the first time by these desert nomads, the camel enabled their forces to move swiftly over long distances without stopping for water.

Like a consuming fire, the Midianites and Amalekites had raged through the tribes of Israel, burning, looting, killing, and bringing them into subjection. Once again the Hebrews were practically enslaved as they had been in Egypt and cried out to the Lord for deliverance from the invaders. And once again God raised up a judge or leader—this time Gideon, the son of Joash.

To Gideon the angel of the Lord spoke as he threshed wheat within the cave in order to hide it from the Midianites and save the grain as food for his family. "The Lord is with you, O mighty man of valor!" the angel greeted him.

"If the Lord is with us, why then has all this befallen us?" Gideon replied shortly, not recognizing the angel as a superhuman being. "Where are all his miracles which our fathers told us about? Now the Lord has forsaken us and delivered us into the hands of the Midianites."

"You shall save Israel from the hands of the Midianites," he was told.

Gideon was a farmer, not a soldier, though his stratagem of threshing wheat in the cave instead of out in the open showed him to be more intelligent than most. "With what shall I save Israel?" he demanded. "My family is poor and I am the least in my father's house."

"I will be with you," the Lord himself assured Gideon. "You shall smite the Midianites as one man."

Gideon was a prudent man; before committing himself he wanted a sign to prove it was indeed God who had spoken.

"I will put a fleece of wool on the floor," he said shrewdly. "If in the morning the dew is upon the fleece only and it is dry upon all the earth besides, then I shall know that you will save Israel by your hand as you have said."

The fleece was wet the next morning, though the rest of the land was dry, and, satisfied now that the Lord would be on his side, Gideon gathered an army to fight against the invaders. In preparation for battle, the Israelites pitched their tents on the northern flank of the Midianite army near the hill of Moreh to the south of Mount Tabor.

"The people with you are too many for me to give the Midianites into their hands, lest Israel vaunt themselves against me saying, 'My own hand has saved me,'" God said to Gideon. "Announce that whoever is afraid can depart."

A large number left, but the Lord told Gideon there were still too many and instructed him to bring the men down to the water and let them drink. "Everyone that laps the water with his tongue as a dog laps, set him by himself," God said. "Likewise everyone that kneels to drink."

Gideon obeyed, and three hundred men lapped the water, lifting it in their hands so they could keep watch even while drinking. The others got down upon their knees to drink and could easily have been surprised by a waiting enemy.

"By the three hundred men that lapped I will save you and deliver the Midianites into your hand," God promised Gideon. "Let all the others go to their places."

A month earlier Gideon would have been appalled at the idea of attacking the Midianites with only three hundred men. But his latent qualities of leadership, and above all his faith in God, had grown tremendously since the angel had hailed him in the cave. With the three hundred men he confidently prepared for battle, even though the forces against him outnumbered his own many times.

As yet Gideon had no plan of attack, but that night the Lord revealed in a dream to one of the soldiers how the enemy would be defeated. And as soon as he heard the dream, Gideon put it into effect, dividing the Israelite warriors into three companies and giving every man a trumpet, together with an empty pitcher to cover the lighted torch that he carried.

"Watch me and do as I do," he directed. "When I and all that are with me blow on the trumpet, then blow your trumpets also on every side of the camp and shout, "The sword of the Lord and of Gideon!""

The Midianites were camped in the bottom of a small valley they had chosen as a battleground, expecting Gideon to attack them in the morning. Sure that the forces of Israel would not dare attack in the night, they had posted only a few guards, and under the cover of darkness Gideon was able to move his three companies secretly into position on the hillside surrounding the valley, boxing the enemy in.

It took a good portion of the night to get the Israelite troops into place, since Gideon had to be very careful not to arouse the sleeping enemy and reveal his stratagem. Finally, in the dead of night about the beginning of the middle watch, Gideon ordered his company to start blowing their trumpets. At the same time, they broke the pitchers which had hidden the torches they carried and held the torches high so that the light could be seen by the Midianites in the valley.

Immediately, on signal, the other two companies began blowing their trumpets, breaking the pitchers to reveal the lights they carried, and shouting, "The sword of the Lord and of Gideon!"

To the surprised Midianites in the valley, the blast of trumpets and the sight of three hundred torches burning on the hillsides around them meant nothing less than an ambush by a superior force of Israelite warriors. Seeking to escape and not able to distinguish their own people from the foe in the darkness, they began to battle among themselves. The entire valley quickly became a melee of shouting, cursing, and fighting men, as the Midianites cut each other to pieces in their crazed desire to escape from the trap, while in the confusion Gideon's forces were able to kill many more.

As he pursued the enemy, Gideon sent messengers ahead to warn the tribe of Ephraim in the direction of whose homes the retreating Midianites were fleeing. These and the neighboring Israelite tribes fell upon them as they passed and killed even more than Gideon had destroyed in the valley before the hill of Moreh, driving them southward across the Jordan at Bethabara opposite Jericho. Nor did Gideon withdraw his men from battle until they had destroyed all their enemies in that region.

When the battle was over, the Hebrews came to Gideon. "Rule over us, both you and your son and your son's son also," they begged. "For you have delivered us from the hands of Midian."

Gideon knew who had really planned the strategy which had let him win such a victory over the Midianites and the Amalekites, however, and refused to let them crown him king. "I will not rule over you nor let my son rule over you," he told the people. "It is the Lord that shall rule over you."

So Gideon returned to his threshing, this time in the open instead of in a hidden cave, and for forty years there was peace in Israel.

But it was an armed peace, one liable to be broken at any time, for a new and formidable power was rapidly growing in strength to the west in the chain of rich and powerful cities of the coastal plain separated from central Canaan by a low mountain range. Into this area a strong and aggressive people had been pouring since about the period when Joshua had conquered central Canaan and divided up the region among the various tribes. This time it was the southern tribe of Judah that suffered most.

# 5. Samson and Delilah

> "And it came to pass afterward, that
> he loved a woman in the valley of
> Sorek, whose name was Delilah."
>
> JUDGES 16:4

IN THE VAST southern district of Israel, inhabited by the descendants of Judah and Simeon, no man was stronger than Samson, the Nazarite. Most populous of the twelve tribes, Judah occupied the whole district south of the Jebusite city of Jerusalem from the coastal plain eastward to the Salt Sea and the Edomite border. And since the coastal plain in this area included the main cities of the Philistines, there was almost constant warfare between them and the Hebrews.

Wide-eyed and not a little fearfully, the Hebrew tribesmen pasturing their flocks and herds on the hillsides of Canaan had watched the great march of the "Sea People" southward along the coastal plains only a few years after Joshua had brought them into the Land of Promise. They could not know whether or not these invaders wanted the land for themselves; only when the newcomers kept on southward in the direction of Egypt, did the Hebrews dare to breathe a sigh of relief.

No one knew exactly the place of origin of the tall men with iron-tipped weapons, shields and caps of bronze, and huge ox-carts piled high with weapons and possessions, beside which the women and children walked. Some said they came from Caphtor, as the island of Crete was called; others said from the country of Greece, though they were not Greeks. But the story of their relentless progress along the entire line of the seacoast at the southern end of the Great Sea was familiar to everyone.

Appearing first in the region of the Sea of Marmora far to the west in the country of the Greeks, the great host had moved steadily and ruthlessly eastward by both land and sea, following the coastline but striking inland at times as far as the fortress of Chattusas on the banks of the river Halys, near the heart of the great Hittite empire. Even the Hittites—a powerful nation for hundreds of years—had yielded to the all-destroying forces of the Sea People, giving up the secret which only they had held until then, that of smelting and forging iron.

Paralleling the movement of the great mass of people along the shore was the progress of a fleet of ships which quickly put the coastal centers between the jaws of a giant pincers. City after city fell to the invaders, the plunder of rich Cilicia, the silver mines of Tarsus, even the riches of Cyprus where a great and enlightened civilization was crushed by the ruthless tall men from the west.

As the invaders moved southward along the coast occupied by the Phoenician people, Ugarit, Byblus, Tyre, and Sidon fell in rapid succession. Another arm of the invasion had turned eastward, to seize the great city of Carchemish on the Euphrates, following part of the route which Abraham had taken many centuries before on his journey from Haran to Canaan. Moving almost without opposition across the border at the River of Egypt, the invaders poured into the rich Nile delta, their main destination. There for the first time they met a force able to stop them and turn them back.

Rameses III had recognized early that the Egyptian delta and its enormously rich cities were the ultimate goal of the Sea People and had been feverishly preparing for their coming. Warships, galleys, and coastal vessels were gathered to oppose the ships of the invaders, while a vast army was mobilized against any further progress by land. Details of the great battle that followed were later pictured in engravings upon the walls of a magnificent temple erected to Amun on the bank of the

Nile west of the city of Thebes. There, for the world to see, a
record of the victory that saved Egypt was preserved for all
time.

When finally the battle was joined, Egyptian chariot squadrons dashed recklessly into the very heart of the enemy lines,
setting them into confusion. Spearmen jabbed at the taller
and stronger Sea People, while bowmen poured arrows into
them. Hampered as to maneuverability by the great solid-
wheeled-ox-drawn wagons in which they carried their supplies
and equipment, and by the presence of their women and children, the invaders were at a disadvantage, and the fleeter, more
maneuverable Egyptian forces hacked away until by sheer
numbers and courage they managed to turn the tide of battle.

On the water too, the advantage went to the Egyptians when
the wind died and the heavier vessels of the invaders could not
be handled easily. Egyptian galleys driven by banks of oars
attacked in swift forays, raining arrows down on the soldiers
massed upon the decks of the enemy ships. Drifting in shallow
water or rammed and sunk by the swifter Egyptian galleys, the
vessels of the Sea People were soon smashed and the occupants
killed when they tried to wade ashore. As the shattered forces
of the invaders reeled backwards, long lines of prisoners, each
branded with the name of the king, were driven into the Egyptian cities to take the place of the Hebrews who not very long
before had escaped from bondage.

After their defeat in the delta, however, the Sea People had
retreated no farther than the rich coastal plain of southern
Canaan. This they had captured on their march into Egypt
and there, in the cities of Ashkelon, Ashdod, Ekron, and Gath,
they set up forges to work iron and began to make pottery and
other products. Known as the Philistines, they were tall, strong,
ruthless men to whom fighting was second nature.

Armor to protect bodies in battle, helmets, weapons of metal,
and chariots of iron the Philistines produced in great amounts.
Some of these objects were sold to the Israelites, but no one
in Israel was allowed to follow the trade of a smith. Thus the
Hebrews were forced to visit the towns and cities of the
Philistines to pay tribute whenever it became necessary to

sharpen the plowshares, colters, axes, and mattocks which they used in clearing fields and tending crops upon the hillsides and valleys of Judah.

As the Philistines became more firmly established, they began to push inland, following the valleys lying between the ranges of hills running from the coastal plains up to the mountain fastnesses of Judah. Inevitably they coveted the rich lands God had assigned to the tribes of Israel, and armed conflict broke out. Sporadic fighting was followed by periods during which an uneasy peace prevailed. Between wars the Israelites traded with the Philistines and, as upon many other occasions, some of them followed pagan gods, a sin which God punished by bringing them under subjection to the enemy.

As a Nazarite—one dedicated to God's service from his birth —Samson of Judah had never drunk wine or other fermented liquor. Nor did he eat anything termed unclean according to the laws received from God by Moses, cut his hair, or shave his beard. At first the Philistines looked upon him with derision, but their opinion changed when he defeated them in battle again and again.

Stories of Samson's strength and prowess were told around the campfires at night, how he slew hundreds of the enemy with only the jawbone of an ass as a weapon, how he set on fire the tails of foxes and turned them loose to burn the fields of the Philistines, and how he killed a lion with his bare hands. Treacherously, his own people had even tried to kill the Israelite champion when the Philistines raided their villages seeking to capture him, but Samson fought the enemy alone and won. In time he became one of the *shophetim*, governing his people and leading them in revolt against the conquerors.

Unable to defeat Samson by military means, the Philistine leaders sought to trap him through his only known weakness, his desire for their women. Their chance came when he fell in love with a woman of Sorek named Delilah. When the Philistine leaders each offered to pay the woman eleven hundred pieces of silver, she agreed to try to discover wherein lay the source of Samson's great strength and betray this information to them.

She was waiting when Samson visited her in the evening. She welcomed him with a kiss and led him to her chamber, but when she tried to worm from him the secret of his great strength, he put her off three times with false answers. Anxious to win the reward that had been promised her, Delilah persevered and when Samson did not give her the answer she sought, pretended to be angry at him.

"How can you say, 'I love you,' when your heart is not with me?" she complained. "You have mocked me three times." Nor would she let him visit her again until he told her what she wanted to know.

Driven by desire for the faithless woman, Samson finally told her the truth. "I have been a Nazarite from my birth," he admitted. "If I am shaven my strength will go from me."

Delilah could not be sure Samson was not putting her off as he had before, but she determined to test his admission. Coaxing him to sleep with his head in her lap, she had a servant shave his head. When he awoke, he did not realize anything had happened and, when the Philistines came to take him, went out confidently to fight them. But with his hair gone, the Hebrew champion was powerless; the Philistines quickly overpowered him and, binding him with chains of brass, took him to prison. There they put out his eyes with a hot iron and kept him as a slave, taunting and deriding him at public gatherings.

Blind and able to move about only when led by a boy, Samson had been in prison many months when the Philistines celebrated a great feast to their god, Dagon. A tremendous crowd had gathered in the temple for the ceremony and, at the height of it, the prisoner was led in like an animal at the end of a rope so that they could gloat over his fall. No one noticed, however, that during the months of prison, Samson's hair had grown back. With it his strength had returned, but he had carefully kept this fact hidden from public notice, husbanding the knowledge against the time when he would have revenge. Now, as he stood beside a pillar at the entrance of the great temple, Samson knew the time had come.

"Let me feel the pillars of the house so that I can lean against them," he whispered to the boy who had led him. And seeing no reason why he should not grant this small favor to a helpless blind man, the boy guided Samson to the main pillars supporting the roof of the temple. Feeling about with his hands, Samson located the two pillars and gripped each of them firmly.

"O Lord God, remember me, I pray you!" he begged. "Strengthen me only this once, O God, that I may be avenged of the Philistines!"

Samson felt the power flowing into his sinews, as his great hands closed slowly upon the pillars. "Let me die with the Philistines!" he prayed as he strained with all his strength and heard the pillars start to crack.

Thousand of startled eyes looked upward when a sudden grinding sound came from the roof of the vast temple. As the two main supports slowly crumpled and the timbers began to crash downward, women screamed in horror and men fought to get out, but the pillars Samson had toppled were near the temple entrance and in falling they shut off any escape.

For a moment Samson stood there, his sightless eyes lifted to heaven in a prayer of thanksgiving while the rubble rained upon his massive shoulders. Then one section of a stone pillar toppled directly upon him and he went down, crushed beneath it. In the agony of death, the cries of the enemy were music in his ears, for even though blinded and a prisoner, Samson had accomplished his greatest single feat, killing three thousand Philistines with his bare hands alone.

Thus died Samson, the mightiest of the judges, a man who sinned and was punished, but lived to revenge himself upon his enemies.

# 6. Ruth and Boaz

*"Thy people shall be my people, and thy God my God."*       RUTH 1:16

"LOVE YOU therefore the stranger, for you were strangers in the land of Egypt," the Lord had instructed his people through Moses. Beset by enemies on every hand, it was hard for the Israelites to obey that commandment during the years when they were busy securing the Land of Promise for themselves. Yet one story they never ceased to tell around the campfires, not only because of its beauty, but for the lessons of tolerance and love for others which it exemplified.

The king of Moab had refused to let the Hebrews pass through his country during the long journey from the Wilderness of Sinai to the Land of Promise. As a result they had been forced to take a long and difficult route around his borders, and the Israelites did not forget this ungenerous act. From time to time there had been conflict, not only between the Moabites and the tribes of Reuben and Gad who dwelt west of the Jordan, but during raids across the river by both sides. Between the raids, however, there were periods of relative truce, as with other peoples of the land.

During one of these truces—according to the story told around the campfires—a great famine had occurred in Judah, and a man named Elimelech from the village of Bethlehem a few miles south of Jerusalem had crossed the Jordan into Moab, where there was plenty of grain. With him were his wife, Naomi, and his two sons, Mahlon and Chilion. Finding homes in the country of the Moabites, Elimelech and his family settled there and, when he died, his body was buried in the foreign land.

Mahlon and Chilion took wives in Moab, one named Ruth and the other Orpah; but about ten years later the sons died, so Naomi decided to go back to her home in the land of Judah.

"Return each of you to your mother's house," she told her daughters-in-law. "The Lord deal kindly with you as you have dealt with the dead and with me, and grant that each of you may find rest in the house of her husband."

Orpah chose to stay with her own people, but Ruth insisted upon accompanying Naomi. "Do not ask me to leave you or to return from following after you," she begged her mother-in-law. "Wherever you go I will go, and where you lodge I will lodge. Your people shall be my people and your God my God. Where you die I will die and there will be buried. The Lord do so to me and more also, if anything but death separate us."

Loving Ruth and knowing her loyalty, Naomi brought her daughter-in-law to Bethlehem at the beginning of the barley harvest. The people welcomed Naomi but, being naturally suspicious of a Moabitess, they shunned the stranger. Ruth did not desert Naomi, however, even when the people of Bethlehem went out of their way to be unkind.

"Let me go into the field and glean ears of grain," she suggested to Naomi when their stock of food ran low, for she had noticed that women who did not have any other means of support were allowed to follow the reapers in the field, gathering for themselves any grain that fell from the sheaves as they were being tied up.

Naomi agreed and sent Ruth to glean in the fields of Boaz, a kinsman of her husband and a man of considerable wealth. The other women shunned Ruth, but she went on with her gleaning, and when Boaz came to the field that afternoon she was still hard at work.

"Who is this woman?" Boaz asked the reapers.

"The Moabitess that came back with Naomi," they told him. "She asked us to let her glean and she has worked from morning until now."

Boaz walked over to where Ruth was picking grain. "Do not glean in another field but stay here with my maidens," he told her kindly. "I have ordered the young men not to touch you, and when you are thirsty, go to the vessels and drink."

Ruth was deeply touched by this first word of kindness from an inhabitant of Bethlehem. "Why have I found grace in your eyes that you should notice me though I am a stranger?" she asked.

"I have heard what you have done for your mother-in-law since the death of your husband," Boaz explained. "How you left your father and your mother in the land of your birth and came to a people you did not know before." He did not add that no man could be insensitive to her quiet loveliness.

When Ruth returned to Naomi's house at the end of the day, her baskets were full, for Boaz had secretly ordered the reapers to drop some of the grain where she could find it easily.

"Boaz is our kinsman," Naomi said when she heard the story of the day's happenings. "He winnows barley tonight on the threshing floor, so wash and anoint yourself and put on your best clothing. Go down to the threshing floor, but do not make yourself known until he finishes eating and lies down. Then mark the place where he lies and later uncover his feet and lie down there."

Ruth did not realize that Naomi was carrying out a plan to make Boaz fall in love with her, so she obeyed, though curious about her mother-in-law's instructions. At the threshing floor Boaz finished the winnowing and, having eaten, lay down at the end of a pile of grain so it would not be stolen during the night before it could be bagged. Ruth waited in the darkness outside the threshing floor until she saw that he was asleep. Then, as Naomi had instructed her, she went in softly and, uncovering Boaz's feet, lay down there and covered herself with the cloth he had drawn over him.

About midnight, Boaz turned and discovered that someone was lying at his feet. "Who are you?" he asked.

"I am Ruth, your handmaiden," the girl answered softly. "Spread the cloth over me, for you are a near kinsman."

According to the custom of the Israelites, if a woman lay under the cloak of a man at night, he was required to marry her or they would both be denounced for lying together in sin. Naomi had know this—hence her instructions to Ruth. As for Boaz, he had already fallen in love with the lovely Ruth, but in this case there was a complication. Another kinsman of Naomi's husband also lived in Bethlehem and, since he was nearer of kin than Boaz, had the right under the law to marry Ruth if he so desired.

Boaz told Ruth not to say anything about having lain at his feet during the night. Early in the morning he consulted with Naomi and then went to the gate of the city. When the other kinsman came by, Boaz stopped him. "Naomi who came out of the country of Moab will sell a parcel of the land that belonged to our brother Elimelech," he said. "If you will redeem it, do so, but if you will not, tell me, for I am next in kin after you."

"I will redeem it," the kinsman said promptly, thinking he could sell it later to Boaz at a greater price.

"When you buy the field from Naomi," Boaz warned him, "you must also marry Ruth the Moabitess, the wife of the dead man, to raise up his name upon his inheritance."

The kinsman had forgotten the custom that when a man died and left a wife without issue, the nearest of kin married the wife in order to produce offspring who would inherit the land he had owned. And though he had been quite willing to make a profit at Boaz's expense, marriage with a foreigner was another matter entirely.

"I cannot redeem it for myself lest I mar my own inheritance," he protested hastily. "Redeem it yourself."

This was what Boaz wanted and he turned at once to the elders who sat at the gates of the city, making available their wisdom and experience to any who sought help. "You are witnesses this day that I have bought all that was Elimelech's and all that was Chilion's and Mahlon's from Naomi," he said. "Moreover I have purchased Ruth, the Moabitess, the wife of Mahlon, to be my wife, to raise up the name of the dead upon his inheritance."

"We are witnesses," the people at the gate and the elders agreed. "The Lord make the woman that has come into your house like Rachel and like Leah who built the house of Israel."

Boaz took Ruth as his wife and when she bore a son, it was given the name of Obed. Thus a hated foreigner, because of her goodness and her devotion to the mother of her dead husband, earned the respect and love of the village of Bethlehem, becoming part of what would soon be the royal line of Israel. And the story of Ruth, the foreigner, set down in due time by scholars, has remained as one of the most eloquent sermons on tolerance and love in all literature.

# 7. Samuel and Saul

*"Make us a king to judge us like all the nations."*     I SAMUEL 8:5

THE PROPHET Samuel was angry with his people, and not without good reason. Dedicated to serve God before the altar at Shiloh—the religious center for all of Israel—since he was a small boy, Samuel had given his whole life to leading his people and, as a prophet, bringing them the word of God. Growing up under the tutelage of Eli, the old chief priest, he had first heard God speak to him from the darkness as he watched before the altar, and had served the Lord faithfully ever since.

Samuel's had not been an easy task, for the early days of his ministry were a time of constant danger, with the Philistines pressing the men of Judah in forays from the southwest, while other enemies waited just across the Jordan and in the north around the Waters of Merom to probe out any weakness in the northern tribes. When, in spite of Samuel's warnings, the Hebrews had persisted in following false gods, the Philistines had defeated them in a great battle at Ebenezer. In another disaster, the Ark had been captured and taken to the Philistine capital of Ashdod, where it had been placed beside the idol of the Philistines' god, Dagon.

138

Yahweh did not tolerate being placed upon an equality with any other god, however, and when a severe pestilence came upon the Philistines, they had hurriedly moved the Ark to Kirjath-Jearim in a relatively neutral area. Not long afterward, the Israelites came together long enough to defeat the Philistines badly, and during much of Samuel's tenure of office as both judge and prophet after that, there had been peace.

Now a new threat had arisen, an expected attack by King Nahash and the Israelites' old enemies from the east, the Ammonites. Faced with this, plus the fact that Samuel was growing old, the elders of Israel came to the prophet at his home in Ramah just south of the ancient shrine of Bethel. They addressed him respectfully, as was his due, but their request was directly to the point.

"You are old and your sons do not walk in your ways," they said. "Make us a king to judge us like all the nations."

Samuel could not help recognizing the justice of their request. The Philistines were pressing the Hebrews again and had even invaded the hill country where heretofore the Israelites had thought themselves safe. The temple—if it could be called such—built at Shiloh to house the Ark of the Covenant had been burned, and neighboring centers had shared the same fate. Israel saw its very future as a people in grave danger and all that had been accomplished in more than two centuries since Joshua had led them into the Land of Promise about to be lost, with themselves put in cruel bondage once more.

To the mind of the elders only one solution presented itself; the entire nation must be placed under the leadership of a strong man who would be what Joshua was in the years following Moses' death, a powerful unifying force. No longer could Israel continue as a loose confederation of tribes which sometimes warred upon one another, held together only by their belief in one god. To be united, the elders decided, they must have a king.

One could hardly blame Samuel, however, for feeling that the request was, in a way, a vote of no confidence in his own leadership and that of God. He was convinced, too, that it would be a mistake to choose an earthly ruler who would represent a separation of civil and military from religious leadership, instead of one appointed by divine will alone—as God had promised centuries before. From Samuel's point of view, the people needed only faith in the God who had brought them out of Egypt in order to triumph over whatever enemies came against them—as Gideon had defeated the host of Midian with only three hundred strong and brave men. But the people were obviously in no mood for such a rededication of themselves, preferring to put their trust in an earthly king rather than an invisible god.

"This will be the kind of king that shall rule over you," the old prophet warned the elders and the people solemnly. "He will take your sons to be his horsemen; and some shall run before his chariot. He will appoint captains over thousands and captains over fifties; and will set them to till his ground, reap his harvest, and make his instruments of war and his chariots. He will take your daughters to be cooks and bakers; he will take your fields and your vineyards and your olive yards, even the best of them, and will give them to his servants. He will take your menservants, and your maidservants, and your goodliest young men and your asses and put them to his work. He will take the tenth of your sheep and you shall be his servants. You shall cry out because of the king you shall have chosen, but the Lord will not hear you."

When the people still insisted upon being governed by a king, Samuel searched until he found a man taller, stronger, and braver than any other in Israel. Saul, the son of Kish, was from the tribe of Benjamin, smallest of the twelve, so that no one could say Samuel sought to win the favor of the larger tribes by choosing the king from among them.

Regal in bearing and fearless in battle, Saul seemed an ideal ruler to lead them against the enemy, and for this he was indeed ideal. But Israel needed more than just a soldier, and moody, vain, temperamental, suspicious that others wished to unseat him, Saul soon showed his inadequacy as a king.

Not all the people would acknowledge Saul at first, largely

because he came from the smallest of the tribes. Then the Ammonites attacked Jabesh-Gilead in the territory of Gad on the east side of the Jordan and, when the besieged city issued a call for help, Saul responded. Leading a band of Israelite warriors in a brilliantly executed military campaign, he soundly defeated the Ammonites and raised the siege from Jabesh-Gilead. After that victory, the Israelite tribes made Saul king by acclamation and Samuel anointed him as their ruler.

Saul took as his capital the town of Gibeah situated upon a height a few miles north of Jerusalem, a strongly fortified center which the Israelites had never wrested from the Jebusites. The palace at Gibeah was a small building among the bean fields covering the hill inside a walled enclosure less than twenty paces square. But since the king and the army of several thousand men he kept ready at all times were usually busy skirmishing with the Philistines, Saul had little opportunity to enjoy his modest luxury.

One of the bravest and most capable of Israel's fighting men —after Saul himself—was the king's son Jonathan. When Jonathan led a foray against an enemy garrison near-by and destroyed it, the Philistines raised a great army to attack the Israelites, setting up camp at Michmash, northeast of Gibeah, with the obvious intention of out-flanking Saul and his army. Saul did not immediately launch the indicated countermovement, however, but waited for Samuel to arrive, since the prophet had promised to make sacrifices and invoke the blessing of God upon the Israelites before going into battle.

Samuel may have been testing Saul to see how great was his trust in God. Or the old prophet could have been displeased with the king because Saul was now the hero of the Israelites after his defeat of the Ammonites and Jonathan's destruction of the Philistine garrison, a feat which had been widely published abroad on Saul's orders. In any event, Samuel delayed his arrival and when Saul saw the confidence of his army growing steadily weaker and defections increasing daily, he ordered the offerings prepared and made the sacrifices himself, a duty ordinarily reserved to the chief priest. Samuel arrived shortly afterward and immediately demanded of Saul what had been done.

"Fearing that the enemy would come down upon me before I had made supplication to the Lord," Saul told him, "I forced myself and made a burnt offering."

"You have not kept the commandment of the Lord your God," Samuel said sternly. "The Lord would have established your kingdom upon Israel forever, but now your kingdom shall not continue. He has sought a man after his own heart and has commanded him to be captain over his people."

Troubled by the break with Samuel, Saul waited indecisively for the Philistines to attack. But not so Jonathan. He, taking his armorbearer, went to spy upon the enemy. Climbing over the hills on hands and knees, the two passed through a narrow defile between sharp crags and found a small Philistine garrison sleeping without guards. When Jonathan and his companion attacked with a great hubbub in the darkness, the Philistines were sure the Israelites had descended upon them in force and fled. Many Israelites who were among the main Philistine party took this opportunity to turn upon their enemies in the disorder and, when Saul finally sent a company of soldiers to pursue the enemy, the Philistines were defeated and driven eastward from Michmash to Aijalon, where Joshua had destroyed the league of the five Canaanite kings.

Saul's victory over the Philistines with only six hundred men restored the confidence of the people in their king, in spite of Samuel's warning to Saul that God had chosen a new leader. He went on to fight and win many battles, but the breach between him and Samuel grew steadily wider. When the prophet gave Saul the command of God to attack the Amalekites, Saul defeated them in a great battle during which their king was captured. Whether from cupidity or failure to understand, however, Saul failed to destroy the Amalekites as Samuel had commanded him and instead took the flocks and the kings as tribute, widening the breach between the two.

"To obey is better than sacrifice and to hearken than the fat of rams," Samuel warned Saul when he heard of this new act of disobedience. "Rebellion is as the sin of witchcraft and stubbornness is as iniquity and idolatry. Because you have rejected the word of the Lord, he has rejected you from being king."

The break between Saul and the prophet who had made him king was now final; its effects were to be felt in Israel for many years.

# 8. The Giant Slayer

*"The Spirit of the* Lord *departed from Saul, and an evil spirit from the* Lord *troubled him."*     I SAMUEL 16:14

"How long will you mourn for Saul, since I have rejected him from reigning over Israel?" God said to Samuel who was saddened by his failure to select a suitable King for his people. "Fill your horn with oil and I will send you to Jesse, for I have provided a king from among his sons."

Near Bethlehem Samuel came to the home of Jesse, a descendant of Boaz and Ruth. There he anointed the youngest of Jesse's sons, a ruddy and handsome boy called David, but cautioned the young man against revealing what he had done.

Saul had been brooding over the break with Samuel and the Prophet's statement that Saul's son should not inherit the throne of Israel. When the king grew daily more moody and preoccupied, someone suggested that a musician be found to play to him and raise his spirits. Several of David's brothers were with Saul's army and when they announced that their younger brother was an accomplished player upon the harp, the youth was brought to the camp. His playing and singing quickly charmed the king, bringing back his spirits, and Saul made the youth his armorbearer or squire.

Once more the Philistines gathered in force, centered at

Shochoh in Judah, south of Jerusalem and Bethlehem. This time the enemy had a new and fearsome weapon in a mighty champion named Goliath of Gath, a giant of a man and a skilled warrior. When he confidently challenged the Hebrews to send any man against him in combat, no one in Israel dared to oppose such a giant.

David had returned to Bethlehem to care for his father's sheep, as the three oldest brothers were with Saul's army. When Jesse sent him to carry food to his brothers, the young musician saw the champion Goliath standing upon the hill and heard him defy the armies of Saul.

"What shall be done for the man who kills this Philistine and takes away the reproach from Israel?" David asked the soldiers in the camp.

"The king will enrich him with great riches and will give him his daughter," they told him.

David went directly to Saul. "Let no man's heart fail because of him," he said, referring to Goliath. "Your servant will go to fight with this Philistine."

"You are only a youth and he is a man of war," Saul said with an amused smile. "How could you go against him?"

"A lion and a bear took a lamb out of my father's flock, but I killed both of them," David said confidently. "The Lord delivered me from the paw of the lion and the paw of the bear. He will deliver me from this Philistine who has defied the armies of the living God."

The youth's faith inspired confidence in the king. "Go," Saul told him. "And the Lord be with you."

David paused only to pick five smooth stones from the bed of a brook and put them in the shepherd's bag he carried, along with the sling that was a shepherd's favorite weapon. Armed only with these and a staff, he confidently approached the Philistine champion.

"Am I a dog that you come at me with staves?" Goliath demanded disdainfully when he saw that his opponent appeared to be armed only with a staff. "I will give your flesh to the fowls and to the beasts of the field."

"You come with a sword, a spear, and a shield but I come

in the name of the Lord of Hosts," David answered confidently.
"This day the Lord will deliver you into my hand and I will
smite you and take your head from you, that all the earth may
know there is a God in Israel. All this assembly shall know
that the Lord does not save by sword and spear, for the battle
is the Lord's and he will give you into our hands."

The Philistine moved contemptuously to attack David, but
the youth did not retreat. Reaching into his bag, he took out
a stone and placed it in the sling. Driven with all the strength
of his strong young arm, the stone struck Goliath on the forehead and the enemy champion dropped to the ground un-
conscious. Having no sword of his own, David killed the
Philistine with his own weapon and cut off his head. And when
the enemy saw that their champion was dead, they were sure
that the powerful Israelite god had intervened and fled in
disorder.

After David's victory over Goliath, Saul would not let him
return home, but kept him by his side and made him one
of his captains. Jonathan and David also became close friends,
swearing a solemn covenant of devotion to each other. By
the time the army returned home to Gibeah, David's feat
in defeating the giant had been announced in the city and the
women came out to greet the army chanting a song composed
in honor of the young champion.

"Saul has slain his thousands and David his ten thousands,"
they sang and thronged about the hero, neglecting the king—
or so Saul felt.

Remembering Samuel's warning that his son should not
rule over Israel and hearing the popular acclaim for David,
Saul was gripped by one of the black moods of suspicion and
distrust which were a major weakness in his character. Deciding to disgrace David, he first removed him from his position as
captain over a thousand and then, having announced that his
older daughter, Merab, would become David's wife—in fulfillment of the promise that whoever overcame Goliath would
marry his daughter—suddenly gave her to another, a gratuitous
insult.

David ignored the insult, however, and when a younger

daughter named Michal was substituted for Merab, accepted her. Saul countered with the provision that, as a dowry, David must kill a hundred Philistines, seeking in this way to force his destruction, but David easily killed the men. Saul had no choice now except to give the lovely Michal to David as his wife.

Becoming the king's son-in-law did not improve David's relationship with Saul, however. Jonathan for the moment argued his father out of a decision to kill David, but when the king tried to thrust him through with a javelin as he was playing upon the harp in Saul's tent, David had no choice except to take his own followers and hide in the mountainous cave region of Judah, south of Jerusalem.

To prove to Saul once and for all that he did not wish the king's life, David slipped into Saul's camp one night and cut off the skirt of Saul's robe as he slept. "I will not put forth my hand against the Lord's anointed, yet you hunt my soul to take it," he told the king when he awakened. "The Lord judge between me and you, but my hand shall not be upon you."

"You are more righteous than I, for you have rewarded me with good whereas I have rewarded you with evil," Saul said contritely in one of the sudden changes of mood that characterized his mental illness. For a short while he gave up his attempts to destroy David, but the black mood soon returned, and with several thousand men he went into the wilderness in pursuit of David, now captain of a guerrilla band.

Once again David stole into Saul's camp at night, taking the spear that stood beside the king's pillow and a cruse of water as evidence that, for a second time, Saul had been in his power. But, though Saul promised amnesty, David knew now that he could not trust him; with his six hundred men, he took service with Achish, the son of Maoch, King of Gath. And hearing that David had left the kingdom of Israel, Saul was satisfied that he was no longer a rival for the throne.

In going over to the Philistines, David did not become an enemy of Israel; rather he used the cover of apparent adherence to the Philistine king to hide his own activities. To this end, he asked Achish to let him and his men live in another part of the kingdom and was given the area of Ziklag, which was to the south on the borders of the Philistine territory. There he carried out succesful raids against many of the ancient enemies of Israel such as the Amalekites. The spoils of these raids he brought to Achish, but pretended that they had been made against Israelites so that Achish would trust him.

When another great Philistine army gathered to fight against Saul and the Israelites, David was in a quandary. He could not fight his own people, yet to refuse to do so would endanger the security he had found in the service of Achish. Luckily for David, some of the Philistine leaders objected to the presence of him and his men, fearing treachery, so they returned to Ziklag.

In the battle with the Philistines, Jonathan and two other of Saul's sons were killed and when Saul's armorbearer refused to thrust him through before he could be captured, the unhappy king took his sword and fell upon it. When the Philistines came to strip the slain, they cut off Saul's head, removed his armor, and put it in the house of their goddess Ashtaroth. Saul's body they impaled upon the wall of Bethshan, a Philistine city lying near the Jordan River east of the plain of Jezreel.

Grief-stricken at the news that Saul and his beloved friend Jonathan were dead, David composed an elegy of lamentation, precursor of a beautiful psalm he later wrote in praise of God. That he could thus weep for the man who had tried on numerous occasions to kill him was a measure of David's greatness, a greatness which was soon to be realized by Israel and the world.

# 9. David and Bathsheba

*"Is not this Bath-sheba, the daughter of Eliam, the wife of Uriah, the Hittite?"*    II SAMUEL 11:3

THOUGH STILL in the very prime of life, David could look back upon an impressive record of conquest and good government for his people. Anointed shortly after the death of Saul as king in Judah, southernmost and largest of the tribes of Israel, he had come to the throne at a time opportune for expansion. A brave military leader, capable of inspiring his men to great feats of arms, he had learned his trade well since the day when, as Saul's armorbearer, he had destroyed the Philistine champion Goliath. More than that, however, he had governed his people wisely and well.

To the south, Egypt maintained a merely nominal suzerainty over Israel, the government being controlled by priests interested only in satisfying their own lust and greed. So far had mighty Egypt fallen, in fact, that when an envoy named Wen Amun was sent to demand from the Phoenicians a gift of their famous cedars to build a royal barge, he was treated with contempt by a Phoenician prince. David's troops had been able to range far to the south without fear of punishment by Egypt, overrunning even the kingdom of Edom on the border between Israel and Egypt. With control of Edom also went access to the

Gulf of Aqabah and ore from which the Philistines smelted copper and iron for weapons.

When David's military successes and his virtues of loyalty, understanding, and tolerance proved him to be a far better ruler than Saul had been, the northern tribes came to him in Hebron and made him king over them as well as Judah. Now at last, the whole of Israel was united under a strong ruler who served the Lord and found favor in his sight. Hebron, the old home of Abraham, was much too far to the south to serve as a capital for the united kingdom of the tribes of Israel, so David set himself the task of taking the Jebusite stronghold of Jerusalem which lay almost between the two regions. Situated upon a mountain called Zion, with powerful and apparently impregnable walls, Jerusalem was no easy conquest, but David's training as a guerrilla fighter had long since taught him the importance of infiltration from within. He sought and soon found a weakness in the city's defenses.

On the east side of Jerusalem, overlooking the Kidron Valley through which passed the brook of that name, there was a spring called Gihon. Many years before—perhaps when Joshua and the Israelites had first come into Canaan—the Jebusites had cut a passageway down through the rocky floor of the city to this spring in order to obtain pure water without having to go outside the walls. This narrow shaft led directly up through the rock from which the spring burst, and opened into a passageway giving access to the center of the city a considerable distance above the fountain in which it began. Entering this "gutter," as he called it, by way of the spring, David sent men by night to infiltrate Jerusalem. In the morning they attacked the inhabitants, taking them by surprise and capturing the city. Having conquered Jerusalem, David then made it his capital, fortifying and enlarging it as the strength of his kingdom grew through conquest.

On the seacoast somewhat to the north stood the Phoenician city of Tyre. When its king, Hiram, sent carpenters and masons to David offering to build him a palace of the famed cedars growing in that land, David had been delighted. After the palace was built, however, his conscience troubled him because the Ark of the Covenant still remained in Judah with no house of its own. To decide what should be done with the Ark, David called his most trusted advisor, the prophet Nathan.

"Thus says the Lord of Hosts," Nathan told the king, " 'When your days are fulfilled and you shall sleep with your fathers, I will set up your seed after you and I will establish his kingdom. He shall build a house for my name and my mercy shall not depart from him. Your kingdom and your throne shall be established forever.' "

In accordance with Nathan's pronouncement, therefore, the Ark continued to be housed only in a tent or tabernacle, since it was God's will that not David, but the son who should rule after him, build a house for it.

With the whole people to govern, David no longer went out to fight the enemies of Israel, but left military matters largely in the hands of Joab, his trusted general. In lightninglike campaigns, the Syrians were conquered as far north as Damascus and great spoils brought to Jerusalem from Moab, Ammon, the kingdom of the Amalekites, and other regions. But when Joab would have destroyed the remaining members of the house of Saul, David protected them and kept them safe. For this act of generosity to the memory of the man he had refused at least twice to kill, although Saul had sought to destroy him on many occasions, David's descendants were later to pay dearly.

The magnificent palace built by King Hiram of Tyre for David was the finest structure in all of Jerusalem. From a commanding platform its terraces and walls looked down upon the entire city. And with leisure to enjoy the luxury which as a guerrilla chieftain had been denied him, David liked to walk upon the roof and watch the manifold activities of the busy and prosperous capital city of Israel. It was while doing this one evening that he saw a woman bathing upon a roof-top near-by.

David had several wives, but though he had been grateful to Michal, the daughter of Saul who had helped save him from death at her father's hands, he'd had little time for women before. Now, as he watched the beautiful woman upon the adjoining roof-top finish her bath and accept the towel a slave girl handed her, he was seized with so violent a desire for her that it left him trembling. Leisurely she dried her body, anointed it, and put on a robe of sheer material before going to her sleeping pallet on the roof-top like thousands of others on a warm summer night.

Calling for a servant, David pointed out the house where the woman had been and sent the man to learn her name. The servant soon returned with the information that she was Bathsheba, the wife of Uriah, a Hittite officer in David's army who was away fighting with the troops against the Ammonites. In the burning fever of his passion, David did not stop to think that he was breaking the laws God had given to Moses, but sent at once and had her brought to the palace.

Bathsheba came willingly, for not only had the king to be obeyed in all things, but it was an honor to be selected by him. In her arms David discovered a passion he'd never before experienced and by the time she returned to her home in the morning, he was thoroughly enchanted by her. Night after night thereafter she was escorted to the king's chamber shortly after dark, to be taken back to her own home in the morning showered with gifts from the now completely enamored David.

When Bathsheba told David she was to bear his child, he was faced with a grave problem. She was still the wife of Uriah the Hittite, away now for many months with the army beyond the Jordan. As soon as her condition became apparent, someone would be sure to bring against her the obvious charge of adultery, to which she could have no plea but guilty, and judgment would then be swift and sure. The place of execution outside the wall of the city was spattered with the dried blood of more than one woman—and man, too, for the partner in adultery was equally guilty—who had been stoned to death by the angry populace.

Only one solution presented itself to David, and a messenger was sent to Joab beyond the Jordan a few days' journey away ordering that Uriah the Hittite be returned to Jerusalem and—presumably—the arms of his wife. Once Uriah had spent the night in his home, David knew, he could be sent back to the battlefield and no odium would then attach itself to Bathsheba because she was to bear a child.

Uriah was puzzled and not particularly pleased by the order to return to Jerusalem. Though not a clever man, he was a strong one, skilled in war and in leading men. Already a minor captain in Joab's command who patterned his every action after the forthright general and was always first in battle, Uriah could hope to gain positions of even greater importance as time went on and might even one day become a general. He knew how the men in the field jeered at those who managed to be sent back home, however. And though Joab had said the order for his return came directly from the king himself, Uriah did not want that to happen to him. Yet even he could understand that a summons from the king might mean a great honor, word of his bravery in battle no doubt having come even to Jerusalem. And such an honor would increase very markedly the chances of his promotion.

Uriah was reassured by his reception, for not only did David greet him warmly, he also asked for a detailed report from the field and congratulated the Hittite upon his battle prowess. "Go down to your house and wash your feet," David said casually at the end of the interview, sure that Uriah was anxious for the embrace of his beautiful wife.

To Uriah's rather slow soldier's mind, to enjoy Bathsheba's embraces while his fellows were enduring the hardship of battle seemed somehow to betray them—and he was first of all a soldier. The answer he worked out was—for him—a logical one. Instead of going home that night, he rolled up in his cloak and slept on the king's doorstep. When the servants opened the door to the palace in the morning, they brought word to David that the Hittite had not visited his home.

David was angry, but carefully hid his feelings when Uriah came before him again, for it would not do to arouse the officer's suspicion concerning the real reason why he had been returned to Jerusalem. "Why did you not go down to your own house?" the king asked.

"The Ark, Israel, and Judah live in tents, and my lord Joab

and his servants are encamped in the open fields," Uriah said honestly. "Should I then go to my house, to eat and drink and lie with my wife? As you live, I will not do this thing."

Baffled for the moment by the man's stubbornness, David told him to stay in the city another day before going back to the army. Secretly, however, he ordered the servants to ply Uriah with wine, thinking that when the man was drunk he would certainly seek out Bathsheba. In the morning, however, the servants brought word that the Hittite, though thoroughly drunk, had still insisted upon sleeping at the palace.

So nothing had been accomplished and David was now reduced to desperate measures, for not even a king was immune from charges of adultery before the people.

To Joab, by Uriah, he therefore sent a letter, ordering that the Hittite be put in the front of the battle and left there so that the enemy would kill him. They did kill him, and a brave man died without knowing the reason why. As for David, he was now free to take Bathsheba as his wife and escape a charge of adultery for them both—at the price of having committed murder.

Uriah himself had carried the letter David sent Joab, so, with the general absent in the field, there was no proof of what really had happened. Naturally, having no proof, no one brought accusations against the king. Word of David's sin did come to Nathan, the prophet, however, and the man of God visited the king in Jerusalem.

"Two men were in a city, the one rich and the other poor," the prophet said, pretending to tell David a story. "The rich man had many flocks and herds, but the poor man had nothing except one little ewe lamb. It ate his food and drank from his cup and lay in his bosom, but when a traveler came to the rich man, he did not pick from his own herd to dress for the wayfarer. Instead he took the poor man's lamb and dressed it."

"As the Lord lives, the man that has done this thing shall surely die." David said indignantly, not suspecting that the wily prophet was tricking him into pronouncing his own guilt. "He shall restore the lamb fourfold, because he did this thing and because he had no pity."

"Thou art the man," Nathan told him sternly. "Thus says the voice of the Lord God of Israel, 'I anointed you king over Israel and I delivered you out of the hands of Saul. I gave you the house of Israel and of Judah, and if that had been too little, I would have given you many other things. Why have you despised the commandment of the Lord, to do evil in his sight? You have killed Uriah the Hittite and have taken his wife to be your wife and have slain him with the sword of the children of Ammon. Now therefore the sword shall never depart from your house because you have despised me and have taken the wife of Uriah the Hittite to be your wife. Behold, I will raise up evil against you out of your own house!'"

As an immediate punishment for David's sin, the first child borne him by Bathsheba became ill. David grieved for it, but when the child died, he mourned no more, recognizing the will of God and bowing himself to it. Soon Bathsheba bore David another son; this one he named Solomon.

# 10. Absalom, My Son

*"Absalom, my son, my son Absalom!*
*Would God I had died for thee."*

II SAMUEL 18:33

ABSALOM WAS a son to gratify any father's heart. His mother was Maachah, daughter of the king of Geshur, so he was of royal blood on both sides. In appearance he was every inch a prince, tall, handsome, with long flowing hair of which he was inordinately proud. A mighty warrior, he was another David in appearance and, though not the first-born, could look forward to a position of great power and importance in the kingdom. In two respects only did Absalom fail to measure up to everything David could have expected of him; he was too clever for his own good, as well as very ambitious.

Few in David's palace paid much attention to Solomon, the son of Bathsheba who had been the wife of Uriah. Many of David's wives were kings' daughters and naturally contemptuous of one who had brought to him only her beauty and her power to stir him to passion. They let Bathsheba live in the palace because David still preferred her to all the others, but they ignored both her and her son. If anyone noticed that Solomon grew up to be very handsome and, in addition, wise beyond his years, the fact was lost sight of in the furious battle of palace intrigue—lost sight of by all except by Bathsheba, whom David

156

had secretly promised that Solomon would succeed him, and Nathan, the prophet, who knew God's will.

When David grew old and his hold on the reins of government began to loosen, palace intrigues grew rapidly more involved as each of his wives sought to have one of her sons inherit the throne. Absalom, however, was busy on his own account and had no intention of waiting patiently for his father to die. First, he secretly trained a force of fiercely loyal young men to drive chariots and fight at his command, and soon had a sizable group built up that answered only to him. And second, he sought to destroy the allegiance of the people to David by implanting the idea that the old king was no longer able to rule them.

Each morning Absalom took up a position just outside the gates of Jerusalem where he could speak to those who came to the city seeking to have their grievances judged by the king as the final authority. Only a few ever reached the king, of course, so there was always much dissatisfaction and grumbling among the petitioners. This discontent Absalom shrewdly used to win their favor for himself.

"No man is deputed by the king to hear you," he would say to those entering the gates with a complaint. "If I were judge in the land, every man with a suit could come to me and I would do him justice."

The petitioners were naturally flattered by such personal attention from handsome Prince Absalom. Through this sort of boring from within, he had managed to build up a considerable following against the day when he planned to force David to turn the throne over to him. And as there had always been a certain amount of ill feeling between the two parts of the kingdom, he had little trouble in convincing the men of the north that David favored the southern tribes from which he had come. Still another factor in Absalom's favor was David's great love for him and his reluctance to hear anything that was not favorable to his handsome prince.

If Absalom was aware that David had secretly pledged to Bathsheba that her son Solomon would succeed him, it made no difference for, having already murdered David's eldest son by a stratagem, the ruthless young prince would not hesitate to destroy the others. Finally, he was ready to make his own move to gain the throne and, in order to get out of Jerusalem with his followers, came to his father and begged permission to go to Hebron to serve the Lord there with a sacrifice in payment of a vow. When David, suspecting nothing, agreed, Absalom left with two hundred men. As he traveled through Judah, he sounded the call for those supporting him to gather, and soon a considerable group of people were in active support of his rebellion against his father's rule.

By the time a messenger reached David with the disturbing report that "the hearts of the men of Israel are after Absalom," the rebellious prince's forces were already approaching Jerusalem to attack the city. In order to avoid as much bloodshed as possible, David decided to evacuate Jerusalem, but when the high priest Zadok and the Levites who served the Ark started to take the sacred symbol out of the capital, David ordered them to carry it back.

"If I find favor in the eyes of the Lord, he will bring me back again and show me both it and his habitation," he said. "But if he says, 'I have no delight in you,' then here I am. Let him do to me as seems good to him."

Thus, unlike Saul, David put his complete trust in God's promises, even in a time of direst peril.

Absalom took Jerusalem without a battle, forcing David to retreat eastward across the Jordan into Gilead. In fact, it seemed that Absalom was on the threshold of becoming king—until overconfidence and vanity proved his worst enemy.

Though blinded earlier to Absalom's ruthless preparations to unseat him, David knew his son well. A clever spy named Hushai was sent into Jerusalem to flatter Absalom and persuade the younger man to leave the protection of the city's walls and pursue his father. When Absalom accepted the counsel of Hushai, David divided his forces into three parts, putting one-third under the leadership of Joab, one-third under Abishai, Joab's brother, and a third part under Ittai, the Gittite, who was loyal to the king.

"Deal gently with the young man," David counseled his captains at the beginning of the battle, but as Absalom sought to escape defeat at the hands of more experienced leaders by riding away upon a mule, his hair caught in the thick boughs of a great oak. Trapped by his own vanity which had made him keep his hair long, he hung suspended and helpless while the mule he was riding ran ahead. Meanwhile Joab, hearing that Absalom was caught in the tree, hurried to kill him, knowing that if he lived, David would only forgive him, leaving him to plot further rebellion.

When David learned that Absalom had been killed, he was disconsolate, even though the treacherous son had almost taken away his kingdom. "O my son Absalom, my son, my son Absalom!" he cried in his grief. "Would God I had died for you, O Absalom, my son, my son!"

Joab was more realistic and had no sympathy for traitors. Hearing that David continued to bemoan the death of his rebellious son, the old captain who had been responsible for many of David's greatest victories went to the king. "By loving your enemies and hating your friends, you have shamed all your servants who saved your life and the lives of your sons and daughters and wives and concubines," he said brusquely. "Now get up and speak encouragingly to those servants or not one of them will remain with you."

David was forced to give up his public mourning to save his kingdom, but for a long time his heart was heavy over the handsome Absalom whom he had loved in spite of his treachery. The palace intrigues continued, however, as did the dissatisfaction of the northern tribes with what they considered the dominance of David's own tribe of Judah.

Once more one of David's sons sought to usurp the place of his father; this time it was Adonijah, the son of Haggith, who was the mother of Absalom. Convinced that the kingdom would break apart without a strong hand at the helm, Joab supported Adonijah against David, but Zadok, the chief priest, Nathan the prophet, and Bathsheba persuaded the old king to proclaim Solomon ruler over both Judah and Israel. When those supporting the rebellion heard this, they ran away, but Adonijah claimed refuge upon the horns of the altar, to which traditionally anyone in Israel could resort and claim immunity.

Solomon, already wise though still young, saw a way to reconcile both the northern and southern tribes for the moment by showing mercy to his brother. "If he will show himself a worthy man," he said of Adonijah, "not a hair of his head shall fall to the earth. But if wickedness is found in him, he shall die."

Trusting in the promise of Solomon, Adonijah came down from the altar and, when he knelt and swore allegiance to the new king, was allowed to go free.

Realizing that death was near, David called Solomon to him. "I go the way of all the earth," he charged the young king. "Be strong therefore. Show yourself a man and keep the charge of the Lord thy God, to walk in his ways, to keep his statutes and his commandments, as it is written in the Law of Moses, that you may prosper in all you do and wherever you turn, and that the Lord may continue his word which he spoke concerning me saying, 'If your children take heed to their ways, to walk before me in truth with all their heart and with all their soul, there shall not fail you a man on the throne of Israel.' "

David had sinned grievously—and had been punished for it. But he had never deserted his God. For his faith the Lord let him see his own son sit upon the throne of Israel as he had been promised. And through David's line, God one day gave his Son to the world that through belief in him men would be able to triumph even over death itself.

# III. The Kingdom and the Glory

"And Solomon sent to Hiram, saying
. . . behold, I purpose to build an house
unto the name of the LORD my God."

I KINGS 5:2, 5

# 1. The House of God

*"Thy son, whom I will set upon thy throne in thy room, he shall build an house unto my name."*   I KINGS 5:5

THE NEW KING of Israel was not a soldier, but then he had little need to be. David had extended the boundaries of Israel beyond what they had ever been, or would be again for nearly a thousand years after Solomon added further to them. From beyond Damascus to the northeast, Israel now encompassed both sides of the Jordan as far as the great desert on the east and southward to Ezion-geber, a port city on the Gulf of Aqabah having access to the Arabian Gulf, or Red Sea, and through it to the Indian Ocean. From Kedesh on the Orontes River in the north the boundary extended southwestward to Mount Carmel, the bold headland jutting out into the Great Sea south of the Phoenician cities of the coast. Thence it ran along the coast to Joppa, giving Israel a seaport on the Mediterranean—the Great Sea—as well as one having access to the Indian Ocean. Bypassing the Philistine centers, the boundary reached the coast again south of Gaza and extended to the usually dry River of Egypt marking the border with that country. From there the line ran eastward again to Ezion-geber, completing the outline of the kingdom of Israel.

From early years Solomon had shown much more wisdom than the other princes of David's court. When this was coupled with the cool ruthlessness which he began to display soon after his father's death, the two qualities operated to make him a very successful ruler, if not to endear him particularly to his subjects.

One of the new king's first acts was to destroy Adonijah, the older brother whose claim to the throne—had not David specifically selected Solomon himself—would have had precedence over the others. Adonijah was killed on Solomon's order when the king decided he was plotting further rebellion. David's great general, Joab, who had backed Adonijah's claim to the throne when David's age seemed to make it impossible for him to maintain an effective rule over the Israelites, was also destroyed.

Joab had not necessarily been treacherous in supporting Adonijah. Through all the history of his relationship with David, the military leader had been a tower of strength, repeatedly putting down rebellion which flared up from time to time between the northern tribes of Israel and the southern tribe of Judah, and keeping the kingdom strong. When he saw that kingdom about to disintegrate because of David's age and weakness, Joab had naturally put his support behind the eldest son, the logical candidate for the throne. Bathsheba, however, had forestalled Adonijah by reminding David of his promise that her son, Solomon, would one day be king, and Solomon never forgave Joab for supporting Adonijah. Thus, by ruthlessly destroying all who might have claim against him for the throne, Solomon gained complete control of the nation.

Solomon's next act was to secure and extend, by negotiation rather than by force, the boundaries of Israel, some of which had been encroached upon by neighboring kingdoms during the latter years of David's reign. A treaty of peace was concluded with the current Pharaoh of Egypt, and one of Pharaoh's daughters became nominally Solomon's wife, though in reality little more than a hostage. This achievement set a pattern by which the young king secured his other boundaries as well, while making contacts with even distant rulers who could add to his riches through favorable trade relations. But as his harem of wives and concubines grew, so did Solomon's riches and the extravagant tastes which were eventually to prove the downfall of his line.

Solomon's reign was a period of peace and great prosperity, but it was this mainly for the nobles of Israel who flocked to his court to flatter him and profit by their connection there. For the common people, whom he did not hesitate to exploit for his own benefit, it was a time of grinding misery. God had promised David that his son would build a house for the Ark, and soon after the old king's death Solomon began construction of a magnificent temple upon the crest of a hill in Jerusalem. At the same time he repaired the break in the walls, made during David's attack upon the city, with a great tower called the Millo.

King Hiram of Tyre had built David's palace and Solomon commissioned him to build the temple at Jerusalem, using the famed Cedars of Lebanon, as well as other fine woods and metal for this structure which the young king confidently expected to outshine any other building in the world as the crowning glory of his kingdom.

Seven years were occupied with the building of the temple. When it was finished, Hiram's artisans stayed on for thirteen more years to build a magnificent palace for Solomon, his hundreds of wives and concubines, and the huge retinue that now served his court.

David had amassed a great store of precious metals in Jerusalem which Solomon used for the temple but, in addition to the skilled workmen of Tyre, thousands of other laborers were needed to prepare the foundation, quarry and haul the stone, and erect the great timbers. To obtain this labor, Solomon decreed the beginning of something which had never existed in Israel before, a *corvee* or conscription under which the common people were forced to work for the king one-third of the time, virtually as slaves.

Naturally there was tremendous resentment throughout the kingdom on the part of the proud and independent Israelites because of the king's decree. For the moment no active rebellion occurred, however, for Solomon had also taken the precaution of establishing a swift chariot corps stationed in various cities of the kingdom and ready to move when trouble arose. The greatest of these cavalry centers was the fortress city of Megiddo guarding both the valley of Jezreel and the coastal plain south of Mount Carmel. There the vast stables required to house the animals and their drivers were ranged along a broad paved street. Built entirely of stone, with separate cubicles for the horses, this army center in itself was a tremendous and expensive undertaking.

Though he gave lip service to the worship of his God at least in the early years of his reign, Solomon was never the devout man that his father was. In fact, his building the temple seems to have been as much to please his own vanity as an act of gratitude to the Lord. When the palace was completed, however, he did not fail to take the opportunity of its dedication to make at least a pretense of humbling himself before divine will, while the people gaped at the magnificence of the house erected in honor of their God.

When the populace was allowed to view the golden vessels, candlesticks, tongs, bowls, snuffers, basins, censors, and even hinges, Solomon also brought out the treasures which his father had dedicated, and placed these in the temple along with precious stones, stores of incense, fragrant woods, and rare things from all parts of the world. Finally, in a vast and solemn procession, the Ark of the Covenant, containing the two tablets of stone engraved with the Law given to Moses when the Lord made a covenant with his people as they were on their way out of Egypt, was escorted by the priests and Levites to its resting place in the holiest part of the temple itself. This done, Solomon invoked the approval of the Lord for the temple he had built according to God's promise to David.

"Now, O Lord God of Israel," he prayed, "let your word be verified which you spoke to your servant David my father. Listen to the supplication of your servant and of your people Israel when they shall pray toward this place. Hear in heaven your dwelling place, and when you hear, forgive. For you did separate them from among all the people of the earth, to be your inheritance as you spoke to Moses your servant when you brought our fathers out of Egypt."

The prayer finished, Solomon blessed the congregation of Israel with these words: "The Lord our God be with us as he was with our fathers. Let him not leave us, nor forsake us. That all the people of the earth may know that the Lord is God, and that there is none else, let your heart therefore be perfect with the Lord our God, to walk in his statutes and to keep his commandments as at this day."

Had Solomon adhered to his own admonitions, he might well have made his nation a truly great power and altered the course of history. But greed, lust, and the desire for personal glory stood in the way.

# 2. The Queen of Sheba

*"And when the queen of Sheba heard
of the fame of Solomon . . . she came
to prove him with hard questions."*

I KINGS 10:1

"Lo, I HAVE GIVEN you a wise and understanding heart,"
God had told Solomon in a dream shortly after he
became king of Israel. And as time went on, stories
about the extent of that wisdom began to be told everywhere.
None of them described a more difficult problem than that
posed by two women of the streets who came before the king
one day, asking that he judge between them.

"O my lord, I and this woman dwell in the same house," one
of the women said. "I was delivered of a child in the house and
on the third day after that this woman was delivered also. There
was no one with us in the house, except we two and, when this
woman's child died in the night because she overlaid it, she
arose at midnight and took my son from beside me and laid
her dead child in my bosom."

"The living child is my son," the other woman insisted. "The
dead is hers."

Solomon considered for a while, and then ordered: "Divide
the living child in two and give half to one and half to the
other."

As he had expected, the real mother protested immediately.
"Give her the child and do not slay it!" she cried, whereas the

168

other woman said with a shrug, "Let it be neither mine nor yours, but divide it."

Solomon told the real mother of the child to come forward. "Give her the living child, for she is its mother," he ordered, and when the people heard of the judgment the king had made, they were amazed at his wisdom.

The Phoenicians, with their seaport cities of Tyre, Sidon, and Byblos, were the seafarers of Solomon's day, as they had been in David's time. Great ships with huge square sails and long banks of slaves straining at the oars traveled the Mediterranean, on regular schedules during the summer months when the weather was generally favorable, carrying goods between all the major seaports of the world and far up the Nile to the Egyptian cities. Phoenician vessels especially built to sail long distances crossed the Mediterranean to bring tin and other valuable cargoes from far distant Tarshish, even venturing past the narrow opening to the west that gave access to a vast sea which no one had explored. Because of their major port of destination, these large and seaworthy vessels became known as "Ships of Tarshish."

King Hiram of Tyre was closely allied to the Israelites and had furnished the skilled workmen and much of the material for building the palace of David, the temple of the Lord, and the magnificent complex of structures that housed Solomon's teeming court, then one of the most luxurious in all the world. Solomon's wisdom warned him against trying to compete with the Phoenicians for trade in the Mediterranean from Joppa, which possessed at best very poor facilities for loading and unloading large vessels. But at Ezion-geber on the Gulf of Aqabah, he possessed a port from which vessels could sail to many of the storied lands of Arabia and the East, perhaps as far as India and Ceylon but certainly to Ophir near the mouth of the gulf, as well as southward along the eastern coast of Africa.

Solomon's shrewdness and his greed for wealth did not long let him overlook the tremendous fortunes to be made by trading in the spices and precious woods so much in demand by the Egyptians for their temples and for preparing the bodies of their kings and nobles for the journey to the afterworld. And so—

perhaps by promising not to interfere with the Phoenician trade in the Mediterranean—he was able to enter into a shrewd partnership with King Hiram.

Soon Phoenician shipbuilders were constructing and launching the great "Ships of Tarshish" at Ezion-geber and sailing them in the Red Sea and along the adjoining coast. There seems little doubt that they sailed as far east also as India and Ceylon, taking advantage of the monsoons which would drive a ship in either direction, depending upon the season. And since the Egyptians did very little long-distance traveling by water, Solomon's navy controlled much of the trade in that region, bringing back exotic things such as ivory, apes, and peacocks.

There was another reason why the southernmost city of Israel prospered. Near Ezion-geber were great deposits of copper, iron, and other metals, and, utilizing the secret processes which David had obtained through his victories over the Philistines, Solomon—again in partnership with Hiram of Tyre —built a great smelter in that area. Ore taken from near-by mines was melted with hot fires of charcoal made from wood brought in great caravans southward along the King's Highway from the regions of Bashan and Gilead on the east side of the Jordan. The metal was then fashioned into tools, weapons, implements, and other products which commanded an immediate market in Egypt and the countries for many hundreds of miles around. Carried to India, Ceylon, Ophir, and the coast of Africa by the ships of Tarshish, these products commanded fantastic prices.

With such widespread trade between Israel and so many countries of the world, it was inevitable that news of Solomon's glory, his riches, and his wisdom, should penetrate even into the relatively isolated area of Sheba or Yemen, lying far to the southeast near the mouth of the Arabian Gulf. There they intrigued the mind of a rich and powerful woman, the queen of that land.

The capital city of Sheba was called Merab, a large and rich center located in an area heavily irrigated by water drawn from a river which had been damned to form a large lake. Here all sorts of fruits and rich spices flourished and were exported, formerly by caravan but more recently by ship, to Egypt, Israel, and many other countries. The people of Sheba worshipped a moon god in a great oval-shaped temple in whose courtyard fountains of water rose to more than twice a man's height, and their queen lived amidst considerable splendor.

As the products of Sheba had for a long time been exported to Israel, it was not unnatural that, at the height of Solomon's fame, the queen should visit his court with her magnificent retinue and many slaves bearing costly gifts. Fully realizing the riches that a monopoly of the trade with Sheba could bring him —and no doubt greatly attracted by the beauty of its queen— Solomon gave the visitor a truly royal welcome.

Besides the beautiful city of Jerusalem with its great golden temple and Solomon's gleaming palace, easily more magnificent than anything that had ever been built in this land before, there were many other places of interest to the visiting monarch. At Beth-Asbea in the south, weavers made the fine, almost transparent cloth called *byssus*, much prized everywhere for making rich garments. From the Phoenician cities on the seacoast came purple, vermilion, and other rich dyes, while Phoenician ships brought cosmetics, stibium, and other exotic products dear to women. Spices of all kinds, cinnamon, balsam and other balms, aloes, wax, honey were sold freely in the markets of the Israelite cities, as were fragrant gums and oils, and women of all stations purchased small bags of myrrh to wear beneath their garments as perfume.

Altogether it was a land of great luxury to which the royal visitor came; nor did the Queen of Sheba visit Jerusalem with empty hands. A long train of camels accompanied her party bearing spices, gold, precious stones, and many other gifts. She talked with Solomon, questioning him closely about many things, and they spent numerous hours alone together. Perhaps she saw the shallowness of the man behind the monarch, for she was not tempted to remain as one of his many wives. But in any event she did not fail to flatter him highly when it came time for her to depart.

"It was a true report that I heard in my own land of your acts and of your wisdom," she told Solomon. "Although I did not believe the words until I came and my eyes had seen it, the half was not told me! Your wisdom and prosperity exceed the fame which I heard. Happy are your men; happy are these your servants who stand continually before you and hear your wisdom. Blessed be the Lord your God who delighted in you to set you upon the throne of Israel."

The Queen of Sheba had given Solomon valuable presents and he in turn gave her many rich gifts so that she and her servants departed as heavily laden with precious goods as when they arrived. One special gift she seems to have taken with her, the faith in the God of Israel which she had seen dominate the life of its people. For, almost a thousand years later, wise men from her country were to return to Jerusalem asking, "Where is he that is born King of the Jews?"

# 3. The Kingdom Divided

*"I will rend the kingdom out of the hand of Solomon, and will give ten tribes to thee."*    I KINGS 11:31

THE RICHEST KING in Israel's history was the last to rule a united people. Ironically enough, Solomon's vaunted wisdom proved his downfall.

Solomon was a great organizer, rightly discerning that Israel could not continue as a power in the world of that day unless it could act as one people in times of stress. In dividing the country into twelve provincial districts, with a governor for each responsible directly to the king, he no doubt greatly increased governmental efficiency. At the same time, he made the mistake of disregarding the old tribal groupings with their fierce loyalties and animosities, as well as the intense individualism of the Hebrews. When he retained control of Judah for himself, the northern tribes—rightly or wrongly—decided that they were being ruled by the larger group, and the seeds of rebellion quickly began to sprout.

Two other sources of discontent arose from Solomon's desires. One was the tremendous expenditure for his palace, the other was his harem.

No one had objected to the construction of the temple; ever since the building of the Ark in the Wilderness of Sinai, it had been understood that a suitable center of worship would one day be constructed. But the magnificence of the royal palace dwarfed the imagination as well as the temple itself—the latter literally. In payment for building the temple and the palace, King Hiram of Tyre had been given twenty Israelite towns near his borders, plus a port on the Red Sea at Elath. This may have been another source of discontent, since at one time or another the Phoenicians had fought against the Israelites, though there had been peace between them for many years.

A considerable source of trouble was the presence of so many foreign women in the king's harem, many of them given to Solomon at the time treaties were made with their home countries, a custom that prevailed widely from ancient times. Perhaps the wife whom Pharaoh sent to Solomon from Egypt started the trouble; or it may have been with the coming of the Queen of Sheba that his greatest failing, the love of strange women, grew into a major source of popular discontent. He had taken wives from among the Moabites, Ammonites, Edomites, Zidonians, Hittites, and others, nations of which the Lord had said to the Children of Israel, "Surely they will turn away your heart after their gods." When Solomon grew old, some of these foreigners did turn his heart away to other deities, particularly such pagon idols as Ashtoreth, the goddess of the Zidonians who was worshipped with rites of almost incredible lasciviousness, and Milcom of the Ammonites.

David had often been weak and temperamental in his personal relationships, but he had never deviated from his loyalty to God. Solomon, however, even built an altar for Chemosh, the god of Moab, on a hill outside Jerusalem and another for Moloch, the hated god of the Ammonite people whose worship included the sacrifice of the first born in great iron furnaces. Before these false deities, Solomon burnt incense and made sacrifices—the ultimate insult to the God of Israel.

One of Solomon's most devoted administrators was a man named Jeroboam and, as a reward for his industry, the king appointed him governor over the descendants of Joseph. As Jeroboam was leaving Jerusalem to take up his new assignment, the prophet Ahijah met him on the road.

Tearing his robe into twelve pieces, Ahijah said to Jeroboam:

"Take ten pieces, for thus says the Lord God of Israel, 'Behold I will rend the kingdom out of the hand of Solomon, and will give ten tribes to you, because Solomon forsook me and worshipped Ashtoreth the goddess of the Zidonians, Chemosh the god of the Moabites, and Milcom the god of the children of Ammon. To his son I will give one tribe, that David my servant may have a light always before me in Jerusalem, the city where I have chosen to put my name, but you shall be king over Israel.' "

A situation almost exactly similar had arisen when Samuel had anointed David as king while Saul still held the throne. And as Saul had sought to kill David, so Solomon now tried to destroy Jeroboam. The latter, however, escaped to Egypt where the Pharaoh Sheshonk, a former soldier of Libya, had developed ambitions of his own, one of them the reconquest of wealthy Israel.

At Solomon's death, the normal successor to the throne of Israel was his oldest son, Prince Rehoboam, an arrogant wastrel who showed no signs of the strength needed to hold the country together. Besides, his mother was a foreigner, an Ammonite, and the council of elders hesitated to choose as their king the son of an enemy with whom they had often fought.

Instinctively realizing that what the country needed most of all was to put the Lord in his proper place as the foremost claimant to the people's loyalties, the religious leaders called for a gathering at Shechem, where Abraham had first made a sacrifice of thanksgiving to God for bringing him and his people into this land. Hearing of this, Jeroboam boldly returned from exile and, with the elders, demanded that Rehoboam guarantee to lighten the burden of taxes and forced labor which Solomon had put upon the people.

Shrewd and able, Jeroboam no doubt realized that the arrogant Rehoboam would not yield, and the crown prince did not disappoint him. Pretending to need three days to consult the elders, Rehoboam actually spent them listening to court sycophants who, by pandering to his vanity, sought to gain positions of influence for themselves.

"Tell the people, 'My little finger shall be thicker than my father's loins,' " they advised him. " 'And whereas my father burdened you with a heavy yoke, I will add to it.' "

Not possessing the intelligence to realize that he was dealing with an aroused and determined people, Rehoboam repeated these words to Jeroboam and the council of the elders at Shechem, and the rupture was complete.

"What portion do we have in David?" the representative of the northern tribes cried in disgust. "To your tents, O Israel!" Only the tribes of Judah and Benjamin remained loyal to Rehoboam, while Jeroboam, as had been prophesied by the prophet Ahijah, was made king of the ten tribes to the north.

Furious at being scorned by fully half the nation, Rehoboam tried to raise an army to fight Jeroboam but, led by a prophet named Shemaiah, the tribes of Judah and Benjamin refused to make war against their own people. Meanwhile Jeroboam, perhaps because of his training as a provincial governor, made the mistake of putting his political judgment before his faith in the god who, through the prophet Ahijah, had selected him to rule over the northern tribes. Fearing that if the people continued to go up to Jerusalem to sacrifice, they might turn again to Rehoboam and the house of David, Jeroboam set up two calves of gold as idols, one in Bethel and one in Dan. Priests were ordained to serve the altars and Jeroboam also sent his wife secretly as an emissary to the prophet Ahijah, who served as the voice of the Lord in that day, hoping to gain his favor. Shrewd though he was, however, Jeroboam had underestimated the prophet.

"Go tell Jeroboam, thus says the Lord God of Israel," Ahijah told her sternly. " 'You have not been as my servant David who kept my commandments, but made other gods and molten images to provoke me to anger and have cast me behind your back. Therefore I will bring evil upon the house of Jeroboam and will raise up a king over Israel who shall cut off your house. The Lord shall smite Israel as a reed is shaken in the water; he shall root up Israel out of this good land which he gave to their fathers and shall scatter them beyond the river."

The union between the northern and southern tribes had never been very strong. Inevitably conflict broke out between

Israel and Judah, beginning the decline in the fortunes of both which was eventually to result in the disappearance of one and the enslavement of the other. As he had punished his people in the wilderness before Sinai for the sin of idolatry, God again chastened them for the same weakness which had brought low even the might and wealth of Solomon, by putting them under the hands of a succession of oppressors.

# 4. The Prophet and the Queen

*"Jezebel sent a messenger unto Elijah, saying, So let the gods do to me, and more also, if I make not thy life as the life of one of them by to morrow about this time."*                    I KINGS 19:2

JEZEBEL MIGHT HAVE succeeded in her determination to destroy the worship of Yahweh in Israel and replace it with the depraved and cruel rites of Baal and Astarte, except for one man—Elijah, the Tishbite, a prophet of God. From the day she came to Samaria as the bride of Prince Ahab, the battle between the prophet and the queen was joined, with the only possible end the destruction of either the one or the other.

The grave sin of Jeroboam in failing to lead the people of the northern kingdom back to God had been visited upon his descendants for several generations, including a bitter civil war. Finally a strong general named Omri welded the warring elements in a ruthless military campaign and, recognizing that the kingdom must have a capital to rival Jerusalem if he were to hold the allegiance of the people, began to build a magnificent walled city called Samaria in the highlands north of Jerusalem.

Near the ancient religious center of Shechem and almost in the center of the northern kingdom, Samaria was built upon an elevation called "Watch-Mountain" rising well above the valley and providing a commanding view of the entire area as well as affording protection for the fortress-palace of the king. In the process of construction, the top of the hill was leveled

178

and its sides were banked, then walls and terraces were built about it so that the city was surrounded by an outer ring of fortifications. Large cisterns furnished an adequate water supply and a secondary wall made of stone blocks surrounded the broad courtyard in which stood the royal palace. An outstanding feature of this court was a large pool enclosed in a basin of stone.

To the northeast, Ashurnasirpal II, king of the Assyrians, had already begun a campaign to conquer Egypt, and his route of march naturally led along the coast almost within sight of Samaria. To help combat this menace, Omri had made an alliance with the Phoenicians on the northern coast, cementing it with a marriage between his son, Ahab, and Jezebel, daughter of Ethbaal, king of the Zidonians. Jezebel brought many rich gifts as her dowry, notably a large quantity of fine Egyptian furniture carved from ivory. In fact, after her arrival the Israelites often referred facetiously to the royal palace as the "House of Ivory."

Jezebel brought a far more sinister gift than these riches, however, one that was to affect seriously the fate of Israel for many years to come. Her father had been a priest of Astarte, the goddess-wife of Baal who was worshipped with voluptuous and perverted rites. When Jezebel introduced this religion into Israel and, in her campaign to destroy the allegiance of the people to Yahweh, assassinated most of the priests of God, she became the Lord's greatest enemy in that day.

Omri had managed to keep his kingdom intact by paying tribute to the Assyrians; in fact, he was so much admired by them that their written records more than a hundred years later still referred to Israel as the "House of Omri." Crowned king after Omri's death, the weak-willed and pleasure-loving Ahab let the domineering and ruthless Jezebel lead him into the lust-filled rites of Baal and Astarte, even building an altar and a temple of Baal in Samaria.

Only one man in the kingdom, Elijah, the Tishbite, dared oppose the vicious queen and her complacent husband. Burning-eyed, with the long hair and beard of a Nazarite, the prophet was a strange figure indeed amidst the magnificence of Ahab's court. But his words of warning were chilling enough, for he spoke of famine, always a danger in a land where rainfall was seldom adequate.

"As the Lord God of Israel lives before whom I stand, there shall not be dew or rain these years but according to my word," Elijah told Ahab sternly.

The weak king might have turned to the Lord had not Jezebel contemptuously dismissed the prophet and sent men to kill him. Elijah was forced to take refuge in the hills, and only at the height of the famine that followed, when the people had been thoroughly chastened by hunger and thirst, did he return.

"Are you he that troubles Israel?" Ahab demanded belligerently when they met.

"I have not troubled Israel but you and your father's house in that you forsook the commandments of the Lord and followed Baal," Elijah corrected him. "Now gather all Israel at Mount Carmel with the prophets of Baal and the prophets of Astarte who eat at Jezebel's table."

When the great congregation of people had come together upon Mount Carmel overlooking the sea, Elijah appeared. Compared to the splendor of Ahab's court and the magnificent trappings of the priests of Baal, the prophet was a solitary and incongruous figure indeed in his girdle of skins with his long hair uncut.

"If the Lord be God, follow him," Elijah challenged the people. "But if Baal, then follow him. Only I remain a prophet of the Lord, but Baal's prophets number four hundred and fifty men. Give us two bullocks and let them choose one and cut it in pieces and lay it upon wood but put no fire under it. I will dress the other bullock and lay it upon wood but will put no fire under it. Then call on the name of your gods and I will call on the name of the Lord, and the god that answers by fire, let him be God."

This was a test which the prophets of Baal could hardly refuse to carry through. While they prayed to their god without effect from morning until midday, Elijah mocked them. "Either Baal is talking or he is on a journey," he said. "Or perhaps he sleeps and must be awakened."

When Baal did not answer the pleas of his priests, Elijah took twelve stones—the number of the tribes of the sons of Jacob. With these he repaired the ancient altar upon the mountain and then dug a trench about it. Next he put wood upon the altar and, cutting the flesh of the bullock in pieces, laid it upon the wood.

"Fill four barrels with water," he directed. "Pour it upon the burnt sacrifice and upon the wood."

This procedure was repeated three times, and when Elijah finally stood before the altar, not only the wood and the flesh were thoroughly soaked but water stood in the trench which had been dug around the altar.

"Lord God of Abraham, Isaac, and of Isreal," he prayed, "let it be known this day that you are God in Israel and that I am your servant and have done all these things at your word. Hear me, O Lord! Hear me that this people may know you are the Lord God and that you have turned their heart back again."

The crowd moaned with terror when a jagged flame plunged from the sky to ignite the wood and the flesh upon the altar. The clap of thunder that followed half-deafened them and, already blinded by the flame, they fell to the earth around the altar while the flames consumed not only the wood, stones, and dust, but even dried up the water in the trench.

"The Lord is God! The Lord is God!" the crowd shouted, and the victory was unquestionably Elijah's—and God's.

"Take the prophets of Baal and let not one of them escape," the prophet commanded sternly, and though the false priests tried to escape, the crowd fell upon them, killing them by the hundreds.

Having shown Ahab and his people that Yahweh was stronger than Baal, Elijah promised that the drought and famine would end. Going to the top of Mount Carmel, he prostrated himself upon the earth in prayer, while his servant took up a position overlooking the sea. Five times the man reported no change in the sky, but the sixth time he said excitedly, "A little cloud arises out of the sea, like a man's hand!"

Elijah sent the servant to warn the crowd and soon the heaven was black with clouds. Even before Ahab and the people reached the plain, the downpour began, ending the long drought and famine.

The destruction of the priests who served the gods which she had brought into Israel was a direct affront to Queen Jezebel. She was more determined now than ever before to destroy Elijah, rightly surmising that only he stood between her and complete control of Israel. Swearing that the gaunt prophet should die before another day had passed, Jezebel sent men to kill him, but again Elijah left before her plan could be carried out. And without the prophet to guide him, the pliant Ahab soon sinned grievously again, this time by coveting the property of another.

Near the palace in Samaria was a beautiful vineyard owned by a man named Naboth. When Ahab demanded the vineyard as a garden for growing herbs, Naboth refused to give it to him, standing upon his right under the Law to keep intact the inheritance of his father and pass it on to his own descendants. Jezebel, however, was not troubled by the Mosaic Law and resolved to get Naboth's vineyard for her husband.

First she ordered letters written in the king's name to the elders of the city where Naboth lived, directing them to proclaim a fast—part of the ritual ordinarily carried out in order to discover who had committed a serious sin. Next she hired two men of Belial—worthless fellows who would not hesitate to perjure themselves for money—to swear that Naboth had blasphemed against God. And since this was the worst possible crime under the Law of Moses, the incensed people dragged Naboth outside the city and stoned him to death.

With Naboth executed for blasphemy, the king was now able to take his vineyard, but when news of Ahab's action came to Elijah, he denounced the king, as Nathan had excoriated David for taking Bathsheba.

"I will bring evil upon you and take your posterity," Elijah said, speaking the words of the Lord to Ahab. "In the place where dogs licked the blood of Naboth, they shall lick your blood and shall eat Jezebel by the wall of Jezreel."

Shortly afterward war broke out again with Syria. And when

the Syrians tried to take Ramoth-Gilead, a city on the eastern side of the Jordan controlling the King's Highway, Ahab ignored Elijah's warning and went into battle. He had taken the precaution of disguising himself as a common soldier. But an arrow fired at random by a bowman struck one of the joints in his armor, giving him a mortal wound. As the dying king was carried away from the field of battle in his chariot, blood from the wound flowed down to form a puddle upon the floor of the vehicle. Later, when the body of Ahab was brought back to Samaria for burial, the chariot was washed in the great pool in the palace courtyard and the dogs licked up his blood. Thus the prophecy of Elijah concerning Ahab's death was dramatically fulfilled.

Equally dramatic was the fate of Jezebel. Some time later during an uprising of the people, she was thrown from the palace and fell, broken and wounded, to die in the street. There the dogs ate her flesh as Elijah had predicted.

# 5. Elisha and the Leper

> "So Naaman came with his horses and with his chariot, and stood at the door of the house of Elisha." II KINGS 5:9

NAAMAN, THE SYRIAN, was desperate. He was wealthy, and as a general in the army of his country and a trusted counselor of the king he occupied a position of importance—until the dreaded pale spots of leprosy began to blotch his skin. Now he saw everything he had worked for about to be destroyed, for a leper was considered unclean and his malady regarded as a loathsome thing associated with filth and degradation.

Under ordinary circumstances Naaman would hardly have listened to the tales of a Hebrew slave in his household concerning a prophet in her land named Elijah who had wrought many miraculous things. In fact, the slave's stories were scarcely believable, for she said that this prophet had been taken up into heaven in the midst of a great whirlwind in a chariot with horses of fire, leaving his mantle to a disciple. Since his disappearance, the servant girl said, he had been known in Israel as "the Angel of the Covenant" who would return one day in glory.

All this seemed no more than the sort of tale a credulous and ignorant girl would repeat, but when she said, "Would God my lord were with the prophet that is in Samaria, for he would cure him of his leprosy," Naaman dared to feel a ray of hope. He was a little discouraged to learn that the man she referred to was not Elijah, but only Elisha his disciple, yet in Naaman's desperate state, he grasped at anything that seemed to offer the slightest hope. Obtaining a letter from his king to the ruler of Israel, he started for Samaria with rich gifts of silver, gold, and clothing.

"I have sent herewith Naaman my servant that you may cure him of leprosy," the Syrian king had written, and the Israelite ruler naturally thought he was expected to heal Naaman, an impossible demand that might be only an excuse for war. Elisha had heard of Naaman's coming, however, and resolved the difficulties for the ruler of Israel.

"Let him come to me and he shall know there is a prophet in Israel," Elisha said, but when Naaman arrived with his horses and chariots, Elisha did not even go out to meet him. "Go and wash in the Jordan seven times and you shall be clean," he directed the Syrian general through a messenger.

Naaman had been somewhat affronted at being sent from the court of Israel to the humble home of a prophet. And when the alleged holy man did not even trouble himself to come out to see him but ordered him to go wash in the river, his indignation boiled. "Are not Abana and Pharpar, the rivers of Damascus, better than all the waters of Israel?" he demanded contemptuously. "May I not wash in them and be clean?"

In his anger, Naaman started back to Damascus, but his servants begged him to try Elisha's remedy, since he had already come that far. "If the prophet had bid you do some great thing, would you not have done it?" his steward reasoned. "How much rather should you obey when he only said, 'Wash and be clean'?"

Finally Naaman humbled himself, a condition Elisha had placed upon him to bring home to him the fact that those who would ask favors of God must do something of themselves. And when he had bathed seven times in the Jordan as Elisha had directed, Naaman was healed immediately. Deeply grateful to the holy man he had not yet even seen, Naaman hurried to Elisha's hut with his gifts, but the prophet only told him to go in peace, refusing to take any pay.

During a long and eventful life, Elisha continued to speak out boldly as the conscience of Israel, reminding even kings of their duty to the Lord.

"I will bring evil upon the house of Jeroboam and will take away the remnant of the house of Jeroboam, as a man takes away dung, until it is all gone," God had said when the first king of the northern kingdom did not follow his precepts. And true to that promise, Israel gradually declined under a succession of weak and vicious rulers of Jeroboam's line. For a brief period only, Jeroboam II was able to take advantage of the weakness of both Syria and Egypt to restore the borders of Israel almost to the extent they had occupied during the reigns of David and Solomon and to bring prosperity to the people, but it was only a temporary condition.

With prosperity came, as in the time of Solomon, the heavy hand of the tax-gatherer, and the soldiers of Jeroboam's army had made many demands upon the people. The prophets Amos and Hosea reminded the king and the people of their evil ways and of how they had strayed from the covenant made so long ago between God and his people, just as Elijah and Elisha had warned the kings before them. With the death of Jeroboam II, Israel became, in the words of Amos, "a basket of summer fruit. The end is come upon my people of Israel, and the songs of the temple shall be howlings." His was indeed the voice of doom for the northern kingdom, a doom already sealed by a power rising rapidly once again in the north—the great nation of Assyria.

In the history of the world few peoples achieved in ruthlessness, sheer ferocity, and cruelty, as well as in the extent of their conquests and the disruption of populations which had been in existence for many centuries, the record left by the Assyrian people on tablets of baked clay and stone obelisks. The ancient records of the Israelites, as set down in the tenth chapter of Genesis, state that Kush, the grandson of Noah, was the

father of "Nimrod the mighty hunter before the Lord. And
the beginning of his kingdom was Babel."

Babel, or Babylon, was the first really great city of the ancient
world, but as its civilization increased, it tended to become
effete and weak through the devotion of its inhabitants to
luxury and physical pleasures. Meanwhile, some three hundred
miles to the north, four other cities, Ashur, Arbelia, Kalakh,
and Nineveh—located upon the Tigris or its tributaries—had
become the centers of a new kingdom which soon began to
dominate the entire region.

The Assyrians were a proud race of mighty warriors, tall,
strong men wearing beards and long hair and prone to boast
of their accomplishments. A steadily widening area of Assyrian
supremacy had been established by the great king Shalmaneser
I, while Moses had been leading the Children of Israel out of
Egypt. And Tiglath-Pileser I had vastly increased the kingdom
at about the time the Philistines were seeking to invade Egypt.
David's and Solomon's kingdoms had existed in a period when
Assyria was comparatively quiet, but after the death of Solomon,
Assyria became more and more of a threat to the northern
kingdom of Israel.

King Omri of Israel had escaped destruction at the hands
of the Assyrian king Ashurbanipal by paying a tribute of two
talents of silver. Later the Israelites under Ahab had raised a
large Syrian and Phoenician army to turn back Shalmaneser III
in Syria. But with the accession to the Assyrian throne of
Tiglath Pileser III—known to the Israelites as Pul—the threat
to the northern kingdom became grave. Pul and his hordes had
moved steadily southward, conquering all the northern kingdom except a small area surrounding the fortress city of Samaria.
Besieged upon its mountain top, Samaria held out for a time,
but was finally taken by Sargon II.

More than twenty-seven thousand people living in Samaria
were carried away into Assyrian cities upon the orders of Sargon,
and the area was repopulated with people brought in from other
parts of his empire. The ten tribes which had constituted the
northern kingdom quickly disappeared into the mass of the

Assyrian empire and were never again identified. And though Samaria as a city and a province of the Assyrian empire continued to exist, the will of God that the northern kingdom should be destroyed because of its sin had now been carried out.

In the south, Judah had suffered much from a succession of weak kings who led her farther and farther into idolatry. For a brief period under King Uzziah, while Jeroboam II ruled in Israel to the north, Judah underwent a period of expansion with the conquest of Edom and the return of the coppermines of Solomon. During this period of prosperity, it had even seemed that both Israel and Judah could prosper without God, but when the northern kingdom was destroyed by Pul and Sargon II, Judah was left standing alone.

# 6. A King's Boil Saves Judah

> "In those days was Hezekiah sick unto
> death. . . . And Isaiah said, Take a
> lump of figs. And they . . . laid it on
> the boil."          II KINGS 20:1, 7

O KING HEZEKIAH, trouble seemed to come in threes. First, the people had accepted only reluctantly his attempts to drive out all forms of foreign worship from Judah and return to following Yahweh alone—in part because there was no known copy of the Law brought down by Moses from Mount Sinai to direct them. Second, the Assyrians were reported to be preparing to attack Judah. Third, and most acute of all for the moment, the king was plagued with a painful boil. And yet—miraculous as it might seem—the third trouble was actually to cure the other two and prove Hezekiah's, and Jerusalem's, salvation—for a while.

Hezekiah's affliction was not simply a boil, though the angry and inflamed swelling was its most prominent symptom. Bubonic plague was endemic throughout the region because of the filth in which the people had been living since they stopped obeying strictly the rules of cleanliness and sanitation that were so prominent a part of the Law of Moses. At times the disease broke out in terrible epidemics which swept city or country, felling people as rapidly as could the sword of an enemy. While not epidemic in Jerusalem at the time, the plague was never absent. Hence the fact that Hezekiah, afflicted with what

189

seemed to be only a boil but was actually the bubo of plague, was gravely ill.

By now, Judah had shrunken to only a portion of its extent at the time Joshua assigned the southern part of the Land of Promise to the most populous tribe of the Israelites. From a few miles north of Jerusalem, it extended southward only to Kadesh-Barnea, the town in southern Canaan from which Moses had sent the spies to seek a route of entry. And from the Salt Sea on the east, its breadth extended only to Lachish, little more than half the distance to the Mediterranean. And yet, even in its shrunken state, Judah was richer than Israel had been, with Lachish, Hebron, Bethlehem, Kerjath-Jearim, Gaza, Beeroth, Gibeon, Gibeah, Jericho, and the capital at Jerusalem as its richest and most populous cities.

The worship of strange gods, allowed to flourish in the time of Solomon, had continued through a succession of kings. One of them, Jehoahaz, had even changed the ritual of the temple to fit the pattern of a pagan altar he had seen at Damascus. Hezekiah, however, was of a different stamp from the rulers who had gone before him. Pious, intelligent, honest, and deeply conscious that his country's destiny lay in obeying the will of God, he tried to return the people to the worship of the Lord. As a result, Hezekiah and Judah prospered, and once again its boundaries were extended to the very walls of the main Philistine city of Gaza.

About this time the prophet Isaiah came into prominence in Judah. Isaiah spoke to the people in the name of the Lord during the reign of four of its kings, Uzziah, Jotham, Ahaz, and Hezekiah, beginning his ministry about the time the Assyrians under Pul, or Tiglath-Pileser, invaded northern Israel and forced its king, Menahem, to pay them a considerable tribute. Condemning the trend away from the worship of God and toward paganism, the oppression of the poor by the rich, and the depravity of the nobles, Isaiah warned sternly against the wrath of God that was to come, predicting that the inhabitants of Judah would be removed from their land, as those of Israel had been removed by the Assyrians.

When Hezekiah ill-advisedly made a disastrous alliance with

Egypt in an attempt to rebel against Assyrian rule, the outlook for Judah seemed grave indeed, but Isaiah sounded a stern call for a return to faith in God, promising deliverance from the enemy. "Thus says the Lord," he told King Hezekiah. " 'Be not afraid of the words with which the servants of the king of Assyria have blasphemed me, for I will send a blast upon him and he shall return to his own land.' "

Isaiah favored Hezekiah because the king was sincere in his desire to return his people to their God, and when he became gravely ill with the bubo, the prophet had directed his treatment by means of a poultice of figs to open the boil and drain out the poisonous matter it contained. Hezekiah recovered and, anticipating the Assyrian attack, began to repair the fortifications of Jerusalem, including the Millo Tower and a tunnel by which additional water was brought into the city against the possibility of a long siege. While these preparations were going on, however, the Assyrian prince Sennacherib encamped his forces around Jerusalem and began the siege.

Had the city been more easily accessible and the forest around it less scanty, the enemy might have used the barbarous tactic which had subdued the great fortress of Lachish some time before. There the Assyrians had cut down wood and piled it against the walls so that when the wood was fired, Lachish was literally turned into an inferno and the people forced to capitulate. Jerusalem, upon its hilltops surrounded by sparsely wooded slopes, was a different matter, so the Assyrian general settled down for a long siege by the more conventional method of cutting off the food supply. It was then that the boil of King Hezekiah became the most effective weapon of the besieged Hebrews, for the Assyrians were not accustomed to bubonic plague. Though burning with a low flame in Jerusalem, the disease quickly became a raging conflagration when it spread to the enemy. Almost overnight the epidemic raced through the Assyrian camp and, before the remnants of the invaders began a dazed retreat, more than a hundred and fifty thousand of them had died.

At Hezekiah's death, his son Manasseh and his grandson Amon ruled successively. Both were weak, however, and most

of the reforms in religion instituted by Hezekiah were allowed
to lapse, particularly the celebration of the Passover feast, commemorating the awful night when the angel of death had passed
over the houses of the Hebrews in Egypt to strike the first-born
even in the house of Pharaoh. Only when Josiah succeeded
Amon was the worship of Jehovah restored to Judah.

In order to pay tribute to the Assyrians, much of the treasure
of the temple had been taken away and the entire structure
allowed to degenerate into an advanced state of disrepair.
Guided by the great priest Hilkiah, Josiah began to restore the
temple, and in carrying out this project a rare find was made, a
scroll of the Law set down by Moses in its original form.

Heretofore the Law had been passed down by word of mouth
among the priests and Levites, and anyone who wished could
claim—often with considerable reason—that no way existed of
knowing whether or not these were the original edicts of God
given to Moses on Mount Sinai. With a scroll of the Law now
in hand, however, Josiah ordered the people to gather about
the temple. There he had the whole of it read to them.

Many of the younger Hebrews had no knowledge of much
that the scroll contained. The logic of its provisions, plus its
undoubted authenticity as divine Law, impressed them deeply.
There before the temple both the people and Josiah swore a
covenant to keep the commandments of God and to walk as
he directed. In fact, so great was the resurgence of faith in
Judah in the succeeding weeks that all idolatrous objects and
the priests of false gods were swept out of the country, and the
greatest Passover ceremony in the history of the people was
celebrated that spring.

Hezekiah and Josiah had both proved faithful servants of the
Lord, but at their deaths the people quickly lapsed into idolatry.
In addition, political forces had long been at work to spell the
end of Judah as an independent kingdom. Egypt had made a
brief bid for world power again when the Pharaoh Necho
launched an attack northward against Assyria and its tributaries—but failed. And Josiah, when he led his small forces
against the Egyptians at Megiddo, was killed in battle.

Meanwhile the Assyrian kingdom had been divided between

the Medes to the north and the Babylonians farther down the Euphrates. Soon a strong and ruthless Babylonian king named Nebuchadnezzar captured Jerusalem, plundering it and taking away into captivity many of the finest youths among the nobility. And when the puppet king, Zedekiah, whom Nebuchadnezzar placed on the throne of Judah, dared to rebel, Jerusalem was leveled and most of its people carried away to Babylon in captivity.

As foretold by the great prophets, both Judah and Israel had ceased to exist. Strangely enough, the rebirth of faith which would see the Hebrews reach their greatest glory was to begin in a distant land.

# 7. Dreams in Babylon

*"Nebuchadnezzar dreamed dreams, wherewith his spirit was troubled."*

DANIEL 2:1

I T WAS A strange captivity indeed that the peole of Judah experienced in Babylon. Inhabiting their own quarter of the renowned and prosperous city, they retained—for the most part—their own customs, had their own homes, and, sometimes, slaves. Allowed to become artisans and enter business, almost the entire nation underwent a remarkable change during the some seventy years of their captivity. What had been a people made up largely of shepherds and farmers had now become one in which a substantial element of the population were teachers, craftsmen, traders, and bankers. Foremost among the Hebrews of Babylon was Daniel who, by insuring freedom of worship for the captives, became one of the heroes in the stories and legends told ever after by his people.

In the days of the Hebrew captivity, Babylon was the political and economic center of the world. Far to the west, the Etruscan civilization that presaged the glory of Rome was at its height, and the Greek cities of Asia Minor were carrying out the judicial reforms which would give the world a new concept of law. In temporal magnificence, however, none of these could equal Babylon. Great walls for defense had been built above and below the city, forming a triangle inside which further fortifications guarded the temples and palaces of the king. The double walls were broad enough to allow a four-horse chariot to turn upon them, and the river banks were lined with great quays or docks where thousands of boats carrying goods both to and from Babylon were able to dock and empty their cargoes.

Babylonian astronomers studied the heavenly bodies nightly and recorded their movements with great accuracy on tablets of clay. Mathematicians carried on their calculations, and companies of scribes imprinted upon the same imperishable records all the knowledge of the world which had been gathered there. Inside Babylon, however, love of luxury and the depravity of the rites used in worshipping its many gods and goddesses were slowly weakening the fiber of the city and its people.

Nebuchadnezzar was a forward-looking and eminently fair ruler, in spite of his ruthlessness with those who rebelled against his rule. One of the reforms he instituted was the organization of a training school in which the most promising young men of the country—including captured youths—were taught the knowledge that the Chaldeans had accumulated over several thousand years. These favored lads were kept at the palace and given a daily provision of food and wine from the king's table. Then, after a three-year period of training, they were assigned to positions of responsibility in the court, if found to deserve such a reward. Among those chosen from the Hebrews was a nobleman named Daniel, with Hananiah, Mishael, and Azariah, the four bearing the Babylonian names respectively of Belteshazzar, Shadrach, Meshach, and Abednego.

Having been brought up strictly in the Law of Moses, Daniel begged the prince of the eunuchs in charge of training the young men to let the four eat only lentils and water instead of the rich food from the king's table. And when at the end of ten days, they were in even better physical condition than those who had eaten of the king's food, they were allowed to select their own diet.

These four Israelites, particularly Daniel, were bright, intelligent young men, and they quickly accumulated considerable knowledge, for the Chaldean teachers were the most learned men in the world of that day. When finally they stood before the king, they excelled so greatly in wisdom and understanding that Nebuchadnezzar assigned them favored positions in his court.

One night the king had a dream, but when he awakened he had forgotten it, remembering only that it had disturbed him very much. "Not a man upon earth can explain this matter," his sorcerers and soothsayers protested when Nebuchadnezzar demanded that they tell him the nature of the forgotten dream, as well as its meaning. "What the king requires is a rare thing and none can make it known except the gods."

Nebuchadnezzar was angry with the soothsayers and decreed they should all be killed. Knowing that Daniel was possessed of great wisdom, the captain who had been ordered to dispatch the wise men came to take him with the others. He begged for a little time, however, and prayed to God for the dream to be revealed with its meaning so that they might all be saved. God heard Daniel's prayer and answered it, so he asked to be brought before the king.

"Can you make known to me the dream I saw and the interpretation of it?" Nebuchadnezzar asked suspiciously, thinking that Daniel was only trying to deceive him and save his own head.

"Wise men, astrologers, magicians, and soothsayers cannot show the king the secret he has demanded," Daniel said. "But there is a God in heaven who does reveal secrets and makes known what shall happen in the future. In your dream you saw a great image. Its head was of fine gold, its breast and arms were of silver, its belly and thighs of brass, its legs of iron, its feet part iron and part clay. You saw also that a stone cut out without hands struck the image upon its feet of iron and clay and broke them to pieces. The iron, the clay, the brass, the silver, and the gold were then broken to pieces together and became like chaff on the summer threshing floors so that the wind carried them away. But the stone that struck the image became a great mountain and filled the whole earth."

"That was the dream!" Nebuchadnezzar cried. "Now tell me its meaning."

"You are this head of gold," Daniel explained. "But after

you shall arise another kingdom inferior to you and a third kingdom of brass that shall rule over all the earth. The fourth kingdom shall be as strong as iron, since iron subdues all things, and it shall break all these in pieces. Because you saw the feet and toes, part of potter's clay and part of iron, the kingdom shall be divided, but it shall contain the strength of the iron. And as the toes of the feet were part of iron and part of clay, so the kingdom shall be partly strong and partly broken. In the days of these kings, the God of heaven shall set up a kingdom which shall never be destroyed but shall break and consume all these kingdoms and stand forever."

Nebuchadnezzar was pleased with Daniel's interpretation of the dream. As a reward he made the Hebrew prince governor over the whole province of Babylon, with Shadrach, Meshach, and Abednego as overseers. Daniel had saved the lives of the soothsayers—the order for their deaths having been rescinded after he interpreted the king's dream—yet some of them envied the Israelite princes and plotted to attack the four through their devotion to the laws of God. Going to the king, they flattered him into having a great image of gold built and issuing an edict that all princes, governors, captains, judges, treasurers, counselors, and rulers of provinces should bow down and worship it. Daniel was away at the time and was not affected, but, obeying the covenant the Israelites had made not to worship any other gods, Shadrach, Meshach, and Abednego refused to make obeisance to the golden image. And since the king had been persuaded to decree that any who did not worship the image would be thrown into the red-hot furnace used in the worship of Moloch, they were brought before him for sentencing.

"Is it true that you do not serve my god or worship the golden image I have set up?" Nebuchadnezzar asked them.

The three explained that their religion forbade such observances, but Nebuchadnezzar was adamant. "If you do not worship, you shall be thrown into the furnace," he decreed. "Then we will see who is the God that shall deliver you out of my hands."

"Our God is able to deliver us from the furnace and out of

your hand, O king," the three men assured him. "But if he will not do so, we still will not serve your gods nor worship the golden image you have set up."

The angry king had the three Hebrews thrown into the furnace, but as Nebuchadnezzar and his counselors watched, they saw inside the furnace not three men but four and they were walking around unharmed.

"I see four men loose, walking in the midst of the fire," the king said in awe. "But the form of the fourth is like the Son of God." Immediately he ordered the three released from the fire, and when he saw that not a hair of their heads was singed nor their clothing burned in any way, he cried, "Blessed is the God of Shadrach, Meshach, and Abednego, who sent his angel and delivered his servants that trusted him! Therefore I make a decree that every people, nation, and language that speaks anything amiss against the God of Shadrach, Meshach, and Abednego shall be cut in pieces."

Nebuchadnezzar later suffered a serious illness of the mind in which he wandered in the fields like an animal and ate grass, but he kept his promise to Daniel's people and their right to freedom of worship was never violated again in his reign.

Belshazzar, who succeeded Nebuchadnezzar, did not share his father's respect for the Israelites or their God. During a great feast he ordered that the gold and silver vessels which Nebuchadnezzar had taken from the temple at Jerusalem be brought out so that he and his guests might drink from them. This deliberate insult to Yahweh did not long go unavenged; while the feast was at its height, the fingers of a man's hand suddenly appeared upon the wall of the palace and began to write.

Stricken with terror, the guests fled from the palace, but none of the astrologers or soothsayers could interpret what was written on the wall. Finally someone thought of Daniel and remembered how he had interpreted the forgotten dream of Nebuchadnezzar long ago.

"You have not humbled your heart," Daniel told Belshazzar sternly. "You have lifted up yourself against the Lord of Heaven and with your lords, your wives, and your concubines have drunk wine from the vessels of his house. You have praised gods of silver and gold, of brass, iron, wood, and stone which neither see nor hear nor know, but you have not glorified the Lord in whose hands your breath is and who knows all your ways.

"This is the writing. Mene, Mene, Tekel, Upharsin," Daniel said, turning to the letters upon the wall. "And this is the interpretation: God has numbered your kingdom and finished it; you are weighed in the balance and found wanting; your kingdom is divided and given to the Medes and the Persians."

As Daniel had foretold, Darius, king of the Medes, soon captured Babylon and Belshazzar was killed. The new ruler appointed Daniel one of the governors of the province, but some of the princes of Darius's court did not like the thought of an Israelite being over them. Nor did it take them long—remembering the case of Meshach, Shadrach, and Abednego—to find a way to attack Daniel. Knowing that he prayed daily to the Lord, they came to King Darius with the flattering proposal that he issue a decree forbidding anyone to ask a petition of any god or man except the king for thirty days, with the added provision that whoever broke this rule should be thrown into a den of lions. They did not fear that Daniel might persuade Darius to rescind the act, since a law of the Medes and Persians could not be changed.

Daniel continued to pray toward Jerusalem three times a day and give thanks to God. Brought before Darius and accused of breaking the law, he had no defense except that of serving his God, and though reluctant to execute a man he respected greatly, Darius could not change his edict. Daniel was placed in the cage with the royal lions, who often were allowed to destroy criminals during public exhibitions.

Concerned at having executed a just man, Darius came early to the lion's cage and found Daniel safe and unharmed. Rejoicing greatly, the king ordered him returned and those who had accused him thrown to the lions instead. Then, as had Nebuchadnezzar, he issued once again a decree giving Daniel's people the right to worship their God unmolested.

# 8. A Queen Saves Her People

*"And so will I go in unto the king,
which is not according to the law: and
if I perish, I perish."* ESTHER 4:16

I N THE HISTORY of the Hebrew people, only one woman
made a contribution to their national welfare valuable
enough to have a religious holiday, the Festival of Purim,
celebrated in her honor. Her Hebrew name was Hadassah, but
as Esther, the queen who risked her life to save her people from
being massacred, the story of her courageous act has been told
for more than two thousand years. It happened while the
Hebrews—now called Jews because formerly they were inhabitants of Judah—were in captivity in Babylon.

The capture of Babylon by Persians under Cyrus had considerably altered the situation of the Jews who were still living
there, for one of his first acts was a decree that people who had
been taken from their own countries by conquering armies
could return home. The decree marked a new era of enlighten-
ment which, unfortunately, did not continue uninterrupted
after the death of Cyrus. Intermittently there were still periods
of persecution, since the Hebrews who remained in Babylon
had powerful enemies.

When Queen Vashti was deposed by Ahasuerus, or Xerxes,
because she disobeyed him, his agents went throughout the
kingdom seeking the fairest among the young virgins for con-

sideration as the new queen. Esther, who lived with her uncle Mordecai, would not ordinarily have been considered, since she was a Hebrew, but Mordecai had carefully kept this fact secret in order to avoid trouble during the occasional periods of persecution. With others of the most beautiful maidens visited by the king's emissaries, Esther was taken to the palace and put into the custody of Hegai, the eunuch who was the keeper of the king's women. There her beauty, her gentleness, and her charm quickly earned her a favored place and when, after a period of purification, she was taken before the king, he fell in love with her and made her his queen.

In order to be near in case Esther needed help, Mordecai made it a point to pass the house of the women every day and pause by the palace gate to talk to the gatekeepers. Naturally he heard a good deal of gossip and one day learned that two of the king's chamberlains, Bigthan and Teresh, intended to assassinate Ahasuerus. This information Mordecai gave to Esther, who revealed it to the king, along with its source. The plot was foiled, but Mordecai, at the moment, was not rewarded.

In the retinue of King Ahasuerus was a man named Haman, an Amalekite and a traditional enemy of Israel. Being shrewd and unscrupulous, Haman had insinuated himself into the king's favor to the point where he was first minister, receiving homage from all except Ahasuerus himself. Mordecai's religion forbade him to bow to earthly nobility, being responsible only to God; when he failed to make obeisance before the Amalekite, Haman demanded to know the reason. Thus it was revealed that Mordecai was a Jew and the wily Amalekite quickly conceived an ingenious plan to destroy not only Mordecai but with him all the Hebrews in the entire kingdom.

In carrying out his plan, Haman went first to the king. "There is a certain people dispersed among all the provinces of your kingdom," he reported. "Their laws are different from ours and they do not keep the king's laws. It is not for the king's profit to suffer them, so let it be written that they shall be destroyed and I will pay ten thousand talents of silver to those that have charge of the business to bring their belongings to the king's treasury."

King Ahasuerus had recently suffered a severe defeat at the hands of a rising new people to the west, the Greeks, and the minister's suggestion of a way by which he could accumulate the belongings of these people that were to be destroyed was very tempting. Haman had been careful not to mention that those he had in mind were Jews, so Ahasuerus issued an order that the people Haman designated should be destroyed, both young and old, women and children, on the thirteenth day of the twelfth month called Adar.

When Mordecai heard the order of the king, he mourned, for not only did it mean the destruction of all his people, but Esther herself would share the same fate when it became known that she was a Jew. At once he sent word to Esther that she must go to Ahasuerus and beg him to save her people.

"Everyone knows that whoever comes to the king without being called will be put to death unless he holds out a golden scepter," she protested. "And I have not been called to come in to the king for thirty days."

"Because you are in the king's house do not think you will escape more than all the other Jews," Mordecai warned her. "If you hold your peace now, deliverance will come from another place, but you and your father's house shall be destroyed. Besides, who knows that you did not come to the kingdom just for such a time as this?"

Esther hesitated no longer. She asked Mordecai to have all the Jews in the province fast and beg God's help while she also fasted in preparation for the supplication she planned to make to King Ahasuerus. "I will go in unto the king though it is not according to the law," she promised. "And if I perish, I perish."

When the fasting period was completed, Esther dressed in her finest royal robes and stood in the inner court of the king's palace before the throne. When Ahasuerus saw her, he held out to her the golden scepter and she was able to approach without being bidden.

"What do you wish, Queen Esther?" Ahasuerus asked. "Ask and it shall be given to you, even to the half of the kingdom."

Esther, too, had a plan, one that if successful would save her people and remove their enemy Haman. "If it seems good to the king, let him and Haman come to the banquet I have prepared," she said, and Ahasuerus agreed.

Haman was pleased by the invitation to a dinner with the king and queen, thinking it meant further honors for him. But as he was hurrying home with the good news, he passed Mordecai and, when the old Jew refused to bow to him, became so angry that his pleasure was destroyed.

"Esther the Queen will let no man but myself come in with the king to the banquet she has prepared," Haman told his family bitterly. "But all this is nothing so long as I see Mordecai, the Jew, sitting at the king's gate."

"Let a gallows be built and speak to the king so that Mordecai will be hanged upon it," his wife and friends suggested. The idea pleased Haman so much that he ordered the scaffold erected immediately, confident that Ahasuerus would leave Mordecai's fate in his hands.

That night the king was not able to sleep and while he was reading the records kept by his scribes, he found the account of how Mordecai had discovered the plot of Bigthan and Teresh and had saved his life.

"What honor has been done to Mordecai for this?" he asked.

The servants could answer only that as far as they knew, nothing had been done. And when Ahasuerus learned that Haman was in the court—having come for permission to hang Mordecai upon the gallows—he ordered the minister to come in.

"What shall be done to the man the king delights to honor?" he demanded before Haman could make his request.

Swollen with vanity as he was, Haman could conceive of no one the king would delight to honor more than himself. "Let the royal apparel be brought, and the horse the king rides upon, and the crown royal," he said immediately, already seeing himself richly arrayed and receiving the homage of the people. "Let this apparel and horse be delivered to the king's most noble princes that they may array the man the king delights to honor and bring him on horseback to the city and proclaim before him.

"Hurry and do as you have said for Mordecai, the Jew, who sits in the king's gate," Ahasuerus ordered.

The idea of honoring Mordecai was gall to Haman's soul, but he had no choice except to obey and issue the orders. While he was trying to devise some way of being revenged upon Mordecai, the king's chamberlains came to take him to the banquet which Esther had prepared.

"What is your petition, Queen Esther?" Ahasuerus asked when they were seated.

"If I have found favor in your sight," Esther said humbly, "let my life and that of my people be given me, for both I and my people are to be destroyed."

"Who presumes to do such a thing?" Ahasuerus demanded indignantly.

"The enemy is this wicked Haman," Esther told him. When she explained how Haman had planned to kill Mordecai and all the Jews, the king ordered the Amalekite hung from the very gallows he had been preparing for Mordecai. It was not possible for Ahasuerus to revoke his order that the Jews could be attacked wherever they were, but he did issue a new edict giving them the right to defend themselves against those who should attempt to slay them. Thus, on the appointed day, the Jews were free to destroy their enemies. As for Mordecai, he was given a high place in the king's house while Esther found even greater favor with Ahasueras than before.

Thus it came about that on the fourteenth and fifteenth days of the month of Adar, Hebrews everywhere celebrate the Feast called Purim, commemorating their deliverance from death at the hands of Haman, the Amalekite, through Mordecai's wisdom and Esther's courage in risking her life to approach Ahasuerus and beg for the lives of her people.

# 9. The Testing of Job

> *"God will not cast away a perfect man,*
> *neither will he help the evildoers."*
>
> JOB 8:20

NOT ALL THE HEBREWS were carried off to Babylon. One of those who remained was named Job. An upright man who feared God and avoided evil, he lived in the southern portion of Judah near the border of Edom. God had favored Job with seven sons and three daughters, but though a rich man, he did not fail to give thanks for all the benefits which had been given him. The Lord was pleased with Job, but the evil spirit called Satan, who was allowed to tempt men so they might be strengthened in their faith, had designs upon him.

"From whence do you come?" the Lord asked when Satan appeared before him one day.

"From going to and fro in the earth and walking up and down in it," the Evil One replied.

"Have you considered my servant Job? None is like him in the earth, a perfect and an upright man who fears God and avoids evil."

"Does Job fear God for nothing?" Satan asked cynically. "Have you not made a hedge about him and his house and everything he has? You have blessed the work of his hands and his substance has increased. But put out your hand now and touch all he has, and he will curse you to your face."

"All he has is in my power," the Lord agreed, confident that Job would survive the test. "Only do not put your hand upon his body."

Satan's first act in tormenting Job was to let a band of Syrian nomads steal his cattle and kill his servant while at the same time a fire consumed most of his sheep. As Job was receiving the report of this catastrophe, a servant came with the news that robbers had stolen his herd of camels and killed the servants who had guarded them.

Before Job could recover from these reverses, still another blow was dealt him. "Your sons and daughters were eating and drinking wine in their eldest brother's house," he was told. "A great wind struck the four corners of the house and it fell upon the young men and killed them."

At this news, Job tore his clothes, shaved his head, and fell upon the ground in mourning. But he did not curse the Lord, as Satan had hoped he would do. "Naked I came out of my mother's womb and naked shall I return there," he said. "The Lord gave and the Lord has taken away. Blessed is the name of the Lord."

Since Job refused to blame God for his troubles, Satan came before the Lord again. "All a man has he will give for his life," the Evil One said. "Now put out your hand and touch his bone and his flesh and he will curse you to your face."

The Lord gave Satan permission to torment Job, but not to kill him, and immediately Job was afflicted by a plague of boils so severe that death would have been a welcome thing. But when Job's wife begged him to curse God and die, he refused. "You speak as one of the foolish women speak," he told her sternly. "Shall we receive good at the hand of God and not receive evil?"

Job had three friends, Eliphaz, Bildad, and Zophar. These came to mourn with him, but when they saw the trouble that had come upon their friend, they could say nothing to comfort him, and as time went on, even Job's faith began to weaken.

Tormented almost beyond bearing by the plague of boils and the reverses which had come to him, he was sorely tempted to curse the God whom he had always served, but who had repaid him thus for his faith.

"Let the day perish wherein I was born and the night in which it was said, 'A man-child is conceived,'" he cried. "Let that day be darkness; let not God regard it from above, neither let the light shine upon it."

"Happy is the man whom God corrects," Eliphaz reproved him. "Do not despise the chastening of the Almighty, for he makes sore and binds up; he wounds and his hands make whole."

"O that my grief were thoroughly weighed and my calamity laid in the balances together!" Job moaned. "For now it would be heavier than the sand of the sea."

Bildad reprimanded Job for cursing the day he was born. "How long will you speak these things and how long shall the words of your mouth be like strong wind?" he demanded. "Does the Almighty pervert justice? God will not cast away a perfect man, neither will he help evildoers. They that hate you shall be clothed with shame and the dwelling place of the wicked shall come to naught."

"How shall man be just with God?" Job asked. "If he contends with him, he cannot answer him once in a thousand. God is wise in heart and mighty in strength. Who has hardened himself against him and has prospered? He is not a man as I am that I should answer him and we should come together in judgment. Neither is there any umpire between us that might lay his hand upon us both. Though he slay me, yet will I trust in him, but I will maintain my own ways before him and he also shall be my salvation, for hypocrites shall not come before him."

As Job and his friends continued to discuss the tribulations God had heaped upon him, the Lord spoke from a whirlwind. "Shall he who contends with the Almighty instruct him?" he asked. "He that reproves God, let him answer it."

"I am vile," Job answered submitting himself at last to God's will even in the depths of his misery. "What shall I answer you?"

"Gird up your loins like a man," God told him. "Will you condemn me that you may be righteous? Have you an arm like God? Can you thunder with a voice like his? Dress yourself now with majesty and excellence and array yourself with glory and beauty. Cast abroad the rage of your wrath and behold everyone that is proud and abase him. Look on everyone that is proud and bring him low and tread down the wicked in their place. Hide them in the dust together and bind their faces in secret. Then will I also confess to you that your own right hand can save you."

At last Job was able to see his wrong in criticizing God for the burdens which had been put upon him and in cursing the day the Lord had given him life. Now he recognized that tribulations are not sent without reason and purpose, although the heart of man cannot always discern the pattern behind such things.

"I know you can do everything and that no thought can be withheld from you," Job admitted humbly. "I have uttered what I did not understand, things too wonderful for me, things which I did not know. I have heard of you by the hearing of the ear, but now my eye sees; therefore I abhor myself and repent in dust and ashes."

Though still in the depths of the misery which had come upon him for reasons he could not understand, Job stopped rebelling against his treatment from God, accepting the fate meted out to him as right and proper, within the infinite pattern of the Lord's purpose for man. And when the Lord would have loosed his anger upon Job's friends who had failed to comfort him, Job interceded for them.

Now God took away Job's tribulations and gave him twice as many blessings as he had had before. For even though sorely tempted, he had realized in the end the justice of God's will and had humbled himself before it, realizing that, as the prophet Micah had said: "He has showed you, O man, what is good. And what does the Lord require of you, but to do justly, and to love mercy, and to walk humbly with your God?"

In captivity in far-off Babylon the Hebrews finally came to

understand what Job had seen in the midst of his own tribulations, namely, that God's purpose, even though not fully comprehended, is ultimately for man's good and that only through humbling himself to God's will can any man approach an understanding of that purpose. Now at last they were ready to return to their homeland when Cyrus revoked the edict which had enslaved them, realizing that the captivity in Babylon was only another manifestation of God's covenant that they should always be his people.

Through periods of enslavement, defeat, and despair, the Hebrews had been buoyed up by three things. Foremost was the covenant that no matter how widely scattered they might be, they should one day return to the Land of Promise, a covenant fulfilled now through the order of Cyrus and the leadership of Ezra, the prophet, and Nehemiah, who went with them as governor to restore Jerusalem and return Judah to its former glory. The second source of courage was God's own word spoken through the prophet Malachi: "Unto you that fear my name shall the Son of Righteousness arise with healing in his wings. You shall tread down the wicked, for they shall be ashes under the soles of your feet, and I will send you Elijah the prophet before the coming of the great and dreadful day of the Lord. He shall turn the heart of the fathers to the children, and the heart of the children to their fathers."

Looking forward to the coming of a leader or Messiah who would reveal their final destiny, the Jews began to rebuild the Holy City of Jerusalem, strengthened by the third and most important prophecy spoken by the prophet Micah:

"But you, Bethlehem Ephratah, though you be little among the thousands of Judah, yet out of you shall he come forth that is to be a ruler in Israel, whose goings forth have been from of old, from everlasting. And he shall stand and feed in the strength of the Lord, in the majesty of the name of the Lord his God. They shall abide, for now shall he be great unto the ends of the earth, and this man shall be the Peace."

This king, they could be sure, would be more to them even than had been David, the greatest of their rulers, or Solomon and all the glory of his kingdom. For the words, "Whose goings forth have been from of old, from everlasting," could only mean that he would be more than human, actually a part of God himself. In him, then, would be carried out the final act in the working out of the covenant which God had made with Abraham, and which now he was to make anew through his Son.

# IV. A New Commandment

"A new commandment I give unto
you, That ye love one another; as I
have loved you."          JOHN 13:34

# 1. The King of the Jews

*"There came wise men from the east to Jerusalem, saying, Where is he that is born King of the Jews?"*

MATTHEW 2:1-2

ORE THAN four hundred years had elapsed since the Jews, under the leadership of Ezra and Nehemiah, had returned home from captivity in Babylon, when one day three strangers appeared at the royal palace in Jerusalem. During those four centuries, the fortunes of the Hebrew nation had undergone many vicissitudes, some brought on by their own sins, others by the marked changes going on in the steadily widening political world of which they were a part.

Servitude in Babylon, plus the fiery exhortations of the prophet Ezekiel, had stirred in the Israelites a renewed faith in their own destiny as God's favored nation under the sacred covenant. Under the inspired leadership of Nehemiah, they had set about rebuilding Jerusalem and establishing themselves in the area formerly occupied by the southern kingdom of Judah, now called Judea. More important to their survival, however, was a renewed dedication to the one thing that could hold them together, the Law of Moses—given directly by God to his people—a distinction possessed by no other nation on earth.

In Jerusalem the prophet Ezra had read publicly the whole of the Law—discovered anew during the reign of King Josiah. Much of it had been forgotten by the people during their

213

years of separation from the fountainhead, so to speak, of their faith, but scholars educated in Babylon had faithfully copied the ancient scrolls. In Jerusalem, too, a new type of government had gradually been evolved, a religious state functioning under the domination of near-by Syria, governed by a High Priest with a *gerousia* or senate.

About a hundred years after the return of the main body of the Israelites from captivity, the conquering tide of Alexander the Great's armies had threatened Jerusalem. When the High Priest surrendered the city, Alexander had spared it, but though saved from destruction, the Hebrews had been subjected to an attack against their minds and their religious faith by the subtle pagan influence called Hellenism spread by the conquering armies of Alexander. In time the worship of Greek gods had spread even to the temple itself, and the High Priest had become hardly more than a Greek puppet.

A few pious men—calling themselves the *Chassidim*—zealously guarded the ancient writings of the Law and refused to espouse the new philosophy of Hellenism. From them grew up a new type of writing, even more moving than the words of the prophets in olden days, strangely poetic and fervent exhortations concerning a Messiah, "Anointed One," or "Son of Man," who would set up the true kingdom of God upon earth with Jerusalem as its center. These forces inevitably came into conflict with Greek influences and fighting soon flared up between the sons of Mattathias, a Jewish priest, led by Judas Maccabeus, called "The Hammerer," and the military forces of Syria which governed Judea as a subprovince.

Judas Maccabeus was spectacularly successful at first and for a time it seemed that the Lord had raised up a deliverer to save the faith of Israel from Greek influences. Much of the glory of David and Solomon was restored when the Maccabees —as Judas' family was called—conquered most of the territory from the hills north and east of the Sea of Chinnereth, now called Galilee, to the border of Egypt on the south and the deserts of Arabia on the east. The ruling line of Judas Maccabeus came to be called the Hasmoneans but, unfortunately, none were as strong as the founder. And a sinister influence soon appeared in the form of Antipater, the Idumean, chief advisor to the Maccabean rulers.

When the Roman Empire finally took over the domain of Alexander, Herod, the son of Antipater, served the Romans so well that he eventually ousted the Hasmonean house entirely and was designated by Emperor Augustus as King of the Jews. Clever, ruthless, and unscrupulous, Herod increased his own power rapidly and sought to insinuate himself into the favor of the pious Jews by building a new temple in place of Solomon's magnificent edifice, which had been destroyed. New palaces were also built in Jerusalem during his kingship, as well as fine cities throughout the land and a great port at Caesarea.

One group of Jews calling themselves Pharisees sought to preserve the ancient Law in as pure a form as possible. Together with a smaller group of lawyers called scribes, they dreamed of re-establishing the religious state which had existed so briefly after their return from captivity. Many of them also eagerly expected the coming of the Messiah—predicted in the prophetic writings—who would use divine power to free his people from tribute to Rome. A third group, the Sadducees, were much more realistic. Denying a life after death—in which most Pharisees believed—they thought Israel's immediate welfare could best be furthered through cooperation with the Roman authorities and with Herod, who ruled there as Roman agent. And since the Sadducees included the High Priest and most of the ranking members of the priesthood, their influence was great.

Herod did not build the temple because he was a devout worshipper of the Most High; he built it to please the influential Jews in his kingdom and thus gain a reputation with his Roman masters for ruling without discord. As a precaution, he built on the west side of the temple area a fortress-palace called the Antonia where the troops under his command could watch everything that happened, not only in the city but in the temple itself.

In spite of his great power, Herod knew the people hated him, not only because he was a lackey of hated Rome, but because of his own ruthlessness and the fact that he was not a Jew by birth and ancestry. Because of his insecure position, Herod lived in constant fear of rebellion or assassination. He had destroyed forty-five of the leading Jews in the kingdom at one time because he thought they intended to oppose him and petition Rome for another ruler. And he had killed perhaps the only woman he had ever loved, one of his wives, the beautiful Hasmonean princess Mariamne, because he feared that a descendant of the Hasmoneans would claim his throne.

Naturally suspicious of strangers, Herod would have put three strangers who one day appeared in Jerusalem under surveillance in any event. But they were taken immediately to him when they asked the question which had brought them there: "Where is he that is born King of the Jews?"

The clothing of the newcomers stamped them as travelers from a distant land, but even Herod was startled when they revealed how far they had come. For they identified themselves as wise men or *magi* from the almost legendary land of Sheba— or Yemen—whose queen almost a thousand years before had journeyed to Jerusalem to visit King Solomon and take back to her home and nourish there the most precious among the gifts he had given her, the faith in Yahweh that was the driving force in the life of every true Jew.

The question of the *magi* started a cancer of fear growing in Herod's heart. He had gone to great lengths to destroy all who might threaten his hold upon the throne, but ruthless as he was, he could not fail to experience some pangs of guilt, especially over the death of Mariamne. Now, if the birth of a new king had been announced by divine means—as seemed likely from the report of the dusty-robed and sunburned men standing before him—it could mean the one thing against which even Herod would be helpless, the coming of the divine ruler called the Messiah who so many Jews expected to free them from Herod's rule, the rule of Rome.

Herod was not one to give up easily, however; he had not reached his present eminence by being soft, and he had no intention of becoming soft now. If this new king could be destroyed, he must be; in coming to him with their question, the wise men of Sheba had unconsciously played directly into his hands.

"Why did you come here?" Herod asked the three travelers.

"We have seen his star in the east and have come to worship him," one of the men answered.

Herod was careful not to let his fear show, for at any sign of weakness, new plots against him would immediately start boiling again in Jerusalem. But there was no denying the probability that a ruler whose birth was announced by a star must indeed have been sent from God. He did not question the *magi* further at the moment, however, but sent them for refreshment, promising to see if he could obtain information about the one they sought.

As soon as the visitors were dismissed, Herod called together the chief priests and the scribes who were familiar with the ancient writings. When he demanded of them where the Messiah would be born, they brought out a scroll containing the writings of the prophet Micah and read these words:

"But you, Bethlehem Ephratah, though you be little among the thousands of Judah, yet out of you shall he come forth that is to be a ruler in Israel."

Herod was pleased by this discovery, for Bethlehem was only a few miles from Jerusalem. If necessary he would not hesitate to destroy all the young children in the city, but there seemed a better and simpler way. Since the wise men had come many hundreds of miles across trackless desert in their quest, they should have no trouble discovering the baby in the town of Bethlehem. Instructing them to bring him word where the child might be found so that he could worship it, Herod sent them on to Bethlehem.

# 2. The Son of God

*"Therefore also that holy thing which shall be born of thee shall be called the Son of God."*   LUKE 1:35

THE STAR which had guided the *magi* from their home in the land of Sheba to Jerusalem did not fail them on the short journey to Bethlehem. Just outside the Holy City it appeared again and went before them until they came to the humble house and carpenter shop of a man named Joseph and his radiant young wife Mary. There they found the child they sought and heard from the mother a strange and wonderful story concerning his conception and birth.

The story really began with a kinswoman of Mary's named Elisabeth, who lived near Hebron—about a day's journey south of Bethlehem—and her husband Zacharias, a priest who often served in the temple at Jerusalem. Zacharias was burning incense in the temple one day when an angel appeared with the astounding news that Elisabeth, though long past the age for childbearing, would give him a son to be called John. "He shall turn many to the Lord their God," the angel promised. "And shall go in the spirit and power of Elijah to make ready a people prepared for the Lord."

Elisabeth had conceived as the angel had predicted, and in the sixth month of her pregnancy, the angel had also appeared to Mary, then a virgin espoused to Joseph of the house of

David. At the time of the angel's visit they were living in Nazareth, far to the north in the hill country of Galilee where Joseph worked as a skilled carpenter and builder.

"Hail, you that are highly favored, the Lord is with you; blessed are you among women," Mary was told by the heavenly visitor. "You shall conceive and bring forth a son and shall call his name Jesus. The Lord shall give to him the throne of his father David, and he shall reign over the house of Jacob forever. Of his kingdom there shall be no end."

"How shall this be," Mary had protested, "seeing I know not a man?"

"The Holy Ghost shall come upon you," the angel told her. "And that holy thing which shall be born of you shall be called the Son of God. Your cousin Elisabeth has also conceived a son in her old age, and this is the sixth month with her who was called barren, for with God nothing shall be impossible."

"Behold the handmaid of the Lord," Mary had said humbly. "Let it be according to your word."

Greatly troubled by the vision, Mary went to visit her cousin Elisabeth in order to see whether or not what the angel had said was true. She had remained there until the child called John was born, but long before that event Mary knew that the angel had spoken the truth and that a child had indeed come into being within her own body.

When Mary returned to Nazareth, Joseph found it hard to believe her story of the visit from the angel. Being a gentle and kind man, he wished to put her away privately with a letter of divorcement rather than make a public example of what had happened. While he was trying to decide what course he should follow, however, an angel appeared to him in a dream. "Joseph, son of David," the angel said. "Fear not to take Mary as your wife, for that which is conceived in her is of the Holy Ghost. She shall bring forth a son and you shall call his name Jesus, for he shall save the people from their sins." No longer doubting then, Joseph had guarded the young mother and her precious gift against the spiteful tongues of those who would not believe that, though still a virgin, she carried a child who was the Son of God.

The year in which these events happened marked the last days for fulfilling a decree by Caesar Augustus, Emperor of Rome, that all the world should be counted in a great census. And since each person was required to return to the city of his birth, Joseph and Mary had traveled to Bethlehem, the city of David a few miles south of Jerusalem, to register for the census.

On a wintry evening they approached Bethlehem and sought shelter at the public caravansery outside the town, but it was already filled, for many of the travelers were poor and could not afford to stay at an inn. Turned away there, Joseph took his wife, her womb already contracting with the early stages of childbirth, to seek accommodation at an inn. No beds were available, however, and the couple were forced to take refuge in the stable where poor folk and the servants of the rich ordinarily slept. There Mary gave birth to a son and, since they had no crib, she wrapped him in swaddling clothes and put him in the manger from which the animals ate.

In the fields between Bethlehem and Jerusalem that night a group of shepherds had been watching the so-called "sacred flocks" from which lambs were taken for sacrifice in the temple. They were terror-stricken when a sudden brilliance shone around them and they heard the voice of an angel saying, "Fear not! For, behold, I bring you good tidings of great joy, which shall be to all people! Unto you is born this day in the city of David a Saviour, who is Christ the Lord. And this shall be a sign to you; you shall find the babe wrapped in swaddling clothes, lying in a manger."

As the voice of the angel died away, the shepherds heard a heavenly host saying, "Glory to God in the highest, and on earth peace, good will toward men."

All this, and many other wondrous things which had happened at the birth of Jesus, Mary told the wise men who had followed the star so many hundreds of miles to find him. They worshipped the newborn babe and gave him gifts of gold, frankincense, and myrrh, valuable and rare spices which grew in great numbers in their land. But being warned by God in a dream that they should not go back to Herod, they left for their own country by another route.

Joseph and Mary were troubled by the knowledge that Herod had learned of Jesus' birth. And when Joseph was warned in a dream that they should flee into Egypt where the unscrupulous king could not harm them, they left Bethlehem at once, taking everything they owned. There in the rich Nile delta where the Hebrews had labored until led out by Moses, the little family of three lived in safety.

Determined to destroy the Messiah when the *magi* did not return to betray his birthplace, Herod now resorted to one of the most brutal acts in history. He executed all children under the age of two in Bethlehem and its environs, certain that by doing so he would include the infant king whom he sought. By this time, however, Joseph, Mary, and Jesus were already on the way to Egypt.

And since Hebron was not included in this sweeping edict, John, the son of Zacharias and Elisabeth, was not killed.

Shortly after this, Herod became the victim of a loathsome disease and died, but not before he had executed several of his own sons whom he judged—rightly enough—to be conspiring against him to usurp the throne. At Herod's death, Archelaus became ruler of Judea. Antipas, Archelaus' younger brother— also called Herod—was made governor of the district of Galilee and Peraea to the east, with the title of tetrarch. Philip, perhaps the best of all Herod's sons, was made tetrarch of a district lying to the northeast of the Jordan, but none of them inherited the title Herod had borne, King of the Jews. Archelaus quickly showed himself to be as cruel as his father and Rome removed him, placing the governorship of Judea in the hands of a series of procurators, Roman officials responsible directly to the emperor.

When word of Herod's death reached Joseph and Mary in Egypt, they decided to return to their homeland, but did not stop at Bethlehem, since it was near to Jerusalem. Instead, they continued on to Nazareth, their old home in Galilee.

# 3. My Father's Business

*"Wist ye not that I must be about my Father's business?"*   LUKE 2:49

GALILEE WAS a lovely land of mountains, fertile valleys, rich vineyards, and verdant pastures. As a skilled carpenter with a special knowledge of woodworking acquired in Egypt, Joseph was very busy. Jesus spent much of his boyhood in the Hebrew schools, usually conducted in the synagogues, which had grown up as centers of worship during the captivity of the Israelites in Babylon when they had been cut off from Jerusalem, their center of religious interest. But whether studying or playing, he was never without something to remind him that the main purpose of Israel lay in serving God according to the ancient covenant.

Attached to the doorpost of every Israelite dwelling was a square of parchment in a little metal case called the *mesusah*, containing exactly twenty-two lines from the words of God to Moses beginning:

"Hear, O Israel! The Lord our God is one Lord.
And thou shalt love the Lord thy God with all thine heart,
And with all thy soul, and with all thy might."
The quotation ended with these words:
"That your days may be multiplied and the days of your
    children,

222

In the land which the Lord sware unto your fathers to give
    them,
As the days of heaven upon the earth."

The passing of the seasons brought the religious festivals,
most important of which was the Passover, held in the spring
on the fourteenth day of Nisan, the first month of the year.
After being blessed—preferably by priests of the great altar at
Jerusalem—the paschal lamb was roasted and eaten in the
evening, along with bitter herbs symbolizing the years of slavery
and captivity in Egypt. At each celebration, the story of how
the angel of death had passed over the Hebrew households in
Egypt was retold so that even the youngest would keep it always
in their minds.

Although the Galileans were about a week's journey from
Jerusalem—the country of the Samaritans lying between Galilee
and Judea being considered a forbidden land—they made the
trip to the Holy City for the Passover as often as possible instead
of celebrating it at home. It was always a festive occasion, with
groups of people joining together along the road until the
joyful procession crossed the Jordan River east of Jericho and,
singing songs and waving fronds and branches as they walked,
passed through the City of Palms and took the long climb of
some fourteen miles to Jerusalem. Many families camped upon
the slopes of Mount Zion overlooking the Holy City rather
than pay the high prices charged by innkeepers and food-sellers
during the religious holidays. These journeys were for many
an opportunity to meet friends and relatives they would not
otherwise see for a number of years.

When Jesus was about twelve years old, Mary and Joseph
took him to Jerusalem in company with a group of friends and
neighbors to celebrate his becoming a "Son of the Commandment," as the puberty rite was called. Jesus' cousins John and
James, the two tall, strong sons of prosperous Zebedee, and the
young fishermen, Andrew and Simon, the sons of Jona, were in
the party. Altogether it was a happy group of friends and kinsmen who wound their way along the banks of the Jordan to

Bethabara—where Joshua and the Israelites had crossed over dryshod—and thence through Jericho up to Jerusalem itself.

At twelve already an accomplished scholar in the history and lore of his people, Jesus' heart was filled with emotion as he stood upon the slope of the Mount of Olives and looked across the brook called Kidron to the great golden temple shining in the afternoon sunlight. Not even the rhythmic tread of Roman half-boots—*caligula*—as the guards patrolled the grim palace fortress of Antonia overlooking the temple courts, could dampen his enthusiasm for the scene he watched. For here, to the devout, was the very wellspring of their faith, the place toward which every Jew turned his eyes when he prayed, and the source of his inspired conviction that, in fulfillment of the promises God had made, he would one day send a deliverer who would set up his earthly kingdom here.

Once the paschal lamb was eaten and the hymn which ended the Passover day sung, many of the visitors began the journey home. With a number of others, the Galilean party which Jesus and his family had accompanied to Jerusalem left early. And since the young people always ran ahead of the procession, investigating every new thing and exulting in the freedom of the road, neither Mary nor Joseph thought it odd when they did not see Jesus for many hours. Only when night fell and he did not come to their tent pitched beside the road near Jericho did they become alarmed. When a thorough search of the camp did not reveal Jesus' whereabouts, Joseph and Mary returned to Jerusalem, but after three days of visiting relatives and friends in the city they still had not found him.

As the highest governing body of the Jewish faith, subject to the Roman Procurator or Governor only in decisions involving the sentence of death, the Sanhedrin sat in formal session during the feast days. During the latter part of the celebration, it was customary for members of the court to descend to the lower levels of the temple where the public gathered and answer questions. Here the anxious Mary finally found Jesus, sitting in a circle before the noble judges, asking questions and discussing points of law with them.

"Why have you dealt with us in this way, son?" she asked him reproachfully.

When Jesus turned to face her, she saw in his eyes a look she had never seen there before, a far-away expression as if he had been communing with something or someone she did not know.

"How is it that you sought me?" he asked. "Do you not know that I must be about my Father's business?"

It would be a long time before Mary would fully understand the meaning of those words, but she could not repress a chill of fear at what she had seen in the eyes of her son, although he made no more objections but went quietly back with them to Galilee.

# 4. Voice in the Wilderness

> *"One mightier than I cometh, the latchet of whose shoes I am not worthy to unloose."*     LUKE 3:16

IT HAD BEEN many hundreds of years since a true prophet had arisen in Israel. Now a new and arresting voice was beginning to be heard. Eyes burning with prophetic fervor and wearing the long hair and beard, the rough robe woven of camel's hair, and the leather sandals of a Nazarite, John, the son of Zacharias and Elisabeth, preached in the wilderness country at the northern end of the Salt Sea near one of the busiest crossings of the Jordan, that at Bethabara, a few miles east of Jericho. His message was one of repentance, but it had a startling character too, for he announced himself as the fore-runner of the true Messiah.

While Jesus had been spending his youth and early manhood in Nazareth working as a carpenter to support the family after the death of Joseph, John had joined the community of the Essenes, a strict and ascetic group living near the Salt Sea. Devoted to obeying the Law of Moses in every detail, the Essenes were dedicated to a life of study, service, and scholarly work, copying and preserving the ancient records of God's covenant with his people. When he became a man, John's fiery spirit had taken him away from the retirement and protection of the Essene community to the near-by fords of the Jordan, where a constant stream of people passed on the way to and from Jerusalem, Galilee, and Peraea. There, in a grove of sycamores, he preached like Elijah of old.

"O generation of vipers!" he lashed those who came to hear him. "Who has warned you to flee from the wrath to come? Bring forth fruits worthy of repentance, for the axe is laid to the root of the trees and every tree which does not bring forth good fruit will be hewn down and cast into the fire!"

"What shall we do?" the people asked him.

"He that has two coats, let him give to him that has none. And he that has meat, let him do likewise. Exact no more than that which is appointed to you, and do violence to no man nor accuse any falsely."

For four centuries no other man had appeared who resembled so closely the old prophets of Israel and it was natural that people should see in John many things. Some thought he was Elijah, who, according to tradition, had been taken up into heaven bodily by the Lord and was expected to return to earth and lead his people to their true destiny. Others named him the "Expected One," the Messiah who would reign as both a spiritual and material king in Israel, freeing his people from the bondage of Rome and setting them over all the nations of the earth. Many young men of Jesus' acquaintance—among them his kinsmen James and John, the sons of Zebedee, and the fishermen of Galilee, Simon and Andrew—had become disciples of the new prophet.

John, however, made no claim to be anything except what he was, a fiery and dedicated preacher, gifted with prophetic vision, who saw the course in which the sins of the people were taking them. Those who repented he led into the Jordan for the symbolic washing, or baptism, practiced by the Essenes. "I baptize you with water," he warned the multitudes, however. "But one mightier than I comes, the latchet of whose shoes I am not worthy to unloose. He shall baptize you with the Holy Spirit and with fire."

Living quietly in Nazareth, teaching the children who flocked to him by telling them simple stories illustrating the greatness of God's love and concern for his people, and often speaking on the Sabbath from the elevated pulpit in the center of the synagogue, Jesus inevitably heard of John's preaching. In fact, many of his friends had already become disciples of the Baptist, as the gaunt Essene was popularly called from his custom of baptizing with water. With the coming of his thirtieth year, bringing maturity and the right to speak in the councils, it was inevitable that Jesus should seek a wider sphere in "going about his Father's business." And while journeying to Jerusalem for one of the religious festivals, he came to John for baptism in the shallow waters of the Jordan at Bethabara.

It was a dramatic moment as the two men faced each other. John was burning-eyed and dramatic with a hot fire of devotion and dedication. Jesus was slender and quiet, with a majesty, strength, and compassion in his face and eyes that already marked him as one set apart. John recognized him immediately.

"Why do you come to me?" he asked humbly. "I have need to be baptized by you."

"Suffer it as it is now," Jesus answered. "For thus it becomes us to fulfill all righteousness."

Because both John and Jesus were filled with the spirit of God, a deep communion existed between them from that moment. To Jesus—John understood—baptism was a public avowal of his subservience to the will of the Father. Through being washed in the water like the humblest repentant sinner, he was announcing his intention to begin a new phase of his life—in a sense making a new covenant with God.

As Jesus stood in the water after his baptism, he was conscious of a deep and pervading communion, a glory and a warmth so great that it seemed to be a light, blinding him. In the midst of the light, he saw a vision like the spirit of God in the shape of a white dove descending to light upon his shoulder, and heard the voice of his Father saying, "This is my beloved son, in whom I am well pleased."

Wishing to search his own heart and spirit concerning his deeply moving experience in the waters of the Jordan, Jesus did not go on directly to Jerusalem but turned aside on a path leading up a mountain overlooking Jericho. Climbing the

precipitous slope to its summit where many rough caves pocketed
the surface, he made camp alone for a period of fasting, self-
study, and search for the will of the Father concerning him.

From the mountaintop Jesus could look down upon the
beautiful palm-bordered streets of Jericho, a true oasis which
had been made into a flourishing garden with water brought by
aqueducts from the near-by village of Neaera and from the
"Fountain of Elisha" at the foot of the mountain. There upon
the heights, Jesus was tempted by the voice of evil which speaks
to every man.

"If you are the Son of God, command that these stones be
made into bread," the voice said, shrewdly selecting as the first
temptation the hunger and thirst which assailed him as it would
any other human being. But Jesus answered without hesitation:
"It is written, 'Man shall not live by bread alone, but by every
word that proceeds out of the mouth of God.'"

His period of fasting completed but with as yet no revelation
of God's purpose for him, Jesus came down to Jericho and took
the road ascending the hills to Jerusalem. As he stood in the
highest place of the temple looking down upon the magnificent
city and its surroundings, the evil voice spoke again with the
very human temptation to proclaim his real identity and receive
the homage which a miraculous proof of that claim would certainly bring him.

"If you are the Son of God, cast yourself down," the voice
said. "For it is written, 'He shall give his angels charge concerning you and in their hands they shall bear you up, lest at
any time you dash your foot against a stone.'"

This temptation, too, Jesus answered as he had the other: "It
is written again, 'You shall not tempt the Lord your God.'"

Not finding in the temple the revelation of God's purpose for
him that he sought, Jesus left Jerusalem for the return journey
to Nazareth. From a mountaintop along the way he looked
upon the rolling expanse of Israel stretching before him and
beyond that, invisible yet certainly present, the vastness and
richness of the kingdoms of the world. "All these things I will
give you if you will fall down and worship me," the evil spirit

offered again, but now the answer came easily to Jesus' tongue, words spoken long ago by God to Moses: "You shall worship the Lord your God, and him only shall you serve."

Defeated, the evil spirit tormented Jesus' human body no longer. He came down from the mountain and continued on toward Galilee, knowing that whenever God's purpose was revealed to him, he was ready to begin his work.

# 5. The First Rejection

> "This day is this scripture fulfilled in
> your ears."                    LUKE 4:21

SIMON OF BETHSAIDA was depressed and a little angry as he
stirred a pot of stew over some glowing coals under a syca-
more tree near the caravansery at Bethabara. A hard worker
accustomed to achieving results, he resented having wasted his
time.

Simon had become an enthusiastic and eager follower of
John, now popularly known as "the Baptist," when the prophet
had begun to preach by the Jordan. Leaving his fishing on the
Sea of Galilee, he had even gone with his brother Andrew and
the sons of Zebedee, James and John, to become the Baptist's
disciple, confident that when the right time arrived John would
announce his identity as the long-expected Messiah. But now
the prophet had definitely denied that he was the Expected
One, and there was nothing left for Simon to do except to
return to Galilee and admit that he had been a fool. One
thing was certain, he vowed to himself as he stirred the stew
with his long fisherman's knife, he would not soon follow another would-be Messiah. Fishing was his business; he'd stay with
that next time.

Still, Simon thought as he watched the glowing coals morosely,
he supposed he should be grateful in a way to the delegation

of Sadducees and Pharisees from Jerusalem who had questioned the Baptist that afternoon, even though Galileans naturally distrusted such haughty churchmen. At least they had determined once and for all that John was not the Messiah when they questioned him and the gaunt prophet answered: "I am the voice of one crying in the wilderness, 'Make straight the way of the Lord,' as the Prophet Elijah said."

"Why do you baptize then if you are not the Christ or Elijah?" the Jerusalem delegation had insisted.

John's eyes had swept over the listeners and when he spoke, it had seemed to Simon that the prophet was looking directly at a slender man standing at the edge of the crowd, a man he knew as Jesus of Nazareth, a cousin of James and John, who often taught in the synagogues on the Sabbath. But the Baptist's words obviously made that impossible.

"I baptize with water, but there stands one among you whom you do not know," John had said. "He it is who coming after me is preferred before me."

The delegation from Jerusalem had left that afternoon, satisfied that John the Baptist did not claim to be the Messiah and was therefore not likely to stir up political trouble with the Romans. Later, as in the case of Simon, many of those closest to John had begun to drift away. Simon had not seen his brother Andrew for several hours, but the two, with the sons of Zebedee and a friend named Philip, had already decided to start back to Galilee in the morning.

The sound of footsteps turned Simon's thoughts from the coals and what had happened that afternoon. Andrew, the younger brother, entered the circle of firelight, his eyes dancing and his face flushed.

"Simon!" he called excitedly. "We have found the Messiah!"

"Did you not hear the son of Zacharias tell the men from Jerusalem he is not the Expected One?" Simon asked a little irritably. "Come and eat."

"This is Jesus of Nazareth! I have been with him all afternoon. Come and see for yourself."

"Perhaps—when I have finished eating. Look. I bought goat's flesh from a seller of meat."

Andrew sniffed the pot and, reaching in with his knife, took out a piece of the meat and accepted a fragment of bread. "You must come and see Jesus tonight, Simon," he insisted. "John and James are there with Philip."

"I will go," Simon promised with a shrug. "Hurry and eat."

Jesus was sitting beneath the shelter of the caravansary when Simon and Andrew arrived. He looked up at the big fisherman and his eyes warmed in a smile. "You are Simon, the son of Jonas," he said gently. "But you shall be called Cephas."

The word meant stone and the Greek equivalent was *Petros*, or Peter. Simon did indeed look like a rock, standing there with his broad shoulders and his powerful body and legs. Rocklike, too, was the obvious resistance in his mind to acknowledging a Nazarene carpenter as the Messiah. And yet, as he stood looking down at the slender man who had just spoken to him, Simon felt a strange warmth begin to permeate his body, a feeling of communion and companionship with one he'd known before only as a casual acquaintance and a kinsman of the family of Zebedee to whose fishing establishment he sold his catch. Thus began a relationship which was to grow stronger through the vicissitudes that were to follow, changing the whole life of Simon called Peter.

The five spent that night with Jesus at the caravansary and in the morning Philip brought his brother Nathanael, or Bartholomew, to join them when they started northward along the road that followed the Jordan to the Sea of Galilee. As they walked and listened to Jesus, these six were welded into an inner circle which was to be closer to him than any other during the succeeding years of his ministry. Of them all, the closest ties were to be with the hulking fisherman he had called Cephas —or Peter—and his dynamic and impulsive cousin John.

When Jesus and the other Galileans reached Nazareth, they found that his family had gone to the near-by town of Cana where a kinsman was being married, so they decided to go there. Jesus' party—many of whom were also relatives of the kinsman whose wedding was being celebrated—had not been expected, and no provision had been made for them. Wine, heavily diluted with water, was the favorite beverage upon such festive occasions, and when the supply ran out, Mary came to her son. It was a humiliating experience for the one giving the feast to fail to provide enough for everyone, and as head of his own household, Jesus had the responsibility of helping his kinsman if he could. This, however, seemed impossible, for the wineshops were already closed.

Several stone water pots stood in the house, having been filled with water from the near-by spring by the women before the feast began. When Jesus instructed the servants to carry some of the water to the steward in charge of the feast, they hesitated, wondering how mere water could be expected to satisfy the thirsty Galileans. But they obeyed the quiet authority in his voice, and after the steward tasted the cup, he sent the servants to pour wine for the guests while he drew the bridegroom aside.

"Every man sets forth good wine at the beginning," the steward said severely. "Then when the men have drunk well, the host brings out the second best. But you have kept the good wine until now."

The guests drank the new wine with gusto, but when word spread of the miracle Jesus had accomplished in turning water to wine, the gaiety of the feast died away. In reaction to something which seemed to be supernatural, even Jesus' friends shunned him, the first of many such experiences he was to have in the months ahead.

Jesus sent his six Galilean companions back to their work after the wedding feast, but word of the miracle at Cana spread rapidly throughout the countryside, eventually coming to the ears of Chuza, Herod's steward in Capernaum. Chuza's son was gravely ill at the time and, having exhausted all other alternatives, he went to Jesus, who was again in Cana, begging him to come and help the boy.

Recognizing that Chuza was a good man, Jesus did not fail him. "Go your way," he said. "Your son lives."

Chuza returned reluctantly to Capernaum, convinced that he had failed and that the boy must die, for it was unbelievable that a man could heal another when they were separated by many miles. Before he reached home, however, his servants met him with the news that his son had suddenly become well—at the exact hour when Jesus had said, "Go your way. Your son lives." In this way Chuza, an important official of Capernaum and Galilee, became a believer in the new Messiah.

The people of Nazareth had known Jesus as a kindly teacher, a pious man, and a skilled carpenter. Even after word of the miracle at Cana and the healing of Chuza's son began to spread abroad, it was difficult for them to understand that he was anything more than one of them. It was Jesus' custom to speak frequently in the synagogue on the Sabbath, interpreting the scripture for the congregation. Many rabbis, as the teachers were called, traveled about preaching in the various synagogues, and Jesus had been doing this for some time in the villages and and towns near Nazareth. Soon after the miracle at Cana and the healing of Chuza's son, he returned home and, as was his custom, read from the scrolls of the ancient writings during the service. This time the scroll was that of Isaiah and his voice took on a resonance and a confidence the people had never heard before as he read:

"The spirit of the Lord is upon me, because he has anointed me to preach the gospel to the poor. He has sent me to heal the brokenhearted, to preach deliverance to the captives and recovery of sight to the blind, to set at liberty them that are bound, to preach the acceptable year of the Lord."

When he finished reading, Jesus put down the scroll but did not speak for a moment. Then quietly, yet loudly enough for his words to fill the synagogue, he said, "This day is the scripture fulfilled in your ears."

It took a moment for the people to realize what he meant. When they did, a murmur of resentment began to arise, for in naming himself as the expected Messiah, Jesus had put himself upon a plane of equality with God. And not willing to accept as the Expected One a man they knew as a carpenter who had grown up in their community, the people of Nazareth naturally felt him to be guilty of blasphemy, the most serious of crimes.

By the time Jesus came out of the synagogue, an angry mob had gathered. Without giving him a chance to explain what he had meant by the statement during the sermon, they seized him and dragged him up the hill behind Nazareth to where an outthrust crag overhung the town from a considerable height. Taking him to the very edge of this cliff, the crowd drew away to stone him before thrusting him over it in retribution for what they considered the crime of blasphemy.

Jesus faced them unafraid and at the quiet courage visible in his face, each man hesitated to take the first step and thrust him over the cliff. When finally he started to walk away, the crowd drew aside and made a path for him. Nor did they follow him as he walked down the path, leaving them standing sheepishly behind.

This first of many rejections took place in his own city, an experience of which one who loved Jesus dearly was later to write: "He came unto his own, and his own received him not."

# 6. The Fishermen of Galilee

*"Come ye after me, and I will make you to become fishers of men."*

MARK 1:17

THE SEA OF GALILEE, a harp-shaped expansion of the Jordan River which in Abraham's day had been called the Sea of Chinnereth, lay within a deep cup surrounded by hills. A narrow strip of lowland bordered part of the lake, widening out toward the northwestern portion in the Plain of Gennesaret, a fertile and fruitful area that was one of the loveliest places in all of Israel. Almost at the edge of the plain lay Capernaum, largest of the teeming communities in the busy lake area. The Way of the Sea, the ancient caravan road from Damascus into Canaan by which Abraham and his followers had traveled some two thousand years before, also passed near-by. Here Jesus came after his rejection at Nazareth to begin his ministry.

The Galileans were composed of many and diverse nationalities. A large proportion of them were Jews only by conquest but, as so often happens, these were even more fervent in their intense national spirit than those whose fathers had known the covenant through the ages. Thus it was a brawling, teeming, exciting little world into which Jesus came when he was slightly over thirty years of age.

237

Galilee itself was ruled by the tetrarch Herod Antipas, but just beyond the Jordan and the lake lay the territory of the tetrarch Philip. A kindly and tolerant man, he had built the city of Bethsaida-Julias a little east of where the Jordan empties into the Sea of Galilee, naming it in honor of his Roman masters. This—with the new city of Caesarea-Philippi on the slopes of Mount Hermon near the cave of Pan, where one of the sources of the Jordan bursts from a rock—served as Philip's seat of government.

The Sea of Galilee lay about six hundred feet beneath the level of the Mediterranean to the west; at its southern end, the Jordan began another precipitous descent to the Sea of Judgment, or Salt Sea, far to the south. This body of water, so salty that no life could exist within it, was some twelve hundred feet below the level of the Mediterranean.

Because of its very diversity of peoples, Galilee was an area much more nationally-minded than Jerusalem and Judea, where the proximity of the temple, with its large number of priests and government officials—plus the fact that it was ruled over by the Roman procurator Pontius Pilate—tended to discourage any feelings of revolt against Rome. Abortive uprisings had occurred at various times in Galilee; during one led by Judas the Gaulonite, some two thousand Jews had been crucified on the slopes before the Roman center of Sepphoris, a few miles north of Nazareth.

No fishing establishment upon the lake was larger than that of Zebedee and his sons who, with their friends and kinsmen Simon and Andrew, were among the leading fishermen of the region. After the miracle at Cana, the four had gone back to their work on the lake, and one morning, as he walked along the shore, Jesus came to where they had brought their boats into shallow water at the end of a night's fishing to wash the nets. Discouraged by a poor catch, Simon started to protest when Jesus told him to launch his boat but, impressed by the Nazarene's quiet air of confidence, he changed his mind.

"Nevertheless, at your word I will let down the nets," the big man said. When he tried to draw them in, they were so full of fish that the boat almost sank and he had to call for James and John and their father to help land the catch.

"Depart from me, O Lord, for I am a sinful man!" Simon begged.

Jesus only smiled. "Come after me, and I will make you fishers of men," he told the four—Simon, Andrew, James, and John—and from that day until their deaths none of them ever turned away from following him.

Word of the forthright teachings of the young rabbi of Nazareth spread quickly around the lake. When he began to perform spectacular miracles of healing too, notably the curing in the synagogue in Capernaum of a man with palsy and the healing of Peter's mother-in-law, such large crowds followed him, seeking to be healed, that he was hardly able to teach any more. Even the men closest to him—now called his disciples— found it hard to understand that Jesus would wish to teach people a new way of life in preference to restoring broken and diseased bodies. But so great was his own humanity for those who suffered that he could not withhold his curative power from them. Such large crowds began to gather wherever he spoke that the synagogues could no longer hold them, and he was forced to teach in the open, as had John the Baptist. For this purpose, the secluded coves and flat lands along the shores of the Sea of Galilee were ideal.

The Pharisees prided themselves upon being the sole interpreters for the people of the Law of Moses. Professing to follow the strict religious Law, they had in fact made so many interpretations of it that an ordinary person could hardly be expected any longer to know just what constituted it. Jesus did not teach outright disobedience to the Law; in fact he was always scrupulous to remind his listeners that the covenant made by Moses was the real basis of their obedience to God. But when it came to the strict observance of the Sabbath—particularly in matters of healing—and the ritual washings and similar prohibitions which the Pharisees had ringed about the great and abiding truths of the Law, he often transgressed what they considered the sacred rules. One such transgression occurred in Capernaum.

Jesus had returned to Capernaum for the Sabbath after a tour of the lake region and when his presence became known, the area around Peter's house where he was staying quickly filled with people seeking to reach him in order to be healed and—secondarily—to hear his teachings. A paralyzed man was unable to reach the house and, knowing that Jesus stayed in Capernaum only a few days at a time, hired four men to pick up the pallet upon which he lay and carry him to Jesus.

Houses in Palestine had flat, connecting roofs upon which the people often slept in hot weather. And since it was possible to cross a good portion of the city by traveling over what was often called the "Road of the Roofs," the men carrying the pallet upon which the paralyzed man lay chose this route. They came to Peter's house without much difficulty and, removing the tiles over the porch, let the suffering man down through the opening.

Jesus could not disappoint the faith which had led the petitioner to take such an unconventional way of reaching him. "Son, be of good cheer," he said. "Your sins are forgiven."

"Blasphemy! Blasphemy!" cried some Pharisees who were listening. "The Nazarene claims to forgive sins, and this only the Most High can do!"

"Is it easier to say, 'Your sins are forgiven'?" Jesus demanded sternly, "Or to say, 'Arise and walk'?"

The Pharisees could not answer, so Jesus turned to the paralyzed man. "That you may know the Son of Man has power on earth to forgive sins," he said, "I say to you arise, take up your bed, and go to your house." When the sick man rolled up the pallet and put it upon his shoulders, the crowd parted in amazement for him to pass through.

Soon afterward, Jesus went to dine at the home of a new disciple, Matthew or Levi, a hated taxgatherer or "publican." When he was reprimanded by the Pharisees for eating and drinking with publicans and sinners, he stated, perhaps more clearly than he yet had, the essence of his earthly mission.

"They that are whole have no need of a physician, but they that are sick," he told his critics sternly. "I came not to call the righteous, but sinners to repentance."

The gulf between Jesus and the Pharisees who taught that God would not look with favor upon any who did not prove their righteousness by strict devotion to the details of Mosaic Law—as they interpreted it—was widening steadily. This conflict with accepted practices was to cause most of the opposition to Jesus by the religious authorities of Israel.

# 7. Nicodemus and the Master

*"For God so loved the world, that he gave his only begotten Son, that whosoever believeth in him should not perish, but have everlasting life."*

JOHN 3:16

S OMETIMES Toah's faith wavered a little, but usually not for very long. For thirty-eight years, ever since a wagon had run over his back while he was carrying a heavy pack containing military supplies for the mile required of any civilian overtaken by a Roman column, he had lain by the Pool of Bethesda every day. Fed by an underground spring, the rush of water from the pool's source periodically caused the surface to boil up and, according to an old tradition, the first person to enter the pool after each such disturbance would be healed. Consequently, a large number of crippled and sick spent the day beside the pool, each seeking to be the first to enter when the surface was disturbed.

The Pool of Bethesda had come to be something of a social center for the afflicted, and passers-by often stopped to ask about those who had been fortunate enough to enter the water and be healed. In this way Toah had come to know many people in Jerusalem: Abiathar, the ruthless captain of the temple guards; Jonas, the hunchbacked woodseller; Joseph, the kind-hearted merchant of Arimathea; and especially Nicodemus, the lawyer, who was his particular friend. As the oldest of those who waited and the most faithful, Toah was something of a celebrity, but he would gladly have given it all for a chance to be first in the water.

Today more than for a long time Toah's faith that he would one day be cured was at a low ebb. Jonas had verified the rumor that the famous teacher of Galilee, Jesus of Nazareth, was in Jerusalem with his disciples to celebrate the Passover. Even without the news, however, Toah would have known something unusual was happening. Only a few of the afflicted were by the pool that morning, the rest having gone in search of the Nazarene who was said to heal even while at a distance from the sufferer.

As he lay by the pool, Toah fought against the temptation to drag his crippled body to the temple where he was sure the others were waiting for the Nazarene, reminding himself that, with so few at the pool, this might be the very day when he would be first into the water. But thirty-eight years was a long time, and the prospect of being healed merely by the touch of the new teacher was so attractive that Toah found it hard not to follow the others. His deep-seated faith in God's justice kept him at the pool, but he could not still the insistent voice warning that he might be throwing away his one chance to be healed by the Galilean.

A shadow fell across Toah's face as he lay on a pallet with his eyes fixed upon the water. Within his field of vision he saw a man's worn sandals and homespun robe but dared not look up at the newcomer's face lest he miss the first stir of the pool's surface. The material of the robe told him that this man was not one of his friends from Jerusalem; he knew their clothing by heart now. Probably some traveler in the city for the Passover, he thought, and steeled himself against being drawn into conversation. But when the stranger spoke, his words startled Toah.

"Would you be made whole?" he asked.

Toah looked up. A slender man in a robe of rough homespun stood beside him. His beard was brown, as was his hair, and his face was tanned from the sun. He was of medium height and build and his head was well formed, the eyes warm and friendly, as was the smile that softened his lips.

Just then the water was disturbed and, with a cry of triumph, one of the cripples waiting at the edge of the pool threw himself into it. But somehow Toah did not feel any resentment against the stranger for keeping him from being the one who felt the healing touch of the water.

"Sir," he said respectfully, "I have no man to put me into the pool when the water is troubled. While I am coming, another steps down before me." Even after thirty-eight years Toah was not complaining, for his faith was still strong that God would some day allow him to reach the pool first.

"Rise. Take up your bed and walk," the man beside him said quietly, and for an instant Toah could hardly believe he had heard aright. Then, as he felt his paralyzed muscles begin to stir with the exquisite pain of returning life, he knew a sudden rush of joy. Rising to his knees, trembling with the excitement of what had happened, he began to roll up the pallet upon which he had been lying. But when he turned to thank the man who had healed him, no one was there. Confident that the cure had somehow come from God, however, Toah started toward the temple, carrying his pallet and shouting to all he met the good news that he had been healed.

At the entrance to the sanctuary Toah was stopped by a Pharisee. "It is not lawful for you to carry your bed on the Sabbath," the man told him sternly, but Toah was little concerned with guilt now.

"The one who made me whole told me to take up my bed and walk," he explained.

"Who told you that?" the Pharisee demanded sharply, and Toah was forced to admit that he did not even know the name of his benefactor. While he was arguing with the Pharisee, who claimed that he was lying and wanted to accuse him then and there of breaking the Law, Toah saw his good friend Nicodemus in the crowd. He was on the point of asking the lawyer for proof of his former paralyzed state, but just then someone else assured the Pharisee that his story was true and he had indeed been healed. And by the time Toah finally convinced the Pharisee, Nicodemus had gone.

That afternoon Nicodemus sought out Toah at his home

and talked with him for a long time, questioning him closely about the miracle of his healing. Toah could tell him nothing, however, except that the Nazarene—whose identity as the one who had healed him he had learned at the temple, had said, "Rise. Take up your bed and walk."

As a member of the great Sanhedrin, Nicodemus had heard of Jesus long before the healing of Toah, but the miracle was the first concrete evidence he had witnessed with his own eyes that the Nazarene teacher possessed an obviously divine power. Being a lawyer, he pondered the weight of the evidence, discussing it that day with some fellow members of the court.

The priests among them could not believe that a Galilean should be the Messiah, as many people now claimed Jesus to be. Wanting to have nothing interfere with their sure hold upon the enormous power and revenues of the temple, they labeled the Nazarene a charlatan. The stricter of the Pharisees could not forgive Jesus for breaking the Law and were blinded to the significance of his healing miracles by the fact that, in their interpretation, the Law forbade healing on the Sabbath. It was a measure of their minds, and their faith, Nicodemus thought ruefully, that the legal questions involved meant more to them than the startling fact that a man paralyzed for thirty-eight years had been instantaneously healed. A few to whom Nicodemus talked mentioned the possibility that Jesus might be a great teacher who could bring the people back to a realization of their duty to God under the covenant. But he found no one who would go so far as to name a Nazarene carpenter the Messiah whose coming they professed to desire.

Nicodemus was not sure in his own mind just what the miracle of Toah had meant so, being a man of action and directness, he went that night to the camp on the Mount of Olives overlooking Jerusalem where Jesus and his followers were staying.

"Rabbi," the lawyer said respectfully, giving Jesus the title by which he was ordinarily known. "We know that you are a teacher come from God, for no man can do the miracles you do unless God is with him."

Jesus recognized Nicodemus' earnestness and the deep-seated

desire for truth that had brought him to the camp that night. "Except a man be born again, he cannot see the kingdom of God," he said kindly.

Nicodemus frowned. "How can a man be born when he is old? Can he enter the second time into his mother's womb and be born?"

"Except a man is born of water and of the Spirit he cannot enter into the kingdom of God," Jesus explained. "That which is born of the flesh is flesh, and that which is born of the spirit is spirit."

Nicodemus was still perplexed. "How can these things be?" he asked.

"God so loved the world that he gave his only begotten Son, that whoever believes in him should not perish but have everlasting life," Jesus said simply. "God did not send his Son into the world to condemn it, but that the world through him might be saved."

Nicodemus had been given the answer to the question foremost in his mind, that Jesus was indeed the Messiah. But the lawyer's voice, though he followed Jesus faithfully after that, was only one raised in the councils against the powerful entrenched hierarchy of the chief priests who had already determined to destroy the gentle Nazarene because through his teachings, he was showing to everyone a way to God over which they exercised no control.

# 8. Sermon upon a Mountain

*"And seeing the multitudes, he went up into a mountain."*  MATTHEW 5:1

SIMON AND ANDREW, James and John, two pairs of fisher- men brothers, had been the first disciples Jesus called, but as time went on, the circle of those nearest him had widened until it included twelve men. Besides the first four, there were Levi or Matthew, with Philip and his brother Na- thanael or Bartholomew, and Thomas, sometimes called Didy- mus because he was one of a pair of twins. Three others of the twelve were relatives of Jesus through Joseph. These were James, usually called the son of Alphaeus to distinguish him from James the son of Zebedee; Judas, called Lebbaeus or Thad- daeus; and another Simon, referred to ordinarily as Zelotes or "The Zealot." The eleven were all Galileans, many of them near members of Jesus' own household, being related to him or friends of boyhood. The twelfth disciple was not a Galilean but a native of Judea; named Judas of Kerioth, he was often called Judas Iscariot.

With the sphere of his ministry rapidly widening, it had be- come obvious that Jesus could not carry the entire burden of healing and teaching; the time had come to ordain men who could be sent out to teach and to preach in his name. For this ceremony, he chose a mountain called the Horns of Hattin

247

near a road leading to the Mediterranean from the beautiful
new city of Tiberias, built by Herod Antipas on the shores of
the Sea of Galilee in honor of the Emperor Tiberius. The top
of the mountain had once been the location of a city and the
ruins formed a fine natural amphitheatre from which a large
number of people could hear a speaker. There Jesus gathered
around him the inner circle of twelve, while a large group
of people waited upon the slopes below to listen. After a
night of prayer, he began his charge to the twelve with these
words:

> "Blessed are the poor in spirit: for their's is the kingdom of
> heaven.
> Blessed are they that mourn: for they shall be comforted.
> Blessed are the meek: for they shall inherit the earth.
> Blessed are they which do hunger and thirst after righteous-
> ness: for they shall be filled.
> Blessed are the merciful: for they shall obtain mercy.
> Blessed are the pure in heart: for they shall see God.
> Blessed are the peacemakers: for they shall be called the chil-
> dren of God.
> Blessed are they which are persecuted for righteousness' sake:
> for their's is the kingdom of heaven.
> Blessed are ye when men shall revile you, and persecute you,
> and shall say all manner of evil against you falsely, for my
> sake.
> Rejoice, and be exceeding glad: for great is your reward in
> heaven: for so persecuted they the prophets which were be-
> fore you."

"You are the light of the world; a city set on a hill cannot be
hid," Jesus continued. As he spoke, he looked across the beautiful Sea of Galilee to the Greek city of Hippos with its shining
columns upon the hill tops east of the lake. Part of the Deca-
polis—the name given to ten Greek cities in that area—Hippos
was visible from all parts of the region, and the comparison of
a light set upon a hill was a particularly apt one.

Jesus continued to teach the disciples and the people who
were gathered upon the mountain, giving them the very essence

of his mission as the Son of God sent as a Saviour. Finally, he taught them how to pray, saying:

"Our Father which art in heaven,
Hallowed be thy name.
Thy kingdom come.
Thy will be done
In earth, as it is in heaven.
Give us this day our daily bread.
And forgive us our debts, as we forgive our debtors,
And lead us not into temptation, but deliver us from evil;
For thine is the kingdom, and the power, and the glory,
    forever. Amen."

"Whoever comes to me and hears my sayings and does them is like a man who built a house and dug deep and laid the foundations on a rock," Jesus concluded, "When the flood rose, the stream beat vehemently upon that house, but could not shake it, for it was founded upon a rock. But he that hears and does not, is like a man that built a house on the surface without a foundation. The stream beat vehemently against it and immediately it fell, and the ruin of that house was great."

Not long after the sermon on the mountaintop, Jesus had word from an old friend. Like Nicodemus in Jerusalem, John the Baptist had a question to ask.

Even though John had denied that he was Elijah returned to earth, he was still regarded by many people as a true prophet. As such, no one found fault with his forthright doctrine demanding repentance and submission to the will of God; when difficulties finally came for John, they stemmed from another source than the people.

Herod Antipas, son of Herod the Great, ruled in Galilee and Peraea, the latter including the area at Bethabara where John preached. While on a visit to Rome, Herod had developed a violent passion for Herodias, the wife of his half-brother Philip. Shortly after his return to Galilee, he had put away his wife, the daughter of King Aretas of Nabatea, and Herodias soon followed him to become his wife, accompanied by her beautiful seventeen-year-old daughter Salome.

According to Jewish Law, Herod had committed adultery in putting aside his wife and taking the wife of another. For this John forthrightly denounced him. Even kings ordinarily did not interfere with the teachings of prophets for fear of stirring up the people, who believed they were actually the words of God spoken through the mouth of a man. Herod would have left John alone, but Herodias was tremendously angered by the temerity of this ragged prophet in denouncing her. She kept nagging Herod until finally he had John arrested and imprisoned in the fortress-palace of Machaerus, which stood on the crest of a mountain overlooking the Sea of Judgment.

Many months had passed since John had baptized Jesus in the Jordan near Bethabara and, except for the one occasion in Nazareth when he had almost been killed by his own people, and the private conversation with Nicodemus, Jesus had not publicly proclaimed himself the Messiah. It was natural therefore that John should begin to doubt, and finally he sent one of his disciples to Jesus with this inquiry: "Are you he that is to come? Or do we look for another?"

"Go and show John again those things which you hear and see," Jesus told the messenger. "The blind receive their sight and the lame walk. The lepers are cleansed and the deaf hear. The dead are raised up and the poor have the gospel preached to them."

Jesus knew John would understand from these words that he was actually the Messiah, for Isaiah had written many centuries before of the Expected One who would be sent to lead Israel back to God:

"Then the eyes of the blind shall be opened,
And the ears of the deaf shall be unstopped.
Then shall the lame man leap as an hart,
And the tongue of the dumb sing."

"Blessed is he who is not offended in me," Jesus added, knowing John would also understand this to be an apology for not freeing him from prison by miraculous means. Jesus had come to establish a new kingdom in the hearts of men and to rule there. If he were to defy the power of Herod and free John now, he would be setting his own material power and authority against that of Rome, and it was not a part of God's plan that this should be done.

When the disciple returned to John with Jesus' words, the Baptist contented himself as best he could in prison, realizing that no miraculous power would be used to release him. Herodias, however, was not content that the gaunt prophet who had denounced her should suffer no worse punishment than being locked up in one of the cells hollowed out of the solid rock beneath the fortress. Determined that John should die, she cleverly planned to dupe Herod into ordering his death.

It was Herod's custom upon his birthday to give in the palace of Machaerus a great feast to which the rich and noble in the tetrarchy were invited. This time, when the party was at its height and both Herod and most of the guests were drunk, Herodias shrewdly sent the beautiful young princess Salome to dance for her husband and the guests. After the dance, Herod drunkenly promised to give the girl whatever she asked, even half his kingdom, but Herodias had instructed Salome what gift she should demand.

"Give me John the Baptist's head on a charger," the girl said.

Herod was troubled and afraid, for if John were indeed a true prophet, he might incur the wrath of God by injuring him. But being a vain man, he was also reluctant to be shamed before the guests for not carrying out his oath. A captain was sent to behead John, and the prophet's head was duly brought to the banquet hall upon a silver charger and given to the girl. She took it to her mother, and Herodias' triumph was complete.

Of the two most eloquent voices in Israel, one was now stilled. Realizing that the danger to himself had increased, Jesus drove even harder to carry out the mission upon which he had embarked that night in Cana when he first revealed his divine power.

# 9. Parables by the Sea

*"And he taught them many things by parables."*

MARK 4:2

To NICODEMUS Jesus had been able to explain his mission in straightforward fashion, but in speaking to the hordes of people who followed him everywhere, he usually employed a different method, the parable. And certainly no teacher in history ever mastered this art so completely as did the Man of Nazareth.

A few miles north of Capernaum, like a pocket set into the rocky shore, was a natural amphitheatre opening upon the water where Jesus could speak from a boat to crowds on the land, yet be heard by all. Here he had called the four closest to him with the challenge to become "Fishers of Men," and here he spoke many of his most revealing parables. As often as not—since the Plain of Gennesaret was fertile and rich—the simple stories had to do with growing things.

"A sower went out to sow," Jesus told the crowd one day. "As he sowed, some seed fell by the wayside, and the fowl of the air came and ate it up. Some fell on stony ground, where it did not have much earth; immediately it sprang up but was scorched, so soon as the sun was high, and because it had no roots, withered away. Some fell among thorns which grew up and choked it so that it yielded no fruit. But other seed fell on good ground and yielded fruit that brought forth some thirty-, some sixty-, and a hundredfold."

When the disciples asked him later the meaning of the parable, Jesus explained: "The sower sows the word, but when those by the wayside have heard it, the Evil One comes immediately and takes away the word that was sown in their hearts. They likewise that are sown on stony ground immediately receive the word with gladness, but have no root in themselves and so endure but for a time. Afterward, when affliction or persecution arises for the word's sake, they are immediately offended. Those sown among thorns are such as hear the word, but the cares of the world and the deceitfulness of riches and lust of other things choke the word and it becomes unfruitful. But those sown on good ground are such as hear the word and receive it and bring forth fruit, some thirtyfold, some sixty-, and some an hundredfold.

"The kingdom of God," he continued, "is like a grain of mustard seed which, when it is sown in the earth, is less than all the seeds that are in the earth. But when it is sown, it grows up to become more than all herbs, and shoots out great branches so the fowl of the air may lodge under the shadow of it."

The listeners understood his meaning fully, for a grain of mustard seed was about the smallest thing they were able to see. Yet they knew that, planted in the fertile soil of the plain and properly watered and cared for, it grew into a plant taller than a man's height with spreading leaves that gave shade to animals and to men who might pause beneath it, and served the birds as a roosting place. Besides, mustard was much prized as a medicine and for seasoning food.

Continuing the parables of sowing, Jesus said, "The kingdom of heaven is like a man who sowed good seed in his field, but while men slept his enemy came and sowed tares among the wheat. When the blade of the wheat sprang up and brought forth fruit, the tares also appeared, so the servants of the household came and said to him, 'Did you not sow good seed in your field? Why then does it have tares?'

" 'An enemy has done this,' the householder said.

" 'Shall we go and gather them up?' the servants asked, but the householder said, 'No, lest while you gather up the tares, you root up also the wheat with them. Let both grow together until the harvest, and I will say to the reapers, 'Gather first the tares and bind them in bundles to be burned, then gather the wheat into my barn.' "

From this they could understand that the righteous, although they must live with the unrighteous, would in the end be separated from them and given their just reward by God.

Excitable by nature, the Galileans were soon stirred to a veritable fever heat by two events that happened close together. First, Jesus raised from the dead the daughter of Jairus, a leader in the synagogue at Capernaum, and many took the feat as certain proof that he was the Messiah. The second event was a startling miracle of quite another nature, one whose tremendous implications were quickly perceived by a group of very practical men. It happened when the Master—as his disciples called him now—sought to withdraw for a period of communion with them to a lonely and largely uninhabited area between Bethsaida and the Greek city of Hippos.

As always, the people followed, some by boat, and Jesus had only a brief period alone with those nearest him. Then, generous as always with those who sought his aid, he went down to the narrow strip of shore where the crowd had gathered, and began to heal the sick and the crippled. It had been afternoon before they arrived and when evening approached, many still remained and had no way of getting food for the evening meal, the only large meal of the entire day.

Judas of Kerioth had charge of the money donated by grateful recipients of Jesus' miraculous powers, and it was his task to provide food and lodging whenever needed for the Master and his disciples. They had brought only a few loaves and fish when they left Capernaum, however, hardly enough for the thirteen of them. When darkness approached and Jesus showed no sign of dismissing the large crowd, Simon Peter and Judas came to him.

"This is a desert place and it grows late," Peter said. "Send the people away so that they can go into the villages and buy bread, for they have nothing to eat."

"Give them food," Jesus said without stopping his work.

"Shall we buy two hundred pennyworth of bread and give them that?" Judas asked scornfully.

"Go and see how many loaves you have," Jesus ordered.

When they could count only five loaves and two fish, he commanded them to divide the people into companies of fifty and, while this was being done, took the five loaves and the two fish, blessing them and breaking them in his hands.

Whenever traveling any distance, the Galileans customarily carried a small basket into which they put whatever they found discarded in the fields or anything they bought on the way. Many among the crowd had these baskets with them, and representatives of each group now brought the empty containers to where Jesus stood. Some of the crowd had begun to laugh at the thought of dividing five loaves and two fish into enough to feed thousands of men, but they ceased when Jesus continued to break the loaves and the fish, putting them into the baskets with no sign of any limit to the supply. In the end, the entire group was fed and twelve baskets of food fragments were collected for the morning meal.

Having miraculously fed the five thousand, Jesus sent the disciples by boat to Capernaum after nightfall while he went up into the hills to pray. The wind was blowing against those in the boat, however, and they had great difficulty in rowing it. Buffeted by the waves and concerned for their safety, they were startled to see someone walking toward them upon the water, but were reassured when Jesus cried out, "Be of good cheer! It is I, do not be afraid."

"Lord, if it is you," Peter said, "bid me come to you upon the water."

"Come," Jesus told him and Peter gathered up his robe and stepped out of the boat. He took a few steps upon the surface of the water but, at the sight of the wind and the waves, his faith deserted him and he began to sink.

"Lord, save me!" Peter begged.

"O you of little faith, why did you doubt?" Jesus said sadly as he reached out his hand and lifted Peter up. When the Master entered the boat with the disciples, the waves quieted and they were able to reach land.

News of the miraculous feeding of the five thousand spread like wildfire and when Jesus went into the synagogue at Capernaum to teach on the following Sabbath, some of the group who had been fed wished to acclaim him king, certain that anyone able to feed a multitude with only a few loaves and fish would easily triumph over the power of Herod Antipas and Rome.

"You did not seek me because you saw the miracles, but because you ate of the loaves and were filled," Jesus reproved them sternly. "Do not labor for the meat which perishes, but for that meat which endures to everlasting life which the Son of Man shall give you."

"What shall we do that we might work the works of God?" they asked, revealing the real reason for their desire to make him king, the wish to enrich themselves.

"This is the work of God," Jesus told them. "That you believe him whom he has sent."

"What sign will you show that we may see and believe you?" they insisted. "Our fathers ate manna in the desert and it is written, 'He gave them bread from heaven to eat.'"

"The bread of God is he who comes down from heaven and gives life to the world," Jesus answered.

"Lord, evermore give us this bread," they begged, still not understanding his meaning.

"I am the bread of life," Jesus said then. "He that comes to me shall never hunger and he that believes in me shall never thirst. This is the will of him that sent me, that everyone who sees the Son and believes on him may have everlasting life."

They were still too concerned with worldly things to understand his meaning, however. Disappointed because he had refused to let himself be acclaimed king and use his divine power for a material purpose, many of the people began to desert him.

Jesus watched them go until only a few besides the disciples remained.

"Will you also go away?" he asked finally.

Simon Peter answered. "Lord, to whom shall we go?" the big disciple said. "You have the words of eternal life."

# 10. The Practical Sister

*"But Martha was cumbered about much serving."* LUKE 10:40

**M**ARTHA was a practical person.

And indeed it was good that she was, for the death of her parents had left her with a sister, Mary, and a brother, Lazarus, to care for. It was true that the parents had left the three fairly well fixed as far as worldly goods were concerned. They had a home in the lovely village of Bethany on the slope of the Mount of Olives beyond Jerusalem toward Jericho. And they had large land holdings in the fields and vineyards outside the village. But with Mary dreamy and impractical, loving flowers and sewing more than working in the kitchen and in the vineyard, and with Lazarus a headstrong boy who badly needed the authority of a father, Martha's work had been cut out for her.

She had done it well, too. Mary and Lazarus had sometimes rebelled against what they considered Martha's harshness, but the three had lacked for little in the years since their parents had died. The inheritance had been well cared for and their holdings were considerably more now than they had been at the parents' death. Lately, too, Lazarus had assumed most of the chores of managing them.

Martha had always run a busy household, cooking, cleaning,

and sweeping and hardly taking time even to go in to Jerusalem
for the religious festivals. She was especially busy with household chores today, for they had a very important guest, the
teacher of Nazareth who many said was the Messiah. Not that
Jesus was much trouble, but the eleven Galileans who accompanied him, and the lean and saturnine man of Kerioth called
Judas, were mighty trenchermen and there was much work to
be done preparing the evening meal.

Ever since the arrival of Jesus, Martha's ire had been rising
steadily against her younger sister. For instead of helping in the
kitchen, Mary sat at the feet of Jesus, drinking in his every
word and caring for his slightest need. The Nazarene looked
worn and tired, Martha had to admit, and from the talk she
heard as she passed the door into the main room of the house,
she judged that he had been on a long journey. They spoke of
Syro-Phoenicia, where he had healed the daughter of a Gentile
—something Martha was not sure she approved of—and mentioned Caesarea-Philippi far to the north on the slope of Mount
Hermon, much farther than Martha had ever been—or wanted
to go.

Had she been less practical, Martha might have left the work
to the servants and come in to listen to what was being said.
But she could never be sure everything was being done right
unless she put her own hands to the task. And whether Jesus
was really the Messiah—which seemed hardly possible or he
would not be here in her own house but in a palace or in the
temple—or among the itinerant teachers who thronged the road
at the time of the religious festivals, really made no difference.
He was a guest in her house and he deserved the best she could
afford.

But she deserved some help from her sister, Mary, the practical side of Martha's nature insisted. She had not even gotten to
speak a dozen words to the guest of honor since he had arrived.
Now she wiped the perspiration from her face and went to the
door.

"Lord," she said to Jesus. "Do you not care that my sister
has left me to serve alone? Bid her help me."

When Jesus looked up and smiled, Martha's weariness

seemed to evaporate as if by magic. "Martha, Martha," he said warmly. "You are careful and troubled about many things! But one thing is needful, and Mary has chosen that good part, which shall not be taken away from her."

Martha was not sure what Jesus meant; she supposed it to be that Mary was serving him by drinking in his teachings just as she herself would serve him by ministering to his physical needs. Something she overheard a disciple who was talking to Lazarus say just then seemed to confirm that assumption, for he was repeating some of Jesus' own words: "If any man will come after me, let him deny himself and take up his cross and follow me. Whoever will save his life shall lose it, and whoever will lose his life for my sake shall find it. For what does a man profit if he shall gain the whole world and lose his own soul?"

Practical Martha was content now. In serving Jesus, she thought, was she not following him? And in selecting her home as his dwelling while attending the religious festival, had he not honored her above other women?

Though he spent the night in Bethany, Jesus went into Jerusalem each day. Naturally he took his place on the so-called Porch of Solomon on the lower terrace where the other rabbis sat, each surrounded by a group of listeners questioning him concerning points of the Law. And because his reputation as a miracle-worker and teacher had spread from Galilee throughout the whole land, a large crowd always gathered quickly when word of his arrival spread.

The temple authorities had already recognized in Jesus a definite threat to their hold over the people and were seeking ways to destroy him. The simplest device seemed to be that of arousing the mob to the point where they would stone him for breaking some of the many tenets of the Mosaic Law. They thought they had found the answer when a woman was caught in adultery and brought before Jesus to be judged.

"Master," they said, pretending that theirs was a simple question. "This woman was taken in adultery, in the very act. Moses and the Law command that such be stoned. What do you say?"

Jesus recognized the double trap in the simple question. If he said the woman should be stoned, he would be going against his own teachings that the sins of the truly repentant would be forgiven. On the other hand, if he said she should be released, he could be accused of breaking the Law of Moses by condoning adultery.

Jesus did not answer at once but stopped and began to write with his finger in the dust as if he were thinking. When they repeated the question, he raised his eyes and said simply, "He that is without sin among you, let him cast the first stone at her."

The questioners were dumbfounded, for if any among them dared to claim he was without sin, he would be putting himself upon a level with God, who alone was recognized as being free from sin—an act of blasphemy in itself. Sheepishly those who had sought to trap Jesus melted away, but the chief priests were more determined now than ever that he must die.

# 11. Triumph over Death

> "He that believeth in me, though he were dead, yet shall he live."
>
> JOHN 11:25

SOME OF Jesus' most pleasant days had been spent in the home of Mary, Martha, and Lazarus in beautiful Bethany. Now a tragedy in that same household forced him to perform here, close to Jerusalem where it was certain to attract considerable notice, his greatest miracle. In saving one he loved from the grave, he set the temple authorities and the Sanhedrin unalterably against him, presaging the greater tragedy of his own death that was to follow. It happened while he was teaching in Peraea across the Jordan, where he had withdrawn to escape the attempts of the temple authorities to arrest him and bring him to trial for breaking the Law.

Spring was in sight on the hillside when Lazarus rode home one afternoon from an inspection tour of the family vineyards. Green sprigs were already appearing on the vines, clusters of violets could be found in protected spots among the rocks, and the burnet thorn on the hillsides was putting forth foliage and getting ready to bloom. There was little warmth in the drizzle foretelling the often torrential rains of the spring *moreh*, however, and Lazarus' lips were blue with cold when he rode into the yard of the house at Bethany.

Mary and Martha scolded him for staying out in the rain.

They plied him with dry clothes and hot drinks and made him sit by the fire, but their scoldings turned to fear when they saw the flush of fever rising in his cheeks. Soon he began to breathe quickly with gasps of pain that bespoke a serious illness. During the night, chills racked his body, and in the morning he was delirious, picking at the bedclothes and muttering wild things. A messenger was sent to Jesus beyond Jordan, telling him what had happened, but well before the man could reach the Master, Lazarus was dead.

The messenger found Jesus in a village beyond the Jordan and gave him Martha's message, the simple words, "Lord, he whom you love is sick." By then, however, not only had Lazarus' body been prepared for burial and placed in the crypt hewn from the rocks in the garden of their home, but the great stone, or *golel*, had been rolled in front of the tomb.

Some of the disciples were in other villages preaching and Jesus waited two days for them to join him before departing for Judea. When he announced that they were going back, there was immediate protest. "Master, the Jews sought to stone you," one of them said. "Why do you go there again?"

"If any man walk in the day he does not stumble, because he sees the light of this world," Jesus answered. "But if a man walk in the night, he stumbles because there is no light in him. Our friend Lazarus is asleep, but I go that I may awake him out of sleep."

"Lord, if he sleeps, he shall do well," one of the disciples who had hurried in from the other villages said a little sarcastically.

"Lazarus is dead," Jesus told them then, although the messenger had not known of Lazarus' death when he arrived. "And to the intent that you may believe, I am glad for your sakes that I was not there. Now let us go to him."

By the time Jesus reached Bethany, Lazarus had already been in the grave four days and the two sisters were surrounded by friends and relatives comforting them in their sorrow. When Martha heard that Jesus was coming, she went out to meet him. "Lord, if you had been here my brother would not have died," she said reproachfully.

"Your brother shall rise again," Jesus assured her.

"I know that he shall rise again in the resurrection at the last day."

Jesus took her by the hand. "I am the resurrection and the life," he said. "He that believes in me, though he were dead, yet shall he live. And whoever lives and believes in me shall never die. Do you believe this?"

"Yes, Lord. I believe you are the Christ, the Son of God which should come into the world."

"Where have you laid him?" Jesus asked her.

Mary had joined her sister now and Jesus followed the sorrowing women through the garden to the tomb. But when he ordered the stone moved, Martha protested. "Lord," she said in horror, "by this time he has been dead for four days."

"Did I not say that if you would believe you should see the glory of God?" Jesus asked her. The stone was quickly removed then and Jesus spoke into the open crypt.

"Lazarus, come forth," he called, and within the tomb the dead man stirred, stood erect, and came out, his body still wrapped in graveclothes and his face covered with a napkin.

Since Bethany was only a short walk from Jerusalem, the miraculous raising of Lazarus quickly came to the attention of the temple authorities. A hurried meeting of the Priestly Council, which largely governed the affairs of the temple, was held to decide what should be done about the Nazarene, who had now defied them in the very gates of Jerusalem. For if the miracle of raising a man who had been dead for four days became widely known, the people would be sure to acclaim Jesus the Messiah, and a full-scale revolt against Roman authority could quickly burst into flame.

Caiaphas, the crafty High Priest, gave an answer that salved the consciences of many on the Council. "It is more expedient that one man should die than that the whole nation should perish," he said, pointing out that if Jesus stirred up the Roman authorities, the vengeance of Rome would be executed upon them all. This practical argument convinced many who had favored treating Jesus as a prophet; with their support Caiaphas and the priests were able to push through a sentence of death over the protests of Nicodemus and a few others. Jesus foiled Caiaphas, however, by leaving Bethany before he could be arrested. Going into the wilderness north of Jerusalem he began to teach in the region of a city called Ephraim just south of the border of Samaria.

When the northern kingdom had been destroyed and many of its people carried into captivity, the Assyrians instituted there the same policy which had proved so effective in holding other rebellious states in check. Large numbers of foreigners were imported to repopulate the land and, as these had married with the few Israelites remaining in Samaria, they had gradually taken up the worship of Yahweh. The people of Judah, especially after they returned to Jerusalem and the homeland from the captivity in Babylon, had looked upon the Samaritans as a mixed breed to be shunned. And in retaliation, the Samaritans had built their own temple upon Mount Gerizim, claiming this to be the true sanctuary. From time to time, hatred between Jews and Samaritans had flared into actual conflict, and the latter had defiled the temple at Jerusalem on several occasions. To call a Jew a Samaritan was to curse him to his face. When, as he went about teaching, a lawyer tried to trap him, Jesus used the enmity of Jew for Samaritan to drive home a potent lesson of tolerance.

"Master," the lawyer inquired. "What shall I do to inherit eternal life?"

"What is written in the Law?" Jesus asked.

"You shall love the Lord your God with all your heart and with all your soul and with all your strength and with all your mind, and your neighbor as yourself," the lawyer answered.

"You have answered right," Jesus told him. "Do this and you shall live."

"But who is my neighbor?" the lawyer insisted.

Jesus chose to answer with a parable: "A certain man went down from Jerusalem to Jericho and fell among thieves who stripped him of his clothing, wounded him, and left him half dead. By chance a priest came that way, but when he saw the man, he passed by on the other side. Likewise a Levite looked on him and passed by on the other side. But a certain Samaritan came where the wounded man was and had compassion upon him. He bound up the wounds, pouring in oil and wine, and put the man on his own animal, and brought him to an inn, and took care of him. On the morrow when he departed, he took out two pence and gave them to the host, saying, 'Take care of him and whatever you spend more, I will repay you when I come again.' "

Jesus looked searchingly at the lawyer. "Which of these three do you think was neighbor to him that fell among thieves?"

The man could give but one answer, yet he boggled at speaking the hated word Samaritan. "He that showed mercy to him," he said lamely.

"Go and do likewise," Jesus told him.

In the midst of controversy such as swirled about him in these last climactic months of his ministry, Jesus spoke many of his deepest truths. One of these came during a warning against the hypocrisy of the Pharisees. It was an assurance to even the least among men of God's concern for them. "Are not five sparrows sold for two farthings but not one of them is forgotten before God?" he said. "Even the very hairs of your head are all numbered. Fear not therefore; you are of more value than many sparrows."

# 12. Triumph at Jerusalem

*"My house shall be called a house of prayer, but ye have made it a den of thieves."* MATTHEW 21:13

JESUS RETURNED to Bethany and the home of Martha, Mary, and Lazarus at the beginning of the Passover season that spring. As on the first occasion when he had visited Jerusalem at the age of twelve for the religious festival, he was accompanied by a festive crowd of Galileans. This time, however, they confidently expected him to announce his identity as the Messiah and seize both the government and the temple in God's name.

More than once in recent weeks, Jesus had tried to tell his followers what would really happen. "Behold, we go up to Jerusalem, and all things that are written by the prophets concerning the Son of Man shall be accomplished," he had said. "He shall be delivered to the Gentiles, and shall be mocked and spitefully treated and spit upon. They shall scourge him, and put him to death, and the third day he shall arise again."

The disciples had refused to listen, however, telling themselves the Master was speaking—as he so often did—in parables. Nor did his actions disillusion them when he made ready to enter Jerusalem, for he sent Peter and John ahead to the village of Bethphage to secure a colt upon which he could ride, fulfilling the prophecy made by Zechariah many centuries before concerning the Messiah:

"Behold thy king cometh unto thee.
He is just and having salvation;
Lowly and riding upon an ass,
And upon a colt the foal of an ass."

Who could have been expected then to believe Jesus was not announcing his real identity when he allowed the jubilant crowd to follow him on the road to Jerusalem in triumph, waving palm fronds and shouting, "Hosannah to the Son of David! Blessed is he that comes in the name of the Lord! Hosannah in the highest!"?

At the ridge marking the highest point of the Mount of Olives, with the glorious beauty of the temple and the Holy City bathed in sunlight across the Kidron valley, Jesus halted the procession. For a moment he looked out over this scene which had meant so much to him since that day in his boyhood when he had first seen it: the beauty of God's house, the walls which had protected Jerusalem from invaders, the plume of black smoke rising into the sky from the altars where the sacrifices to God were being made. Those near by saw his face torn with anguish and heard him cry:

"O Jerusalem! Jerusalem! If you had known, at least in this day, the things which belong to your peace! But now they are hid from your eyes. The day shall come when your enemy shall cast a trench about you, and compass you round, and keep you in on every side. And shall lay you even with the ground and your children with you. They shall not leave in you one stone upon another, because you knew not the time of your visitation."

Only those nearest him heard the cry, however, or knew anything unusual had happened. With the crowd still shouting and singing and spreading palm branches before him, Jesus rode into Jerusalem in triumph.

At the temple he went directly to the market located beneath the royal porch that formed the southern portico. Stalls for the sellers of animals used in the sacrifices occupied one entire wall of the Sanctuary; on the inside aisle were located the booths of the moneychangers. Because only one coin, the Tyrian shekel, was allowed in the temple, all foreign money had to be changed. And since rates of exchange were set by the moneychangers, they often took advantage of this monopoly to defraud pilgrims who thronged to pay the temple tribute required of all Jews and to make gifts. Both the moneychangers and the sellers of sacrificial animals shared a portion of their profit with the priests in return for the privilege of setting up their booths inside the temple. Thus the whole lower area of the Sanctuary had become one vast market where the shrill voices of men haggling over prices were heard far more often than prayers.

This was the busy area into which Jesus entered when he came into the temple. His face grim, he strode forward and, seizing the first cabinet containing the coins of a moneychanger, tumbled it over, spilling the contents upon the floor while he went on to overturn another table. Amidst cries of indignation and protest he turned and spoke, his voice filled with anger and sorrow.

"It is written, 'My house is a house of prayer,'" he said loudly enough for all in the market area to hear. "But you have made it a den of thieves!"

For a moment Jesus stood looking at the moneychangers and the sellers who cringed before the accusing light in his eyes. When finally he turned away toward the eastern side and Solomon's Porch, even the disciples could not fail to realize that the time of decision between him and the temple authorities had arrived. Either the priests must accept his authority or they must destroy him; there could be no other end to what had begun.

With the crowd shouting acclaim and drinking in Jesus' every word, the priestly hierarchy did not dare to arrest him openly. Instead they tried to discredit him as a teacher, hoping to weaken his popular support. While he was teaching from Solomon's Porch, a delegation from the chief priests, with some lawyers and elders in the congregation at Jerusalem, approached. "By what authority do you do these things and who gave you this authority?" they demanded.

"I will ask you one question and if you tell me, I will tell you by what authority I do these things," Jesus answered. "Whence was the baptism of John? From heaven or from men?"

The questioners were taken aback and withdrew to confer among themselves. If they said that the baptism of John came from heaven, Jesus could ask why they had not believed him. But if they said that it came from men, they would discredit John, and the people in general had held the Baptist to be a prophet. Finally they admitted they could not answer.

"Neither will I tell you by what authority I do these things," Jesus told them then.

Defeated in the attempt to discredit him on matters of their own law, the temple authorities next sought to embroil him with the Romans.

"Master, what do you think?" one of the students who called themselves Herodians, asked. "Is it lawful to give tribute to Caesar or not?"

Jesus understood the purpose of the question. If he said it was not lawful to give tribute to Caesar, he could get in trouble with the Roman authorities. On the other hand, if he supported Rome, many of the people would turn away from him.

"Why do you tempt me, you hypocrites?" he demanded scornfully. "Show me the tribute money."

When they brought him a penny he held it up and asked, "Whose is this image and superscription?"

"Caesar's," they replied.

"Render therefore to Caesar the things which are Caesar's," he told them. "And to God the things that are God's."

The Pharisees and Herodians were discomfited, but Jesus had answered them truly. In return for the benefits Rome had brought to the Israelites, things such as peace, protection from their enemies, and the building of roads, it was only fair that they should pay a tribute to Rome. But God had brought them benefits, too, in the covenant he had kept with them down through the ages. Thus it was right for men to pay tribute both to Rome and to God.

Foiled in their attempt to discredit Jesus, Caiaphas and his group now tried more forthright means to destroy him.

# 13. Betrayer's Bargain

*"They covenanted with him for thirty pieces of silver."*     MATTHEW 26:15

JUDAS OF KERIOTH was a greedy man. Worse than that, he was a thief.

Of the twelve, only he was not a Galilean. Many of the others were friends and kinsmen of the Master, so that naturally Jesus was closer to them than to the brooding Judas. And when the man of Kerioth was given the most unpleasant task of all, that of keeping the common purse, the cancer of greed and resentment which was to destroy him began to grow.

Grateful recipients of Jesus' healing miracles often made gifts, all of which went into the common purse from which Judas purchased food, clothing, and other necessities. But since Jesus was as generous with their funds as he was with his healing power, the purse was often empty, squandered—in Judas' opinion—upon beggars and thieves. From this belief it was a short step to the act of taking from the purse for his own use.

Judas had joined the twelve with great hopes that Jesus would proclaim himself king, certain that as one of the Master's trusted disciples he would occupy a high place in the kingdom with unrivaled opportunities for self-aggrandizement and perhaps for self-enrichment. His first disillusionment had come when Jesus refused to let the crowd name him king in Capernaum after the miraculous feeding of the five thousand. And now, when the days passed after the triumphal entry into Jerusalem and Jesus did not take control, Judas' resentment steadily increased.

Judas had taken Peter aside, assuming that as the one closest to Jesus and the designated leader after him, the tall fisherman would know the Master's plans. But Peter could only tell him that they must follow Jesus without question, and this did not satisfy the man of Kerioth. Judas knew the temple authorities were anxious to arrest Jesus, being held back only by the fact that large crowds were still following him everywhere in Jerusalem. And he could not forget that Jesus had predicted his own death in Jerusalem during this visit. The time was certain to come, probably just after the Passover, Judas reasoned, when Caiaphas would be sure enough of himself to take Jesus prisoner. When that happened, it was logical to suppose that the twelve would also be arrested. From this thought, it did not take the man of Kerioth long to convince himself that Jesus had failed him personally in putting his life in danger, and that he no longer owed any loyalty to the Master.

Two things happened next, crystallizing Judas' determination to betray Jesus to the authorities. One was the Master's denunciation of the Pharisees from the very steps of the temple, using language that could only drive away the support of the one group who could hold the priests in check and save him from destruction if he refused to use divine power.

"Woe unto you, scribes and Pharisees, hypocrites!" Jesus cried. "For you shut up the kingdom of heaven against men; you neither go in yourselves nor suffer them that are entering to go in. Hypocrites! You pay tithe of mint and cummin but have omitted the weightier matters of the Law—judgment, mercy, and faith. You make clean the outside of the cup and platter, but within they are full of extortion and excess. You blind Pharisees! First cleanse that which is within the cup and the platter so that the outside of them may be clean also. You are like whited sepulchers which indeed appear beautiful outwardly, but are full of dead men's bones and all uncleanness.

You serpents! You generation of vipers! How can you escape the damnation of hell?"

The second thing occurred when Jesus attended a dinner in Bethany given by a man named Simon who had been cured of leprosy. The house was filled with guests, and as they reclined at the table, Mary, the sister of Lazarus and Martha, came in with a small alabaster box of a precious and very expensive ointment made from spikenard. The women were coming and going with the serving, so no one noticed Mary as she approached Jesus. But when she opened the jar and, pouring the ointment into her hand, knelt and began to anoint his feet, the rich fragrance of the spikenard quickly permeated every corner of the room, bringing the conversation to a halt. In the silence, Mary took down the lustrous masses of her hair and wiped the Master's feet, while an indrawn sigh of amazement came from the guests.

Judas was the first to speak and, in his anger at what he could only consider waste, he overreached himself. "Why was this ointment not sold for three hundred pence and given to the poor?" he demanded.

A murmur of agreement rose from some of the guests, but Jesus silenced them. "Let her alone," he said sharply. "She has kept this against the day of my burial. The poor you have with you always, but me you will not always have."

Jesus had spoken directly to Judas, publicly reproving him and, in Judas' mind, shaming him for making what had been only a reasonable protest. But more than that, the sharpness of Jesus' tone made Judas wonder if the Master did not know of his thefts from the common purse. In any event, he felt a surge of anger and indignation at being thus publicly reprimanded and, rising to his feet, plunged from the room. Nor did he hesitate outside, but took the road to Jerusalem though it was night. There he demanded, and was given, an immediate audience with the High Priest.

When Judas came out of Caiaphas's palace, the details of his act of betrayal had been arranged. For a reward of thirty pieces of silver—the price of a common slave contemptuously set by

Caiaphas—he had agreed to lead the agents of the Hight Priest to a spot where Jesus could be seized with only his disciples around him and no crowds to interfere.

The opportunity to carry out his part of the betrayal came to Judas sooner than he expected. Jesus had made it his custom each evening to leave Jerusalem—where he might have been arrested at night—and return to Bethany where he was surrounded by friends. But on the night of the Passover, he chose to eat the sacred meal in Jerusalem.

Peter and John had been sent into the city early on the morning of the feast day to prepare for the paschal supper at the home of Mary, mother of John Mark, and aunt of Barnabas, all of them devoted followers of the Master. In the upper room while they were preparing to eat, the disciples began to argue among themselves as to who should occupy the place of honor, but Jesus silenced them.

"He that is greatest among you, let him be as the youngest," he told them. "And he that is chief, as he who serves."

While they were eating, Jesus said, "I do not speak of you all, for I know whom I have chosen. But that the scriptures may be fulfilled, he that eats bread with me has lifted up his heel against me. Truly I say to you that one of you shall betray me."

The disciples began to clamor for the name of the betrayer, but Jesus only picked up a piece of bread and dipped it in gravy to form what was called the sop. Handing it to Judas, he said in a low voice which only a few of the disciples could hear, "It is he to whom I shall give the sop." Then he spoke directly to Judas: "That which you do, do quickly."

The taste of the bread was suddenly bitter in Judas' mouth. Pushing himself away from the table, he left the room, but since he carried the purse and often went out to purchase supplies that were needed from time to time, no one particularly noticed his absence. Jesus, however, knew Judas had gone to notify the Hight Priest that he was in Jerusalem accompanied only by the twelve and could be taken in the night without stirring up the crowds.

"Children, yet a little time will I be with you," he told the disciples. "So now I give a new commandment to you, that you love one another as I have loved you. By this shall men know that you are my disciples, if you have love one for another."

"Lord, where are you going?" Simon Peter asked, still not comprehending what Jesus had been telling them throughout the past several months.

"Where I go you cannot follow me now," Jesus told Peter. "But you shall follow me afterwards."

The meal was nearly at an end when Jesus took a piece of bread in his hand and began to break it into pieces. "Take, eat, this is my body which is given for you," he told them. "Do this in remembrance of me."

When they had each eaten a piece of bread—although without as yet fully realizing its significance—he took a cup of wine and gave it to them to drink, saying, "This cup is the new covenant in my blood which is shed for you."

The Passover ceremony always ended with the singing of a hymn. Its strains were floating over the city from thousands of throats when Jesus and his disciples made their way from the upper room in Jerusalem and started across the Kidron valley toward the beautiful garden on the slopes of the Mount of Olives called Gethsemane, a place where he had often gone to pray during his visits in Jerusalem. Leaving the disciples at the entrance to the garden, he took Peter, James, and John farther into the garden and there, a little distance from the three, prostrated himself in prayer.

"O Father, if it be possible let this cup pass from me," he said humbly. "Nevertheless, not as I will but as you will."

After a while Jesus returned to where he had left the three and found them asleep. "Could you not watch one hour?" he asked sadly. "Watch and pray lest you enter into temptation. The spirit truly is ready, but the flesh is weak."

Jesus went away to pray again and when he came back a little while later, he found the three asleep again. "Sleep on now and take your rest," he told them. "It is enough, the hour is come. Behold the Son of Man is betrayed into the hands of sinners." Then his voice rose. "Rise up, let us go! He that betrays me is at hand!"

Already the sound of marching soldiers had broken the stillness of the garden. Judas had done his work well; only Peter tried to resist when the temple guard and a detail from the Roman garrison came to arrest Jesus, but he was quickly disarmed and fled after the others. Alone, Jesus received the embrace of Judas identifying him in the final act of betrayal, and was led down the road in fetters to be judged by men who had already ordered his death.

Inside the palace of the Hight Priest, a small portion of the Sanhedrin, hurriedly summoned by Caiaphas, met for the final act of condemnation. The witnesses had been carefully coached to swear that Jesus had blasphemed against the temple and against God. When he refused even to answer their lying charges, Caiaphas demanded furiously, "Are you the Christ, the Son of the Blessed?"

Jesus spoke then for the first time since he had been brought to the palace a prisoner: "I am. And you shall see the Son of Man sitting on the right hand of power and coming in the clouds of heaven."

"Blasphemy!" the listeners cried self-righteously, and the final sentence of death was passed.

Judas, waiting at the edge of the crowd that filled the palace courtyard, saw the man he had betrayed being led away for approval of the sentence of death by the Roman procurator. His eyes met those of the Master and, stricken by an overpowering sense of guilt, he turned away. The thirty pieces of silver in the purse at his girdle grew heavier and heavier as he walked, while what was left of good in him spoke with a louder and louder voice. Finally, tormented beyond bearing by his guilt, he sought out a priest and gave him the silver but the act brought him no relief from the voice of conscience.

Stumbling along the road to Bethany, instinctively trying to get as far as he could from what he knew would happen next, Judas came to where a tree grew from the rocky hillside and overhung the path. Convinced now that he could expiate in only one way—with his own life—the crime of having betrayed the man who had loved him, Judas climbed upon the rocks and, removing the girdle wound about his waist, secured one end to the limb and the other about his own neck.

With a despairing cry, he who had betrayed the Son of God stepped off the rock, but his punishment was not yet complete. The weight of his body at the end of the improvised rope failed to snap his neck as he had intended. Instead, the noose suddenly drew tight and, struggling desperately with his feet almost touching the ground, Judas slowly and painfully choked to death.

# 14. Pilate's Guilt

> "I am innocent of the blood of this just person."  MATTHEW 27:24

**P**ONTIUS PILATE, procurator of Judas, had not slept well. He did not like Jerusalem, where he had suffered a humiliating defeat when he had ordered the imperial standards brought into the Holy City on his accession to the governorship, seeking to impress the people of this benighted land with the might and glory of Rome. Pious Jews had been horrified at the insult to their God, who forbade any graven image, and a delegation of their leaders had walked across the hills to Caesarea to protest, baring their necks to the sword rather than yield. Pilate had been forced to give in and remove the hated emblems, but he had never overcome his resentment. In time he learned to handle these contentious people—or so he thought—by letting the priestly hierarchy have its way so it would be loyal to him. But he never felt really secure in Jerusalem, knowing that the intense nationalistic fervor of the Jews might explode into violence at any time.

The most dangerous period of all was the Passover when the city teemed with people, and Pilate had made it his business to be at Jerusalem every spring with extra legionnaires from Caesarea. He'd be happy when he was finished with this chore and could return to Herod Antipas' lovely place at Jericho where it was always warm at this time of year and pleasant company could be expected.

All through the night, after the singing of the *hallel* that marked the end of the Passover supper, the city had been alive with furtive goings and comings, as if some mischief were afoot. And since Pilate knew he could count on any disturbance in Jerusalem to mean trouble for him, he had lain awake, wondering when the first clash would come. Once, hearing the sound of marching men, he'd even considered turning out the guard and sending them through the sleeping city to see what was happening. But that, he knew, would only create a commotion, and with the festival so nearly over and the people about ready to start streaming out of the city, he decided to leave well enough alone.

Then there had been that mysterious request from Caiaphas for a detail of soldiers to supplement the regular temple police. The High Priest had justified the request by the need to be sure that no group of Galileans in Jerusalem for the Passover created a disturbance. It was true that Galileans caused more trouble at the religious festivals than all others put together, but Pilate suspected that this particular request might have more behind it than was apparent, for he knew the wily Caiaphas well by now. The detail of soldiers had not returned to the Antonia yet, he was sure, and he resolved to demand an explanation from the High Priest the first thing in the morning as to just how they had been used.

The faint glow of dawn was already gilding the Mount of Olives when Pilate heard the clank of marching feet below, and stepped out on the balcony of his suite in the Antonia. He saw the column approaching the fortress and heard the challenge of the guard at the gate. Behind them the sound of excited jabbering rising on the cool night air told him that some of the people were out even this early, but he could not as yet see whether they were merely following the soldiers or were pursuing them.

The gate of the court around which the palace was built was opened by the guard and, as the detail of legionnaires marched in, Pilate saw that a number of temple guards accompanied them, distinguishable by their more colorful dress and the burly form of Abiathar, the captain, at their head. Sure now that there was trouble, Pilate stepped inside the suite and began to put on his toga. By the time he was dressed, the centurion in charge of the guard was knocking at his door.

"What is it, Pelonius?" he called.

"A prisoner sent from the Sanhedrin, sir. He has been condemned to death and they wish your approval."

"Take him to the audience chamber."

"The Jews who accuse him will not come into the fortress, sir," Pelonius said.

Pilate curbed his anger at the stupidity of people who considered themselves defiled even by entering a Roman building. For a moment he considered refusing to judge the prisoner if they did not give in, but the difficult time was so nearly over and, if nothing more important stood between him and another year of peace than the execution of some poor wretch for disobeying the strict religious laws of the Jews, he could afford to meet them half way.

"Bring them into the court," Pilate directed. "I will be there in a moment."

Pilate deliberately extended the moment considerably—to teach a lesson to the Jews—before appearing in the court. Pelonius, he noted, had everything well under control; guards stood on either side of the prisoner who had obviously been beaten and cuffed about. But then that was characteristic of what was called justice among these excitable people.

That this, however, was no groveling wretch hoping for a reprieve from the death by stoning that so delighted the crowd, Pilate saw at once. Slender, clear-eyed, almost regal in his bearing, the prisoner faced the Roman governor more like an equal—or even a superior—than like a condemned man whose death Pilate alone could now prevent.

A group of priests and members of the Sanhedrin stood behind the prisoner, whose name Pelonius read from a scroll as Jesus of Nazareth. They were careful to stand so that the shadow of the Antonia, just now taking form in the early morning sunlight, did not fall upon them, since that in their eyes would have been a defilement.

"Of what crime is this man accused?" the governor demanded coldly.

One of the priests spoke. "He claims to be King of the Jews, noble Pilate."

"The Jews have no king! Rome rules here!"

"He blasphemes by saying he is the Son of God."

"Take him and judge him according to your law, then."

"The Sanhedrin has already sentenced this man," the priest insisted. "But it is not lawful for us to put anyone to death."

Pilate turned somber eyes upon Jesus. "Are you the King of the Jews?" he asked. There was no mockery in his voice; rather it held a tone almost of respect, for, being himself a soldier, he recognized a brave man who showed no fear at facing death.

"Do you say this of yourself?" Jesus asked him, "Or did others tell it to you concerning me?"

Pilate shrugged. "Am I a Jew? Your own nation and the chief priests have delivered you to me. What have you done?"

"My kingdom is not of this world," Jesus answered. "If my kingdom were of this world, then my servants would fight."

"Are you a king then?" Pilate insisted.

"To this end I was born and came into the world," Jesus said quietly, "that I should bear witness to the truth."

Ordinarily Pilate would hardly have glanced twice at a prisoner sent by the Sanhedrin for sentencing, but there was something oddly compelling about this man. He was tempted to take him inside the palace and discuss with him this question of truth, for Pilate, too, was interested in matters of philosophy. But he knew quite well what an outcry the Sanhedrin would make were he to reverse one of their sentences. Jealous of any power besides their own, they would carry the affair to Rome and, with the end of his tenure of office as procurator almost in sight, Pilate wanted no adverse reports going to the Emperor Tiberius. At the same time, the prisoner obviously was no ordinary malefactor and deserved more consideration than a simple ratification of the sentence passed by the Sanhedrin.

Then Pilate remembered something that seemed to offer a way out of this difficulty. Pelonius had called the man Jesus of Nazareth, which meant that his home was in Galilee; and Herod Antipas, tetrarch of Galilee, was in Jerusalem for the Passover. "I find no fault in him," Pilate told the Sanhedrists. "Take him to Herod; a man should be judged by his own ruler."

The priest who was the spokesman started to protest, but Pilate waved him off and went inside the palace, calling the servants to bring him the morning meal. He had barely finished eating, however, when Pelonius returned with word that the prisoner was again in the courtyard, sent back by Herod who refused to take jurisdiction over him. This time, Pelonius added, the angry Sanhedrists were demanding the death of the condemned man without further delay.

When Pilate stepped out into the open court again, he saw that Herod had been playing one of his jokes. The Nazarene now wore one of the tetrarch's own purple robes, and purple sandals had been laced on his feet. By refusing to judge the prisoner, and flauntingly arraying him in royal robes, Herod was obviously telling Pilate that this was a Roman matter now, a case of rebellion against the empire for which he alone must take the responsibility. And to make the situation worse, a considerable crowd of jeering rabble, the very dregs of Jerusalem, now followed the slender man in the purple robe. Pilate could not get out of his mind the odd conviction that the Nazarene wore the robe with far more authority and kingly bearing than Herod ever had, and, angry at Herod for placing him in such position, he vented his spleen upon the Sanhedrists.

"You have brought this man before me as one who perverts the people," he said sharply. "I have examined him before you and found no fault in him concerning the things of which you accuse him, and neither has Herod. I will therefore chastise him and release him."

"Noble Pilate!" the leader of the priests said in a loud voice. "We have a custom that on this day, you release one prisoner to us. Will you follow that custom again at this season?"

Pilate looked at him narrowly, sure that more was behind the request than the simple custom he had followed, like most

governors, of freeing an important prisoner during occasions of
particular public interest.

"Do you wish me to release the King of the Jews?" he asked.

"Release Barabbas," the priest said promptly and, as if this
were the signal for which they had been coached, the rabble
began to shout, "Release Barabbas! Give us Barabbas!"

Pilate saw a way out of the dilemma in which he had been
placed, the choice between on one hand stirring up the Sanhedrin and perhaps having a protest sent to Rome, and on the
other sentencing a man who seemed to be innocent. Barabbas
was a hardened criminal, a known murderer and revolutionary.
If the crowd insisted upon releasing him instead of the Nazarene, the responsibility for what happened to Jesus of Nazareth
would not be Pilate's, and the blood of an innocent man would
not be upon his conscience. While he was considering, a priest
heading the delegation from the Sanhedrin demanding the
death sentence added shrewdly, "If you let this man go, you
are not Caesar's friend."

The threat that the Jewish court would go over his head to
Rome was in the open now; the priest's words could mean
nothing else, and Pilate was suddenly afraid. Another tenure of
office in this land he hated would be the end of his career, he
was sure. And being intensely ambitious, he could let nothing
interfere at this point.

"What shall I do with Jesus who is called the Christ?" the
governor demanded lamely, and the answer he expected came
back to him.

"Crucify him!" the crowd shouted. "Crucify him!"

Crucifixion was the Roman form of execution, while stoning
was the Jewish. The Sanhedrists, abetted by Herod, had shrewdly
maneuvered Pilate into a position where it was Rome who
must destroy the man who had stood through all this without
cringing or begging.

"Shall I crucify your king?" Pilate asked again but only as a
sop to his conscience.

"We have no king but Caesar!" the people shouted—by their
own words committing the sin of blasphemy.

"Bring me a bowl of water," Pilate called to a servant. When it came, he ceremonially washed his hands and dried them upon a towel, holding them out for all the world to see. "I am innocent of the blood of this just person," he told them. "See you to it."

"His blood be upon us and on our children," the crowd shouted.

"Release Barabbas," Pilate ordered the centurion in charge. "And give the Nazarene to them to be crucified."

He turned away without meeting the eyes of the man he had refused to save from death because he was afraid to risk his own career by insisting upon the one thing that Roman law guaranteed to even the least person in the empire—absolute justice.

In his apartment Pilate shivered as he heard the animal-baying of the crowd receding down the hill upon which the Antonia stood. From the balcony he could see the Nazarene in their midst, a crown of thorns so pressed upon his forehead that the blood dripped down his face, and bearing on his shoulders the heavy crossbeam or *patibulum* to which his arms would be secured. The procession swirled through the streets toward the gate leading to Golgotha, the "Place of the Skull," so named not because it was a favorite place for execution but from the appearance of the rocky crest. There seemed to be difficulty for a moment and when the procession got under way again, Pilate saw that a stronger figure seemed to be bearing the patibulum as they swept on toward the gate leading to the place of execution.

While the governor watched, the procession wound its way up the hill to where three tall poles lay upon the ground. Shortly the center one with the patibulum now attached—though at that distance he could not make out the identity of the man nailed to it—rose into the air. Familiar with many another crucifixion, he knew the agony that would strike through the body of the victim when the bottom of the upright was dropped into the deep hole, and the slow, tortured death that would follow.

It was only a few hours afterward—though to guilty, brooding Pilate it seemed an eternity—before a servant brought word that the merchant, Joseph of Arimathea, wished to speak to the governor. Joseph was a leading businessman of Jerusalem and Pilate greeted him courteously.

"I wish to claim the body of Jesus of Nazareth," Joseph said respectfully.

"Is he dead already?" Pilate was surprised, for victims of crucifixion sometimes hung on the cross for days, the whole purpose of the method being to cause a lingering and extremely painful death.

"Just now," the merchant confirmed. "We wish to put his body in the tomb in my garden before the Sabbath begins at sunset."

"Take it down," Pilate said. "Tell Pelonius you have my permission."

Joseph left at once, and as he closed the curtains shutting off the balcony, Pilate thought that even the elements seemed to be in mourning for the dead man. A dark cloud hung over the city, and it was almost as if night had already fallen when a jagged bolt of lightning struck, so close that it seemed to touch the temple itself. Pilate cringed, and shouted for the servants to pull the other curtains and bring wine.

"If Jesus of Nazareth were really the Son of God," the faint voice of conscience said in his heart, "perhaps God is now wreaking his vengeance upon the man who could have saved him and failed."

The lightning flashed again, so near that its brilliance penetrated even the drawn curtains, illumining the apartment with an eerie glow and leaving the sharp, acrid odor in the air that always followed a bolt striking near-by.

"Wine! Wine!" Pilate shouted to the servants. But when the filled cup was given him, his hands shook so badly that some of the wine spilled over. Pilate's eyes dilated with fright as he stared at his hands—for the color seemed to be no longer that of wine, but of blood.

"The basin!" he screamed. "Bring me water in a basin!" But deep in his heart Pilate knew he could never wash away the stain of an innocent man's blood. Worst of all, he would never know whether or not he had allowed the Son of God to go to his death, thus damning himself for all eternity.

# 15. The Testing of Peter

*"Woman, I know him not."*

O F ALL THE TWELVE, it had been from the first the bond
between Simon Peter, the hulking, impetuous fisherman, and Jesus that was the closest. On the slopes of
Mount Hermon near Caesarea Philippi, when Jesus had asked
the disciples who they considered him to be, Peter alone had
given the true answer: "You are the Christ, the son of the
living God."

"Blessed are you, Simon, son of Jonas," Jesus had told Peter
then. "For flesh and blood did not reveal it to you but my
father which is in heaven. Upon this rock I will build my
church, and the gates of hell shall not prevail against it."

After that Peter had been the acknowledged leader of the
disciples, even though Salome, wife of Zebedee and mother of
James and John, had asked during the final trip to Jerusalem
that her sons be given the places of honor in Christ's kingdom,
on his right and on his left hand. Jesus had warned them all at
the time against striving for honor among themselves, saying:
"Whoever will be great among you, let him be your minister.
And whoever will be chief among you, let him be your servant,
even as the Son of Man came not to be ministered to but to
minister, and to give his life a ransom for many."

286

None of them had understood Jesus' meaning then; nor did Peter understand it when, in Jerusalem during the paschal supper there in the upper room at the home of Mary, the mother of Mark, Jesus had said: "You shall seek me, but where I go you cannot come."

"Lord, where are you going?" Peter had asked.

"Where I go you cannot follow me now," Jesus answered. "But you shall follow me afterward."

"Why cannot I follow you now?" Peter had insisted, distressed that Jesus should speak of leaving him behind. "I will lay down my life for your sake."

"Will you lay down your life for my sake?" Jesus had asked him in a melancholy voice. "Truly I say to you, the cock shall not crow until you have denied me three times."

Peter had been a little offended by the suggestion that he might ever deny the Master. And when the soldiers had come to arrest Jesus in the Garden of Gethsemane shortly after midnight, he had impetuously seized one of the swords and tried to resist. The soldier he attacked parried his stroke easily, so he had succeeded only in slicing off the ear of one of the bystanders. But when he saw a sword raised to thrust him through for daring to resist, the suddenly panic-stricken Peter had broken loose from the crowd and rushed into the underbrush. There, as he stumbled around in a daze, Mark found him, and they went together to the palace of the High Priest where Jesus had been taken.

The night was cold and the bystanders had built a fire in the courtyard while they waited to see what would happen to the prisoner. As Peter and Mark approached the fire, a servant girl from the palace looked up at the big man curiously. "You were with Jesus of Galilee!" she accused him. But Peter, seized again with the terror that had overtaken him when Jesus was arrested, cried: "I know not what you say," and moved to another part of the court. There he was seen by another woman who also accused him of being with Jesus of Nazareth, but Peter again denied it, shouting desperately, "I do not know the man."

For a while they had let him alone, then a merchant who

heard him speak to some of the others said, "Surely you are one of them. Your speech betrays you."

"I know not the man!" Peter shouted with a curse, and started to leave the courtyard, but he was brought up short by a familiar sound, the crowing of a cock announcing the coming of dawn. Only then did he remember the words Jesus had spoken to him but a few hours before at their last supper: "Before the cock crows this night, you shall deny me thrice."

Overcome with grief and shame, Peter let Mark lead him to his house and hid there, sure that the soldiers would come to arrest him at any moment. It was much later that the youth burst in with the news that Jesus had been crucified between two thieves on the hill of Golgotha.

"What of the others?" Peter asked, his voice hoarse with grief and shame.

"The Master gave John charge of his mother," Mark told him. "Some of the women wait at the foot of the cross; the rest have gone away."

Peter began to lace on his sandals. "You will be recognized if you go out," Mark protested. "You were the only one to resist last night."

"I am going to the hill and demand that I be crucified beside Jesus," Peter said quietly, voicing a resolve that had come to him with the news of the Master's execution. "They can put me with my head down, for I deserve no more."

Mark still protested, but Peter was insistent and left the house, even though the black storm cloud still hung over the city and lightning cracked down every few moments. The crowd had been driven away by the storm and no one molested him as he climbed to the summit of Golgotha where the crosses were placed. Two men hung on either side, but the center upright was now empty.

"Did you know him?" a voice said beside him, and Peter turned to see a Roman officer.

"I knew him and loved him," Peter said with a sob.

"He must have trusted you; now I remember seeing you once here in the city, walking just behind him."

"Nail me to that," Peter begged, pointing to the blood-stained patibulum lying at the foot of the empty upright. "And let me die here."

The centurion shook his head. "From the cross the Nazarene forgave those who persecuted him. You cannot serve him now by sacrificing yourself."

Peter looked again at the empty upright and then down at the patibulum with the bloodstains from the nail wounds still damp upon the surface of the wood. Once again he seemed to hear a familiar, gentle voice saying, "You are Peter. Upon this rock I will build my church and the gates of hell shall not prevail against it." Now, at last, with the Master gone, Peter understood what his own particular task would be.

"Where did they take his body?" he asked the centurion.

"Joseph of Arimathea is laying the Nazarene in his own tomb. But be careful; Caiaphas asked Pilate for a guard to keep the tomb sealed."

A sorrowing little band gathered at Joseph's garden to keep the death watch: a few women, several of the disciples—and Peter. But this was not the same Peter who had denied Jesus in the courtyard the night before, the Peter who had hidden in Mark's home. His face still ravaged by grief, his eyes filled with pain, the tall disciple was now a rock, their acknowledged leader to whom they all instinctively came for strength. And when Mary of Magdala—having visited the tomb early on the morning the third day to prepare Jesus for burial, since they had not been able to make the normal preparations before the sabbath—came running with the news that his body had been taken from the sepulcher, Peter was first at the tomb.

Only one explanation seemed to fit the enigma of the empty crypt at first; Caiaphas must have stolen Jesus' body away lest the disciples claim that he had arisen from the dead. But while Peter was awakening the others to tell them of this unexpected turn of events, Mary came again crying out, "Jesus is risen! Jesus is risen! I have seen the Master!"

Peter's first reaction was that Mary's excitement had led her to imagine the presence of Jesus, for after all, she had been healed of epileptic seizures by the Master. But when she repeated Jesus' own words: "Go to my disciples and say to them,

'I ascend to my Father and to your Father and to my God and your God,'" he dared to believe Jesus had indeed fulfilled his promise that on the third day he would arise from the dead.

In the weeks that followed, Jesus appeared to a number of the disciples and, with word spreading rapidly that he had risen from the dead, the authorities at Jerusalem decided to seize those who could testify to having seen him. The disciples, being Galileans, decided to return to Galilee where they would feel safer than in the region where Jesus had been condemned and crucified.

So it was that Peter returned to his fishing on the Sea of Galilee. But one morning when he and some of the others were rowing back empty-handed, he saw a man standing there on the shore.

"Children, have you any meat?" the man asked and, not recognizing Jesus, they answered, "No."

"Cast the net on the right side of the ship," the man told them and when they obeyed, it was so full of fish that they were not able to draw it in. And Peter, remembering how almost exactly this same thing had happened on the day Jesus had called him, realized the identity of the stranger. "It is the Lord!" he cried joyfully, and leaped from the ship to help drag the net ashore where Jesus stood.

"Bring the fish you have caught," Jesus commanded, and Peter picked out a number of them from the net. There on the shore they cooked some of the fish and ate them together while Jesus taught them once again as he had so many times before.

"Simon, son of Jonas," he said. "Do you love me more than these?"

"Yes, Lord, you know that I love you," Simon said, and Jesus replied, "Feed my lambs."

"Simon, son of Jonas, do you love me?" Jesus asked the tall fisherman a second time.

"Yes, Lord, you know that I love you," Simon answered, and again Jesus said, "Feed my sheep."

When Jesus said the third time, "Simon, son of Jonas, do you love me?" Peter was a little grieved.

"Lord, you know all things," he protested. "You know that I love you."

"Feed my sheep," Jesus said once again, and then he added, "Follow me."

Jesus had used the same words on this very shore only a little more than two years before. Peter understood at last why the Master had asked him to feed the sheep and knew the task that now lay before them all.

For forty days Jesus remained near those he had loved. Then, when they went to Jerusalem and Bethany to continue preaching the word there, he appeared before them a last time and, lifting up his hands and blessing them, disappeared into heaven while they watched.

As they were sorrowing for the Master, two men in white garments appeared. "You men of Galilee, why do you stand looking up into heaven?" they asked. "Jesus who was received into heaven shall come again in the same manner."

Sure now that the beloved Master would fulfill his promise to return, the disciples began to preach everywhere the glad tidings which had been given them, that Jesus had risen from the dead, had joined his Father in heaven as he had promised, and would one day come to lead them once again.

Since Judas was dead, the disciples chose Matthias, or Matthew, to bring their number up to twelve, and began to preach with a new inspiration. None could equal Simon Peter in eloquence, however, for it seemed that—as Elijah had given his mantle to Elisha when he was taken up into heaven—the mantle of Jesus had fallen upon the big disciple.

"You men of Israel, hear these words," Peter told a great audience on the day of Pentecost. "You have crucified and slain Jesus of Nazareth, a man approved of God among you by miracles and wonders and signs. Him God has raised up, having loosed the pains of death because it was not possible that he should be held by it. Concerning him, David said, 'I foresaw the Lord always before my face, for he is on my right hand, that I should not be moved. Therefore my heart rejoiced and my tongue was glad. Moreover also, my flesh shall rest in hope, because you will not leave my soul in hell, neither will you suffer your Holy One to see corruption. You have made known to me the ways of life; you shall make me full of joy with your countenance.'

"Men and brethren," Peter continued. "Let me speak freely to you concerning the patriarch David who is both dead and buried, for his sepulcher is known to us this day. Being a prophet and knowing God had sworn with an oath that from the fruit of his loins he would raise up Christ to sit on his throne, he spoke of the resurrection of Christ, that his soul was not left in hell, neither did his flesh see corruption. This Jesus God has raised up, whereof we all are witnesses. Therefore being exalted by the right hand of God and having received of the Father the promise of the Holy Spirit, he has shed forth this which you now see and hear and has let all the house of Israel know assuredly that God has made that same Jesus, whom you have crucified, both Lord and Christ."

"What shall we do?" the people begged him, as they had asked John the Baptist.

"Repent and be baptized in the name of Jesus Christ for the remission of sins and you shall receive the gift of the Holy Spirit," Peter told them. "For the promise is to you and your children and to all that are afar off, even as many as the Lord our God shall call. Save yourselves from this untoward generation."

This was the Peter upon whom had fallen the mantle of Jesus, speaking in a voice so moving and eloquent that on one day alone, three thousand people were added to the fellowship of those who followed Jesus. Fired with his zeal, the other disciples also carried throughout the land the good news that God had renewed the ancient covenant by sending his Son to earth and raising him from the dead that all might witness his power to triumph over death.

Soon word of a new covenant would be preached, a covenant not simply for the Hebrews but for all the world. News of it was brought by another eloquent voice, that of a tentmaker from Tarsus whose name was Saul.

# V. The Armor of God

"Put on the whole armour of God,
that ye may be able to stand against
the wiles of the devil."

EPHESIANS 6:11

# 1. The First Martyr

*"And Stephen, full of faith and power, did great wonders and miracles among the people."*  ACTS 6:8

ONCE AGAIN the great Sanhedrin had been called to sentence a man to death. This, however, was a regularly appointed meeting of the Jewish high court, not the hurried, furtive conclave of only a small portion of its members which had illegally condemned Jesus of Nazareth. Caiaphas, the High Priest, presided and the members—mostly bearded men of considerable age, for the Hebrews believed wisdom increased steadily with advancing years—were ranged behind a long table at one end of a room in the palace of the Sanhedrin near the Sanctuary area.

Two men stood out from all others in the room. One was short and broad-shouldered, with a majestic, almost godlike head. His mouth was wide and mobile, his cheekbones broad, and his deep-set eyes burned with intelligence and a fanatic zeal. He was not one of the court itself but stood to one side, near the clerks who kept the records. Obviousy highly respected by the court, he conferred from time to time with the officer charged with prosecuting the prisoner standing manacled before the tribunal.

His name was Saul of Tarsus.

The prisoner was taller than Saul, his body wiry and his

face clean-cut with almost Grecian features. His eyes, too,
burned, but with love and compassion even for those who had
the power to sentence him to death.

His name was Stephen.

In one of his last appearances to the disciples, Jesus had told
them to return to Jerusalem and preach to all nations repentance
and forgiveness of sins, the doctrines he had taught while on
earth. In the Holy City, they had received, at a climactic miracle
during Pentecost, some six or seven weeks after the crucifixion,
the Holy Spirit which Jesus promised would come upon them.

At first disciples and converts had lived together, sharing
everything in the same way that Jesus and the disciples had
shared a common purse. But soon minor difficulties arose. In
the early church, all converts were required to sell their property
and give it into the common fund. A man named Ananias and
his wife Sapphira had witheld part of their possessions, however, and had suffered death for their sin.

On another occasion, the authorities had tried to hold John
and Peter in prison, but had been forestalled when one of the
leading teachers of Jerusalem, a member of the Sanhedrin
named Gamaliel, advised caution. If the power which the followers of Jesus seemed to possess did indeed come from heaven,
Gamaliel warned the high court, the people in Jerusalem could
do nothing against them; if it did not, the disciples would fail of
their own accord.

The teachings of Jesus, as expounded by Peter and the others,
had a particular appeal for Jews whose ways of thought had
been considerably influenced by the Greek customs prevalent
in other parts of the world. These so-called Hellenists were
much more liberal in thought and in their worship than were
the other inhabitants of Jerusalem, and the Sadducees of the
priesthood were particularly concerned when more and more of
them joined the new faith. In fact, so many of the Hellenist
Jews came to follow Jesus that a part of its assembly came to be
known by the Greek word, *Ecclesia*—or church—and eventually
the whole body adopted that designation.

The *Ecclesia*, composed of those who were baptized as followers of Jesus' doctrines, had as yet made no attempt to break

away from the temple. Its teachers spoke from Solomon's Porch, as did the other teachers of Israel, and were accepted generally as another sect within the faith, like the Pharisees or the Essenes. In time it became impossible for the disciples themselves to carry on all the administrative duties of looking after the church as well as the teaching and, since so many of the new converts were from among the Grecian Jews, a group of men were elected to serve as assistants or deacons in the routine affairs of the community. Stephen had been chosen for this honor along with Philip, Prochorus, Nicanor, Timon, Parmenas, and Nicolas. Barnabas, the cousin of John Mark—in whose mother's home Jesus and the disciples had eaten the last Passover supper—was also active in this community, having sold all of his goods and given them to the church.

Crowds soon flocked to hear the fiery preaching of Stephen and witness the miracles he accomplished. But when many people began to leave the Jerusalem synagogues and go over to the new sect, the irate leaders had Stephen brought before the Sanhedrin. There, as had been the case with Jesus, hired men perjured themselves to testify against him.

"We heard him speak blasphemous words against Moses and against God," one avowed.

"This man does not cease to speak blasphemous words against this holy place and the Law," another testified.

"We have heard him say that Jesus of Nazareth shall destroy the temple and change the customs Moses delivered to us," another added. One by one the witnesses piled up their false testimony, crowning it with the one statement calculated to prejudice the minds of the Sanhedrin against Stephen more than any other, the accusation that he had been heard preaching that Jesus of Nazareth was King of the Jews.

As the list of charges mounted, Saul nodded in agreement from time to time, obviously approving everything that was being done. Finally, when the list of witnesses had been exhausted, Caiaphas turned to Stephen.

"Are these things true?" he demanded.

Stephen's voice was firm as he addressed the Sanhedrin, but he still gave them the courtesy and reverence due the highest court in Israel from every Jew. "Men, brethren, and fathers, hearken," he began. "The God of glory appeared to our father Abraham and said, 'Get you out of your country and from your kindred and come into the land which I shall show you.'"

Clearly and forcefully he went on to deliver a brief history of God's people since God had made the covenant with Abraham. When he finished describing how Solomon built the first temple, Stephen's voice rose accusingly so that no longer was he on trial, it seemed, but the Sanhedrin itself.

"Nevertheless the Most High does not dwell in temples made with hands," he thundered at them. "As the prophet says, 'Heaven is my home and earth is my footstool. Has not my hand made all these things?' You stiff-necked in heart and ears, will you always resist the Holy Spirit as did your fathers? Which of the prophets did your fathers not persecute? And they slew them who foretold the coming of the Just One, of whom you were the betrayers and murderers!"

The direct accusation of murder in the death of Jesus brought angry murmurs from the court, but Stephen had not finished speaking. Raising his eyes, which now glowed with a strange fire as if he were seeing something beyond the ken of mortal men, he cried, "Behold! I see the heavens opened and the Son of Man standing on the right hand of God!"

"Blasphemy!" one of the court shouted, and the excited crowd took up the cry until even the members of the Sanhedrin were echoing it. Without waiting for an official verdict, the people rushed into the room and seized Stephen from the guards. As with Jesus, they dragged him from the room and out into the streets leading to one of the gates, since it was not legal to execute a man by stoning—the traditional punishment for blasphemy—inside the walls of the city.

A secluded corner in a small rocky clearing outside the gates was the traditional place of execution. Here the wall and the rocks were stained by the blood of other victims spattered upon them. Foremost among the crowd that dragged Stephen to the place of execution was Saul of Tarsus. When the battered and bruised body was thrown against the wall and the people began to gather missiles, the man of Tarsus kept custody over the robes of the witnesses who, as custom dictated, had the right to cast the first stone.

Soon a veritable hail of missiles rained down upon the already grievously wounded man. Almost at once a cut was opened above his eye and at the sight of the blood the crowd seemed to go mad. The sickening thump of stones against flesh and the crack of breaking bones filled the air, along with the shouts and screams of the bloodthirsty mob. Above it all, one voice was distinctly heard, stilling momentarily the howls of the crowd.

"Lord Jesus, receive my spirit," Stephen cried. Then, forgiving his tormentors even in agony, "Lay not this sin to their charge."

Moments later a large stone struck the doomed man's temple and his body became limp. Ordering the stoning to stop—for it was a sin to desecrate the dead—Saul went over to look at the body. A cursory examination told him that Stephen was dead and, shrugging his shoulders, he went to notify the Sanhedrin that the punishment prescribed for blasphemy had been carried out.

# 2. The Road to Damascus

*"Saul, Saul, why persecutest thou me?"*
ACTS 9:4

T HE SMALL CARAVAN plodding along the road to Damascus was grateful for the coolness of the air in the highlands north of the Sea of Galilee—looking like a deep green jewel in its cup-shaped setting—and for the sight of the snow-capped peak of Mount Hermon to the north. The travelers had crossed the Jordan River at the Bridge of Jacob's Daughters, where the narrow, rushing torrent flowed through a thicket of flowering oleanders, papyrus, and the balsam trees from which came the famous Balm of Gilead. But even in the presence of so much beauty, the short, broad-shouldered man walking with an eager, springy gait at the head of the caravan seemed reluctant to pause and examine the scene, so driven was he by the fanatic determination that showed in his eyes. Days later, as the caravan plodded on, even the broad shoulders of Saul of Tarsus had begun to droop with weariness from the long trek across the rough desert path, but the eagerness in his eyes had not abated, and his gaze was turned always toward Damascus, now only a short distance ahead.

Saul was not a native of Jerusalem but had grown up in Tarsus of Cilicia, a far more Grecian city. Reared in the strictest traditions of the Pharisees, he had been sent as a youth to study under Gamaliel, who had succeeded Hillel as the great-est teacher of his day. Gamaliel preached tolerance and, in the early days after Jesus was crucified, had convinced the priests and the Sanhedrin not to persecute Peter and John, but to see what was the will of God concerning their activities.

Little if any of Gamaliel's broad outlook seemed to have been absorbed by Saul, however. Brilliant, intense, thoroughly devout, he was obviously destined for a high place in the re-ligious hierarchy connected with the temple. As such he had been present in the Sanhedrin at the time of Stephen's trial, and had officiated as the observer who guarded the cloaks of the witnesses while they stoned Stephen. More recently Saul's tremendous zeal had been unloosed against the followers of Jesus in Jerusalem. Houses had been entered and men and women who confessed belief in the Galilean whom the Jewish authorities considered an imposter had been summarily carried away to prison. As a result, many of those actively concerned with the young and growing *Ecclesia* had been scattered abroad.

Saul's persecutions had an effect he could not possibly have foreseen. Like the mustard seed Jesus had used in his parables to illustrate the growth of a mighty plant from the tiniest visible thing, his teachings had fallen on rich ground outside Jerusalem and had sprung up some sixty- and some an hundredfold. In Samaria, Syria, and even far off Damascus, groups following the teachings of Jesus quickly formed, to act as parent churches for others. Determined to stamp out these seedlings for whose spread he had largely been responsible, Saul had asked the high priest for letters of authority to the synagogues in Damascus and was journeying there to bring followers of Jesus to Jerusalem for trial before the Sanhedrin.

The day was warm and it was almost noon but in his zeal to go on, Saul had denied the weariness of his body so long that he no longer noticed fatigue. What he could not fail to notice now though was the sudden light that struck him full in the eyes, blinding and stunning him so that he fell on his face. As he lay on the hot sand with the sun beating down upon his head, the man of Tarsus heard a voice saying, "Saul! Saul! Why do you persecute me?"

"Who are you, Lord?" Saul asked, instinctively realizing that this was a divine vision.

"I am Jesus whom you persecute," the voice said. "It is hard for you to kick against the goad."

Not even to his inmost self had Saul admitted the pricks of conscience which lately had been growing stronger and stronger as he witnessed the amazing faith and courage of the people he was persecuting. That faith had carried Stephen unflinchingly through even the second most cruel of deaths and, being a brave man himself, Saul could not help admiring such a quality in others. In fact, much of the urgency which had driven him to expand his activities from Jerusalem to Damascus was in resistance to a deep inner doubt concerning the justice of what he was doing; for, however intolerant he might be, Saul was, above all, an honest man.

"Lord, what will you have me do?" he asked, and the voice answered, "Arise and go into the city and it shall be told what you must do."

In addition to being one of the oldest cities in the world, Damascus was also among the busiest. Great ungainly camels bearing huge packs of precious goods, spices, jewels and other articles of great value from far to the east plodded through the narrow streets, traveling the centuries-old Way of the Sea toward the coastal cities of Canaan and Egypt to the south. Furnaces glowed in the shops of the metalsmiths as great bellows were pumped to keep the flames burning brightly. Swords of Damascene steel were prized in the far corners of the earth, and the narrow streets were lined with shops, booths, and bazaars selling anything the buyer could wish.

A cosmopolitan city where as many tongues were spoken as gods were worshipped, Damascus was also the home of many Jews whose ancestors had been brought there during the dispersion of the northern kingdom and the captivity of Judah in Babylon far to the south. The Street called Straight ran entirely through the city. Lined with beautiful colonnades and partially roofed over for much of its length, it was the most important thoroughfare in Damascus. As he had trudged into the city led by one of those in the caravan, God had revealed to the now blind Saul that he should seek out on that street the shop of one Judas, a cobbler, and there await further instructions.

During three days while, blind and helpless, he waited for God to reveal his purpose, Saul's soul was in torment, torn between sincere belief in the rightness of what he had been doing in persecuting the followers of Jesus in Jerusalem and the revelation of Jesus himself which had been granted him upon the road. To an ambitious and forceful man, blindness was naturally a severe shock. Saul had been told by God in a vision that someone would come and give him his sight, but he still could hardly believe such a miracle possible.

Then, on the third day after his blinding, Ananias, one of the leading followers of Jesus in Damascus, appeared in the shop of Judas. His manner was not particularly friendly, for Ananias could hardly believe that one who had been responsible for persecuting the church in Jerusalem could have changed so suddenly. But he did not question the orders of the Lord.

"Brother Saul," he told the blind man. "Jesus, who appeared to you as you came, has sent me that you might receive your sight and be filled with the Holy Spirit."

As suddenly as he had been blinded, Saul's vision returned. He saw the well in the corner of the courtyard of Judas' home, the rows of newly fashioned shoes lining the shop, and the soft leather sheets awaiting the cobbler's knife. He could not fail to see the doubt and suspicion in the faces of Ananias and Judas, however, and instinctively did the only thing that would convince them of his changed state. He begged them to baptize him at once so that his conversion might be complete.

Characteristically, now that he had set out upon a new course, Saul went before the synagogues of Damascus and told of the wondrous thing that had happened to him upon the road. The people were naturally doubtful at first, as Judas and Ananias had been, but they could not long resist the eloquence and the obvious conviction and fervor of Saul's words. Soon so many were being converted by his preaching that the leaders of the synagogues began to seek some way to stop this man who was now actively furthering the spread of the very teachings he had come there to suppress. In secret meetings they decreed Saul's death but, resourceful as ever, he had himself lowered from the walls in a basket during the night and, when morning came, was far away from Damascus in the desert.

Saul had deliberately chosen the desert country for a period of meditation, as had Jesus after his baptism by John. The revelation on the road to Damascus had obviously brought to an abrupt end his promising career as one of the Jerusalem teachers who were considered the very cream of the rabbinical authorities. Equally obvious was the fact that in espousing the cause of a man who had been shamefully put to death as a false King of the Jews, he had embarked upon a road which could bring only persecution, odium, and perhaps death.

During the weeks in the desert, Saul had slowly come to understand the forces which had been in operation in his soul for many months, certainly as far back as the stoning of Stephen, and perhaps even before that. Having lived in the predominantly Grecian city of Tarsus and being familiar with the philosophies of the Greeks, he could appreciate how Jesus of Nazareth had opened up a whole new world of hope and faith in God for every man. It was a new Saul who now went to Jerusalem to consult with Peter about his future course, a man who preached boldly in the name of Jesus Christ.

# 3. Peter and the Gentiles

*"Of a truth I perceive that God is no respecter of persons."* ACTS 10:34

THE LEGIONS OF ROME were often known by special names, usually because the members had come from a particular city or region, or had excelled in some battle. Among them none was more highly regarded than the Italian band under the leadership of the centurion Cornelius, a just and devout man who had listened to the teachings of the apostles in Jerusalem and come to believe in Jesus Christ.

"Your prayers and your alms have come to the attention of God," an angel said to Cornelius in a vision while he was praying one day at his home in Caesarea. "Send men to Joppa and call for Simon whose surname is Peter. He lodges with a tanner whose house is by the seaside, and he will tell you what you ought to do."

Cornelius immediately sent two servants and a soldier on a brief journey to Joppa in search of Peter. Meanwhile, at the home of a tanner where he was staying in the seaport city, Peter had gone up to the roof to pray while the women were preparing the evening meal. There he fell asleep and in a vision or dream saw the heavens opened and a great sheet gathered at the four corners being let down to the earth. All kinds of wild beasts, creeping things and fowl of the air—

most of their flesh forbidden to Jews by Mosaic Law—were in
the sheet. As he watched, Peter heard a familiar voice say,
"Rise, Peter, kill and eat."

"Not so, Lord!" Peter protested in horror, for he followed
the Law like any pious Jew. "I have never eaten anything
common or unclean!"

"What God has cleansed, do not call common," the voice
said sternly and, when Peter still demurred, the vision was
repeated twice more.

Peter awoke much concerned about the meaning of the
dream, but before he could find an answer, the three men from
Caesarea arrived with the request that he go with them to their
master Cornelius. When they added that an angel had instructed Cornelius in a dream to send for him, Peter understood that this must be in some way connected with his own
vision, and accompanied them to the Roman capital of the
district.

A large number of Cornelius' friends and kinsmen had
gathered at his home to hear Peter. Under ordinary circumstances the tall apostle—as those who had known Jesus now
called him—would have shunned the company of Gentiles and
unbelievers, but when Cornelius told him of his own vision,
Peter understood the meaning of the dream he'd had on the
rooftop in Joppa.

"You know it is unlawful for a Jew to keep company or to
come unto one of another nation," he told the people gathered
to hear him. "But God has showed me that I should not call
any man common or unclean. In truth, I perceive that God
is no respecter of persons, but in every nation whoever fears
him and works righteousness is accepted with him. You know
the word which God sent to the Children of Israel, preaching
peace by Jesus Christ who is Lord of all, for it was published
throughout all Judea and began from Galilee. We are witnesses
of all things which Jesus did, both in the land of the Jews and
in Jerusalem. They slew him and hung him upon a cross, but
God raised him up the third day and showed him openly to us
who ate and drank with him after he had risen from the dead.
He commanded us to preach to the people, and to testify that

it is he who was ordained of God to be the judge of the living and the dead. To him all prophets witness that through his name whoever believes in him shall receive forgiveness of sins."

A new eloquence had come upon one who had been only a rough and impulsive fisherman of Galilee, and even the Romans who heard him were moved. When Peter returned to Jerusalem and told how many had been converted in Caesarea and how the Holy Spirit had come upon them, some of the more conservative among the apostles disagreed with his action. Peter, however, silenced them with a logic they could not deny: "Since God gave them the same gift of the Holy Spirit that he gave to us who believed on the Lord Jesus Christ, who was I to withstand God?"

To the temple authorities, the news that a Jewish sect was now actively soliciting Gentile converts, was the last insult. Pontius Pilate had been relieved of his duties as Procurator of Judea and Samaria when he had ordered the massacre of a large number of Samaritans on Mount Gerizim. In his stead Rome had sent a new ruler, Herod Agrippa, and the temple authorities now shrewdly enlisted his aid to help stamp out the new faith.

Agrippa had lived in Rome during most of the reign of Herod Antipas as tetrarch of Galilee and although largely a wastrel, an odd occurrence there had convinced him that he was destined to be even greater than his grandfather, Herod the Great. While he had been sitting beneath a tree, considering the perversity of fate which had made him a refugee from his own country, an owl had lit upon a branch over Agrippa's head. A German soldier passing by had explained that such an occurrence meant exceedingly good luck, and Agrippa had interpreted it as a sign that he would soon take up his rightful position as king in Judea where his grandfather had ruled. Even the German's admonition that the second time the owl appeared, he would die had not dampened the young man's spirits.

Agrippa had continued to plot against his uncle, Herod Antipas, and after the death of Caligula had been rewarded for his part in helping gain the kingship for Claudius by being made ruler in both Judea and Samaria. In Jerusalem he sought the favor of the leading Jews with the same shrewdness which had gained him so much in Rome. Although a wastrel and a pagan, he enforced strictly the Mosaic Law which had fallen into disuse, particularly those having to do with commerce with Gentiles. Shrewdly sensing that he could endear himself most quickly to the temple authorities by persecuting the new sect which—following the lead of a small group of Jesus' followers in Antioch had now begun to call themselves Christians— he arrested James, the son of Zebedee, one of the three leaders among the apostles, and had him beheaded. At the same time, Agrippa seized Peter and threw him into prison, intending to humiliate the chief apostle publicly in the hope of destroying the movement of which he was leader.

Forced to remain in hiding to avoid arrest, the Christians of Jerusalem were powerless to help Peter by any physical means. They could only pray day and night for his release, remembering the promise of Jesus that if their faith equalled a grain of mustard seed, even mountains could be moved. Nor did God fail to reward their trust; one night Peter's chains dropped away and the doors of the prison opened, allowing him to walk out a free man.

Furious at Peter's escape, Herod Agrippa gave orders that the Christians remaining in Jerusalem be persecuted all the more, but this only served to sow the seed more widely, as Jesus had predicted in the parable of the sower. Later, retribution came to Herod Agrippa when he gave a great celebration at Caesarea honoring himself. Arrayed in royal apparel like a king, although technically only a tetrarch and a puppet of Rome, he addressed the crowd, promising them many things as a result of his rule. And, seeking to curry favor with Agrippa, some courtiers raised the cry, "It is the voice of a god, and not of a man."

To the vain grandson of Herod the Great the words were like strong wine, but in his moment of triumph he forgot the omen he had first seen in Rome. An owl suddenly swooped down to perch above his head and in the same moment, God struck him dead.

# 4. The Christians

*"Separate me Barnabas and Saul for the work whereunto I have called them."* ACTS 13:2

ARNABAS HAD LITTLE TROUBLE finding the Street of Tentmakers in Tarsus where Saul was plying the trade he had learned in his youth and preaching the good news of Jesus' resurrection from the dead and the promise of eternal life. Though not one of the twelve, big, patient Barnabas had been one of the most faithful followers of Jesus in Jerusalem.

Later, when persecution by Herod Agrippa drove him from the Holy City, he had joined several others in establishing a strong and growing church in the great city of Antioch in Syria. There the followers of Jesus had first been called Christians as an act of derision and had proudly taken the name.

Several years had elapsed since Saul's conversion on the road to Damascus. When it became apparent that the help of a dynamic and eloquent voice was needed in Antioch, Barnabas had thought of Saul, who had been sent back to Tarsus from Jerusalem by Peter in order to save his life from the Jews who sought to kill him there.

Journeying northward from Antioch on one of the regular caravan routes, Barnabas had passed through the narrow defile in the Taurus mountains called the Cilician Gates, near where the city of Tarsus stood. Guarding the teeming Lycaonian

Plains from the lands to the east and south, the strategic pass
lay at one of the main junctions of the trade routes from the
Euphrates far to the east with a road from Syrian Antioch to
the south and Pontus, Bithynia, and other districts to the
north.

Beside the narrow road leading to Tarsus, a stream tumbled
through the chasm. Here Hattic races from Cappadocia had
burst through into the fertile basin between the Euphrates
and the Orontes rivers, separating the Babylonians and Assyrians to the east from the Egyptians to the south. Persian
armies under Cyrus and Darius had poured through this same
pass to conquer lesser Asia, and through it in the opposite direction again had come the legions of Alexander to fight Darius
on the Plains of Isis.

A natural seaport by virtue of the River Cydnus which divided
the city, Tarsus had been an important shipping and trade
center long before the Romans appeared, but it had flourished
even more under Roman rule. As he paused before the shops
to inquire for Saul, Barnabas could see weavers busy making
the tough cloth called cilicium after the province in which
Tarsus stood. The threads were first spun from goat hair on
machines operated by treadles before going to the weavers,
who worked in pits over which the heavy looms rested. Else-
where the craftsmen who made the famous tents of Tarsus
were busy cutting and sewing the cloth which was also used
widely as sails for the many ships visiting this particular area.

Saul was glad to see Barnabas and particularly pleased to
learn that a wider field for his services and his dynamic energy
as a preacher was now available in Antioch. Actually, however, the Syrian capital was to be only the beginning of his
real ministry, for soon the elders of he church there heard the
summons of the Holy Spirit: "Separate Barnabas and Saul
for the work whereunto I have called them."

First, Peter had seen the vision which had led him to Cornelius at Caesarea and to a new realization of the widening
character of the ministry to which they had commited their
lives. Now, from Antioch the gospel was to be spread to Gen-

tiles everywhere, fulfilling the instructions of Jesus before his ascension that his followers were to preach the good news to all the world. And since they were going to lands characterized by a predominantly Greek culture, the dynamic apostle—for he, too, had seen Jesus on the road to Damascus—was now called by the Greek version of his name, Paulos, or Paul. With Barnabas and young John Mark, he set sail from the port of Seleucia for Cyprus, Barnabas' home island, to begin the first phase of the ministry to the Gentiles.

Debarking at Salamis on the eastern end of Cyprus, they traveled across the island, teaching in towns and villages until they reached the city of Paphos. There they came to the attention of the Roman governor of Cyprus, Sergius Paulus. Moved by Paul's eloquent preaching, the governor was about to be baptized as a convert to the new Christian faith, but a sorcerer named Elymas saw in the influence of Paul and Barnabas over the Roman governor a threat to his own formerly secure position there. Elymas derided the Christians and tried to delude the governor with feats of magic and lies into believing he possessed a power greater than theirs.

"O full of all subtlety and all mischief!" Paul denounced the magician forthrightly. "You child of the devil and enemy of all righteousness! Since you pervert the right ways of the Lord, the hand of the Lord is upon you and you shall be blind."

When the magician was stricken blind upon the spot and had to be led away, Sergius Paulus no longer doubted that the two travelers preached in the name of the Son of God. He was converted immediately and became a devoted follower of the Lord.

Moving to the mainland of Asia Minor, Paul and Barnabas came to Perga, a seaport city in the district of Pamphylia. There John Mark left them to return to Jerusalem and take a position as assistant, or secretary, to Peter, a job he was to hold for many years.

Paul was not pleased by what he considered Mark's defection, but though Barnabas was Mark's kinsman and sponsor, he went on with Paul. Leaving Perga, they traveled northward through Pamphylia and came to Pisidian-Antioch, the largest city in the Galatian uplands. Antioch-in-Pisidia was one of sixteen cities of the same name established by Seleucus Nicator, and occupied the slope of a mountain range upon the bank of the Anthias River. Built mainly as a military outpost and center of government, it lay upon the Via Augusta, the Roman road leading from Babylon to Ephesus, a great seaport center to the west. As usual in a large Roman city of this size, there was a Jewish synagogue, and here Paul and Barnabas came on the Sabbath.

The service followed the formula of worship developed through the ages by the people with whom God had made a permanent covenant. Prayers were first recited in Hebrew by the *chazzan* or leader of the congregation, after which the scrolls of the Law were read first in Hebrew and then in Greek, since many Jews in this area no longer spoke the mother tongue. The reading finished, anyone who wished to address the congregation was invited to do so. This was what Paul had been waiting for, and he ascended to the elevated pulpit or *shema* to face the congregation.

"Men of Israel, and you that fear God, give audience," he said in the magnetic voice that drew listeners by the hundreds wherever he went. "The God of this people chose our fathers and exalted our people when they dwelt as strangers in the land of Egypt, and brought them out of it. When he had destroyed seven nations in the land of Canaan, he divided the land to them by lot and afterwards gave them judges for about four hundred and fifty years, until the time of the prophet Samuel. Afterward they desired a king, and God gave them Saul, the son of Kish, a man of the tribe of Benjamin. And when he removed Saul, he raised up David to be their king.

"Of David's seed God has given to Israel a saviour, Jesus," Paul continued, his voice now like a trumpet, filling the room. "Men and brethren, children of the stock of Abraham, and whoever among you fears God, the word of this salvation is sent to you. They that dwell in Jerusalem and their rulers, though they found no cause of death in him, yet desired that

Pilate slay Jesus. And when they had fulfilled all that was written, they took him down from the tree and laid him in a sepulcher."

Paul paused a moment, before going on. When he spoke again, his voice was joyful like the bringer of glad tidings. "But God raised Jesus from the dead, and he was seen many days by those who came up with him from Galilee to Jerusalem. Now we declare to you the glad tidings of how God has fulfilled to us their children the promise made to the fathers in that he has raised up Jesus from the dead and through this man I preach to you the forgiveness of sins. By him all that believe are justified from all things from which you could not be justified by the Law of Moses."

Here in Pisidian-Antioch Paul was declaring without equivocation that faith in Jesus and his ability to forgive sin could free Jews from the requirements of the Law. Had the announcement been made in Jerusalem, he would undoubtedly have been stoned, but here in a Greek city far away—where not even the Hebrew in which the scrolls of the Law and the prophets were written was understood by most of the younger members of the congregation—such a doctrine found many eager listeners. When Paul and Barnabas left the synagogue, the Gentiles, too, crowded around him, begging that he tell them more of this good news.

Paul's startling doctrine that belief in Jesus could bring forgiveness of sin and eternal life found many adherents in Pisidian-Antioch, but a small, hard core of ultra-conservative Jews in the synagogues refused to listen. Instead they sought to accuse him and Barnabas of blasphemy.

"It was necessary that the word of God should first have been spoken to you," Paul lashed them bitterly from the pulpit after the charge was made. "But since you put it from you, and judge yourselves unworthy of everlasting life, we turn to the Gentiles. For so has the Lord commanded us, saying, 'I have sent you to be a light to the Gentiles, that you should be for salvation to the ends of the earth.'"

Those who opposed the two missionaries were not moved,

and in the end managed to have Paul and Barnabas driven from the city. Thus began a pattern of rejection and even violence at the hands of his own people which was to be enacted over and over again as Paul journeyed from city to city, bringing the glad tidings of Jesus' resurrection and the forgiveness of sins to men everywhere, whether Gentile or Jew.

# 5. The Godlike Men

> "And they called Barnabas, Jupiter;
> and Paul, Mercurius, because he was
> the chief speaker."    ACTS 14:12

LUCIUS, THE BEGGER, had never walked. Born with flaccid and useless limbs, he had been carried as a child by his father to a place beside the road from Iconium to Lystra, his home city, where he cried for alms in a childish treble. A grown man now, he still kept his old begging place, for, being near the temple of Jupiter, he was able to ask alms not only of wayfarers on one of the most heavily traveled roads crossing the Galatian uplands, but also of those who came to worship. Lucius was not hoping simply for alms today, however, but for a greater gift, that of being made whole.

As yet it was only a faint hope, based on reports of travelers entering Lystra over the past several days concerning strange and wonderful things accomplished by two men journeying from city to city, preaching belief in a new god who had sent his son to earth to die for others. More important at the moment to Lucius, the men were said to heal the sick and cast out evil spirits, and word had come that they were only a few hours' journey away. As he sat by the roadside, Lucius even forgot to cry for alms in the urgency of watching the road so that he would not miss the strangers when they passed.

Had he known the truth of what had happened to Paul and

Barnabas on their journey through Galatia, Lucius might not have been so hopeful. At Iconium their experience in Pisidian-Antioch had been repeated. Successful at first beyond their expectations in preaching to both Jews and Gentiles, they had been opposed by a group of each who had convinced the authorities that they were troublemakers and had brought about their expulsion from the cities. A nucleus of Gentile converts had been left behind in each place, however, and these continued to spread the good news.

It was late afternoon when Paul and Barnabas approached Lystra, and the sight of so many people entering and leaving the beautiful temple of Jupiter near the road made them stop beside the spot where Lucius sat. Climbing upon a large boulder, Paul began to preach and, as always, his eloquent voice and compelling personality quickly drew a crowd. Lucius was sitting almost at his feet, looking up at him and drinking in every word. In fact, the cripple had for the moment forgotten his own need in the desire to hear this new gospel of a god who required only love and obedience from his subjects, instead of bestial sacrifices and lascivious orgies.

While he was preaching, Paul happened to look down and see the begger. His quick glance took in the shriveled limbs and the glow of dawning faith in Lucius' eyes. Moved with compassion for the man, he said, "Stand upon your feet."

For a moment Lucius did not even realize that Paul was speaking to him, so intent was he upon what the eloquent apostle was saying. Then, as he felt his muscles stir with a power they had never known, a floodtide of incredulous joy surged through him and he leaped to his feet.

Many in the crowd had known Lucius for a long time. Startled by the miracle of his being healed, their first reaction was that the men who had accomplished such a feat must be gods.

"It is Jupiter and Mercurius, come to earth in human form!" someone shouted, and others took up the cry until even Paul's protests were drowned out. In the midst of the excitement, several men ran to the near-by temple of Jupiter and called for the priests to bring oxen and flowers so that a sacrifice could be made to the gods who had honored Lystra with a personal visit.

With the miracle occurring in the very shadow of the temple of Jupiter, it was only natural for the pagans of Lystra to confuse the two men with gods. Barnabas was big and broad-shouldered, as in their estimation Jupiter would have been. And who could be more like the messenger of the gods, Mercury, than dynamic, eloquent Paul? In the confusion, Paul did not at first understand what was happening. But when the priests of Jupiter pushed their way through the crowd and prostrated themselves before him, he recoiled in horror.

"Sirs, why do you do these things?" he shouted. "We are men of like passions with you and preach to you that you should turn from these vanities to the living God, who made heaven and earth and the sea and all things that are therein."

The jubilant people of Lystra were too happy and proud that the gods had chosen to honor their city to listen to Paul's protests that he and Barnabas were human, and started to prepare a great sacrifice and celebration in their honor. But some Jews from the synagogues in Antioch and Iconium who had been following close behind Paul and Barnabas and seeking to undo what they had been accomplishing, arrived upon the scene. These succeeded in persuading the people that the two were followers of a false god, and, as angry now as they had been jubilant before, the Lystrans stoned Paul and left him at the edge of the city for dead.

Paul was only stunned, however. As soon as he was able to travel, he and Barnabas went on to Derbe. From there they revisited the cities where they had established churches before coming again to Perga and Attalia, from which port they sailed directly to Antioch.

News of the accomplishments of Paul and Barnabas in Galatia and the churches they had established among the Gentiles was as a new infusion of the Holy Spirit for the church at Antioch. But in spite of this, Paul found grave trouble there that threatened to choke off his mission to the Gentiles almost before it had begun.

James, a member of Jesus' own family, had come to Jerusalem in the early days of the church and, with Peter, John, and the other apostles going out to preach the gospel in various parts of the surrounding area, had become head of the group at Jerusalem. When representatives came from Jerusalem to Antioch with orders that Gentiles could not be accepted into the church unless they underwent the ritual of circumcision and became, in effect, Jews, Paul was forced to protest vigorously for, if carried out, this provision would throttle further spread of the gospel to the Gentiles.

After considerable discussion in Antioch, it was decided that a delegation including Paul and Barnabas should go up to Jerusalem and discuss the matter with the apostles and the elders who were recognized as the legitimate leaders of the church. There Paul, in his usual eloquent fashion, told of the great things which had been done in Galatia and how the power of the Holy Spirit had operated to spread the gospel in that region. Speaking against him, the more conservative members of the Jerusalem church repeated the charges that they had made in Antioch, namely, that no one could be accepted unless he was circumcised and followed strictly the Laws of Moses.

In this grave crisis, many of the apostles looked to Simon Peter and waited to see how he would vote before deciding whether to support Paul's broader concept of the church's purpose. Peter would have been less than human if he had not realized that Paul's almost meteoric rise to prominence in the church already threatened to eclipse his own role, although the man of Tarsus had neither been among those who had known Jesus nor had been chosen by the Master as a disciple before his crucifixion. The tall fisherman did not hesitate, however. With a few words he proved just how far he had come in the steps of the Master whom he had denied three times on that fateful morning, while Jesus was being mocked by Caiaphas and the members of the Sanhedrin.

"Men and brethren," he said. "You know that a good while ago God chose that by my mouth the Gentiles should hear the word of the Gospel and believe. And God—who knows the heart —bears them witness, giving to them the Holy Spirit as he gives it to us, and puts no difference between us and them, purifying their hearts by faith. Why then do you tempt God to put a yoke upon the neck of believers which neither our fathers nor we were able to bear? Instead, we believe that through the grace of the Lord Jesus Christ, we shall be saved even as they."

This simple statement of the saving grace of Jesus as the key unlocking the kingdom of God to all who believed moved the men of Jerusalem even more than had Paul's eloquent description of the miracles and wonders wrought in Galatia. James, the acknowledged head of the church at Jerusalem, gave the final verdict.

"My decision is that we do not trouble them who are turned to God from among the Gentiles," he said solemnly, "but that we write to them to abstain from pollution by idols, fornication, and from things strangled and from blood."

James' decision was not entirely pleasing to Paul, who would have preferred that no restrictions whatever be placed upon the faith he preached. But he recognized that only Peter's forthright support had removed the major stumblingblock to his program of preaching to the Gentiles, and was thankful. The whole Roman world was open to him now, a challenge which Paul—as the official apostle to the Gentiles—joyfully accepted.

As for Simon Peter, in acknowledging Paul's leadership in the Gentile field, he had assumed the lesser position of apostle to the Jews. But that, too, was in the tradition of the man he served, who had said: "Whoever will be chief among you, let him be your servant."

# 6. Mission to Macedonia

> *"Come over into Macedonia, and help us."*
> ACTS 16:9

THE COUNCIL OF JERUSALEM had largely freed Paul's ministry from the old restrictive bonds of the Mosaic Law. But it was far away, at Troas on the Asian coast, that he saw a new and broader vision. It came as a dream in which a man from the heartland of Greece across the Aegean Sea said, "Come over into Macedonia and help us."

A new group of co-workers had accompanied Paul on his second missionary journey. Barnabas had wished to take Mark with them, but not trusting the young man—partly perhaps because he was very close to Simon Peter, but largely because Mark had returned home at the beginning of the first venture into Gentile territory—Paul had demurred. As a result, Barnabas had gone his own way and Silas from the Jerusalem church had become Paul's traveling companion. Visiting the churches of the Galatian highlands, they had picked up Timothy, a young convert, at Lystra, and at Troas had been joined by the physician, Luke, who was to become Paul's biographer. Driving himself beyond the limits of human endurance most of the time, Paul had frequent need of a physician, and Luke filled an important role in the company from then on.

As he approached Troas, Paul was tempted strongly to go into Bithynia, a province on the south shore of the Black Sea and famous for its climate and fertility. But God had a broader purpose for him, a purpose which was revealed in the dream at Troas. And always ambitious to carry the glad tidings of Jesus to new fields, Paul did not "kick against the goad" but set sail immediately from Troas, landing at Samothrace, an island lying between Troas and Neapolis, the nearest port city on the Macedonian coast.

Populous, teeming, and highly civilized, Macedonia was a logical field for Paul's newest missionary venture. The churches in the provinces of Asia and Galatia were now fairly well established, at least enough so to carry on with only an occasional visit or letter from their founder. But Macedonia was the very gateway to Greece itself, and it was in the Greek-speaking provinces that Paul had found the most eager reception for his preaching. Nor was this entirely unexpected, for the philosophy of love and understanding preached by Jesus was close to that taught by many of the great philosophers of Greece and had a natural appeal to a people hungering for a sounder religion than one based upon the whims of capricious pagan gods.

Neapolis was the coastal terminus of a famous Roman road called the *Via Egnatia* leading through Macedonia. From there Paul and his three companions journeyed to Philippi, the leading city of that area. A large and busy center overlooking the plain between Mount Hamas and Mount Pangaeus, upon whose slopes roses were already blooming in the spring warmth, Philippi was the logical place to begin the ministry in Macedonia.

Near the plain lay the marsh across which Mark Antony had led his army to attack the murderers of Caesar, and where, before the gates of the city, Antony and Cleopatra had been overcome by Augustus. Entering Philippi through a magnificent archway spanning the Via Egnatia, Paul and his companions took up residence in the city. Since the worship of foreign gods was not permitted within the *pomerium*—a line inside the archway giving entrance to the center of the city itself—they preached outside Philippi. There Paul converted a woman named Lydia, a dealer in rich goods from the near-by town of Thyatira, and her household.

The Greeks were especially tolerant in religious matters so that Paul had little trouble in Philippi until his presence there interfered with the lucrative business of some unscrupulous men. These were keeping in bondage a poor, demented slave girl who they claimed could look into the future. When the girl saw Paul and Silas one day, she cried, "These men are the servants of the most High God who show us the way to salvation," and began to follow them. Paul healed her of the disorder of her mind which had caused the peculiar behavior, but healed, she was worth nothing to her masters and in revenge they conspired to have Paul and Silas arrested and brought before the magistrates.

"These men are Jews and trouble our city," the owners of the slave girl complained. "They teach customs which, it is not lawful for us, being Romans, to receive or observe."

Paul and Silas would not deny the truth which they were preaching, so the magistrates had them beaten and thrown into prison without further hearing. Actually, Paul could have saved himself the ignominy of being beaten publicly, since he was a Roman citizen by virtue of having been born in Tarsus, but he took the beating and imprisonment along with Silas. They were singing hymns and telling the other prisoners the wondrous story of Jesus when the ground began to quiver from an earthquake, a not infrequent occurrence in that region. In fact, so severe was this tremor that the foundations of the prison were shaken and the prisoners were able to open the doors.

The keeper of the prison was about to fall upon his sword, sure that the prisoners had escaped, when Paul called out to him, "Do yourself no harm, for we are all here!" And when he saw that none had escaped, the keeper knelt before Paul and Silas asking, "What must I do to be saved?"

"Believe on the Lord Jesus Christ and you shall be saved with your household," Paul told him, and that very day the keeper was baptized with his household.

In the morning, messengers came from the magistrates with

orders that Paul and Silas were to be released, but Paul had no intention of letting off so easily the people who had unjustly imprisoned him. "They have beaten us openly though we are Romans and have not been condemned. And they have cast us into prison," he said. "Now they would thrust us out privately, so let them come themselves and bring us out."

Legally every Roman citizen had the right to take his case to the emperor, and when the magistrates heard that it was Roman citizens they had mistreated, they came to the prison and begged Paul and his companions to forget the incident and leave Philippi. Paul's work was finished with the establishment of a church there, so he went on with Silas to Thessalonica and preached, as was his custom, in the synagogue. Many Hellenist Jews to whom Paul's teachings always appealed were converted, but as usual, a small group conspired against him and created a tremendous uproar around the house of a man named Jason with whom Paul and Silas were staying.

In order not to cause any more trouble for their new converts, Paul and Silas left Thessalonica for Berea; then leaving Silas and Timothy there, the apostle went on alone to Athens, the chief city of Greece. There he preached daily in the marketplace, but soon found himself disputing with Jews who sought to condemn him. And since the Greeks liked nothing better than a public debate, the Epicureans and Stoics brought Paul to the central court of the city called the Areopagus.

"Let us know what is this new doctrine of which you speak," they begged him. "For you bring strange things to our ears, and we would know what they mean."

Always welcoming an opportunity to preach the gospel, Paul stood in the Areopagus of Athens and spoke fearlessly to the people gathered there. "You men of Athens," he said, "I perceive that in all things you are too superstitious. For as I passed by and beheld your devotions, I found an altar with this inscription, 'TO THE UNKNOWN GOD.' The one you ignorantly worship I now declare to you. God who made the world and all things in it, since he is Lord of heaven and earth, does not dwell in temples made with hands. Neither is he worshipped with men's hands as though he needed anything, as it is he that gives life, death, and everything to all. And since we are the offspring of God, we ought not to think that the godhead is like gold or silver or stone graven by art and man's device. Now, he commands all men everywhere to repent because he has appointed a day on which to judge the world in righteousness by Jesus, his Son, whom he has ordained and through whom he has given assurance to all men by raising him from the dead."

The sophisticated Greeks of Athens scoffed at the idea of a resurrection, and only a few converts were made there, but at Corinth, where Paul went next, the story was very different. There he spoke in the synagogue on every Sabbath, and many were converted. Nevertheless, his enemies managed to have him brought before the famous Roman judge, Gallio, complaining that he persuaded men to worship God contrary to the Jewish Law. Before Paul could speak in his own defense, however, Gallio lashed out at the accusers.

"If it were a matter of wrong or wicked lewdness, reason would lead me to bear with you," Gallio told them. "But if it is a question of words and names and your Law, look to it yourselves, for I will be no judge of such matters."

Paul won a major legal victory in the Gallio decision that his preaching broke no Roman law, opening up the whole vast Roman empire to him. The ministry at Corinth had prospered greatly, and he left behind a strong church when he sailed for Ephesus en route to Caesarea and Jerusalem to report to the elders there.

Before undertaking the journey to Jerusalem, Paul paused long enough in Corinth to write the first of a series of letters to the churches he had founded. These eloquent and moving epistles were to establish him once and for all as—after Jesus himself—the most important figure in early Christianity.

The first two letters were written to the church at Thessalonica and contained, in addition to expressions of Paul's great love for those he had brought to Jesus, sound advice as to how the members should live. Most important of all was his ringing exhortation to continue diligently at work in the cause of the Lord, since no man knew the day when Jesus would return in glory to demand an accounting of them.

# 7. Incident at Ephesus

*"And God wrought special miracles by
the hands of Paul."*     ACTS 19:11

"ALL ROADS lead to Ephesus" was a saying current in
the world of Paul's day. Capital of the province of
Asia and the greatest city in Asia Minor, Ephesus
was more than simply the seat of Roman government in that
area. A great seaport, constantly visited by ships traveling to and
from Rome, Antioch, Alexandria, and other important cities,
it was a thriving center of business as well as of philosophy,
literature, and art.

The pride of Ephesus was the great temple of Diana, one of
the wonders of the world. Four hundred and twenty-five feet
long and two hundred and twenty feet wide, it had one hundred
and sixty-seven columns. In the very heart of the temple was
the priceless image of the goddess Artemis, or Diana, to which
came worshippers from all that part of the world. Silversmiths
particularly did a thriving business there, making small images
of the goddess which were sold to visitors. And since the religion of Artemis was one of the most corrupt and depraved of all
the pagan cults, Ephesus was naturally a center for every sort
of vice.

Paul had stopped at Ephesus only briefly on the way home
from Macedonia and Greece. On his third misionary journey,

during which he visited the churches he had established across the face of Asia Minor and Macedonia, he came eventually to Ephesus once again. And seeing an unparalleled opportunity to spread the good news about Jesus, he took up residence there, supporting himself by working as a tentmaker.

In a large hall rented from a philosopher named Tyrannus, Paul taught and conversed with people through the hot part of the day when they left their work, healing hundreds who were sick and afflicted. Large numbers came to believe in Jesus during this period of active missionary work and, since a great flux of people constantly poured through the city, some of those whom Paul had converted returned to their own local communities to tell the thrilling story they had heard from the apostle's own lips. In this way small groups of Christians at Colossae, Laodicea, Hierapolis, Smyrna, Pergamos, Thyatira, Sardis, and Philadelphia organized churches in which they taught their own people.

To Paul at Ephesus came word of continuing difficulties in the church at Corinth. The temple authorities at Jerusalem, alarmed by the progress Paul had made in converting the Jews of Asia Minor and Macedonia to the Christian faith, had sent out a group of men to follow him and teach in the synagogues that Christianity was a rejected sect whose leader had been executed as a traitor. Paul had fought and practically put an end to the infiltration of his young churches by people seeking to destroy his work; in Corinth, however, the difficulties were immeasurably greater. There factions claiming to follow Paul contended with disciples of a man named Apollos who also claimed to be an apostle, while another group announced themselves as disciples of Peter, and a fourth clique gave allegiance only to Jesus. With so much contention among themselves, many Christians of Corinth had lost sight of the simple truth that Jesus had given his life to save sinners and, through his resurrection, brought eternal life to all who believed.

In an eloquent series of letters addressed to the Corinthians, Paul expounded the truth in words simple enough for anyone to understand. And in one of the most beautiful passages ever written or spoken, he lectured the church at Corinth concern-

ing the love for each other which Jesus had indicated as the new
commandment for those who would follow him:
"Love suffers long, and is kind;
Love does not envy;
Love does not vaunt itself, is not puffed up.
It does not behave itself unseemly.
It does not seek its own, is not easily provoked, thinks no
    evil;
It does not rejoice in iniquity, but rejoices in the truth;
It bears all things, believes all things, hopes all things, en-
    dures all things.
Love never fails:
But whether there be prophecies, they shall fail;
Whether there be tongues, they shall cease;
Whether there be knowledge, it shall vanish away,
For we know in part, and we prophesy in part.
But when that which is perfect is come,
Then that which is in part shall be done away.
When I was a child, I spoke as a child,
I understood as a child, I thought as a child:
But when I became a man, I put away childish things.
For now we see through a glass, darkly; but then face to face:
Now I know in part; but then shall I know even as I am
    known.
And now abide faith, hope, love, these three;
But the greatest of these is love."
The months of teaching and ministering at Ephesus formed
one of the most satisfying periods in Paul's entire career. Yet,
paradoxically, his very success there almost cost him his life.
Since his preaching turned many away from the worship of
Artemis, the sale of the small images made by the silversmiths
decreased rapidly. Finally, one of the smiths, a man named
Demetrius, rallied the workmen in that field to save their dying
profession.
"Sirs," he told them, "you know that by this craft we have
our wealth. Moreover, you see and hear that, not alone at
Ephesus, but almost throughout all Asia, this Paul has persuaded and turned away many people, saying that there are no

gods made with hands. Not only is our craft in danger of being set at nothing, but also the temple of the great goddess Diana is being despised and her magnificence may be destroyed, although all Asia and the world worships her."

Roused by Demetrius, the silversmiths began a concerted campaign to prejudice the people against Paul and his followers. Seizing two of his companions, Gaius and Aristarchus, they rushed them to the amphitheater where the gladiatorial games were held, planning to execute them publicly as a lesson to Paul. The apostle wished to go before the crowd and try to dissuade them from murdering the two men, but his disciples would not let him. The cause seemed lost, until help came from an unexpected source, the clerk of the city who was responsible to the asiarch, the provincial governor, for the government of Ephesus.

"Men of Ephesus," the clerk pleaded. "What man is there who does not know how the whole city of the Ephesians worships the great goddess Diana and the images which fell down from Jupiter? Seeing that these things cannot be denied, you ought to be quiet and to do nothing rashly. You have brought here men who are neither robbers of churches nor blasphemers of your goddess. If Demetrius and the craftsmen with him have a matter against any man, the law is open and there are judges; let them plead against each other. But if you inquire anything concerning other matters, it shall be determined in a lawful assembly, for we are in danger of being called into question for this day's uproar, there being no cause whereby we may give an account of this concourse."

The clerk's plea reminded even the silversmiths that Roman law was very strict against mob violence and that they might get into considerable trouble if they took matters into their own hands, especially with a Roman citizen. So Gaius and Aristarchus were released, but Paul realized that he could accomplish no more in Ephesus at the moment, and crossed the narrow sea separating Asia Minor from Macedonia.

At Philippi he was met by a convert named Titus who brought the good news that Paul's letter to the Corinthians had eased considerably the difficult situation there. From Philippi,

Paul wrote another letter to the rebellious church, telling them of his grief and sorrow at the difficulties which had come upon them, and of his great joy that they had at last turned back to the simple principles he had taught them.

# 8. The New Covenant

*"But ye are come . . . to Jesus, the
mediator of the new covenant."*

HEBREWS 12:22, 24

T HE FIRST BRIGHT FLUSH of success which had characterized Paul's earlier work in the churches of Galatia and
Macedonia had now faded. On his third missionary journey, he paused for several months to strengthen the church at
Corinth and gather money to help sustain the group in Jerusalem who, with James as their leader, carried on there.

At Corinth disturbing reports reached Paul of difficulties in
many of the churches, particularly those of the Galatian uplands. As usual, most of the trouble came from Jews sent out
by the temple authorities at Jerusalem to follow Paul and undo
his work by teaching that no one could be saved except through
circumcision and a strict obedience to the Law of Moses. Busy
as he was, Paul paused long enough to compose a letter to the
Galatian churches, a little gem containing the essence of his
faith in his own selection by Christ to preach one gospel alone.

"I certify to you brethren that the gospel preached by me
is not from man," he told the Galatians. "For I neither received
it of a man, nor was I taught it except by the revelation of Jesus
Christ. And though we or an angel from heaven should preach
any other gospel to you than that which we have preached, let
him be accursed."

330

In the letter, Paul went on to tell the story of his own conversion, and how he had contended even against Peter when the question of imposing the strict Law of Moses upon Gentile converts had ben raised. "O foolish Galatians!" he said. "Who has bewitched you that you should not obey the truth that Jesus Christ has been set forth crucified among you? This only would I learn of you; did you receive the Spirit by the works of the Law or by the hearing of faith? Are you so foolish that, having begun in the Spirit, you think now to be made perfect by the flesh? He that ministers to you the Spirit and works miracles among you, does he do it by the works of the Law or by the hearing of faith? Abraham believed God, and they who are of the faith are the children of Abraham. The blessing of Abraham has come upon the Gentiles through Jesus Christ, that we might receive the promise of the spirit through faith.

"You are all the children of God by faith in Christ Jesus," he concluded. "And all the law is fulfilled in one word, even in this: 'You shall love your neighbor as yourself.' "

Travel between Rome and the other cities of the empire was frequent and, when the persecution of the early church in Jerusalem had scattered many of its adherents abroad, some had gone to the capital. There a vigorous and healthy church had quickly sprung up and, with his work in Asia Minor and Macedonia now firmly established, Paul turned his eyes eagerly to Rome and Spain in the west, all virgin territory. Once he had completed his duty toward the church at Jerusalem by bringing the collection from the churches he had visited, he planned to go on to Rome. Now in a letter written to the Roman Christians while in Corinth, he stated clearly his conviction regarding the purpose of Christ's coming to earth and of selecting him as an apostle, summarizing these principles in simple words.

Man, in Paul's eyes, had broken the original covenant made with God and, as a result, both Gentiles and Jews had earned the wrath of the Lord. But as God had proved himself willing to forgive man's failings through the ages, he had now made a second covenant that, through faith in the blood of Jesus Christ, a means of redemption and the attainment of eternal life was provided for all.

"All have sinned and come short of the glory of God," Paul wrote to the Romans—and to all the churches, for this letter was circulated among them. "Being justified freely by his grace through the redemption which is in Christ Jesus, whom God set forth to be a propitiation through faith in his blood. Therefore being justified by faith, we have peace with God through our Lord Jesus Christ by whom also we have access into this grace wherein we stand and rejoice in hope of the glory of God."

Jew and Gentile alike, Paul told the Roman Christians, should know that belief in Jesus as the Son of God was the only hope of redemption and eternal life. This simple statement of man's new relationship to God through his Son was the firm rock that was to sustain Christians through centuries of persecution and, with his eloquent appeals to the Corinthians, the Galatians, and the Romans completed, Paul started upon the return journey to Jerusalem.

Paradoxically, the movement begun by Christ's crucifixion and resurrection, now reaching the world through the eloquent voice and pen of Paul, was weakest in Jerusalem. Patriarch of the church was James the Just, but none of the original twelve disciples were there now, and it had actually become merely a small sect of Jews living quietly in Jerusalem with the knowledge and forbearance of the temple authorities. Like Christians everywhere, those in Jerusalem looked forward constantly to the return of Jesus as the Messiah, but they continued to observe the Law of Moses scrupulously. In this respect they actually differed little from other Jewish sects, such as the Essenes, or the Therapeutae, who had a large colony just outside the city of Alexandria in Egypt.

There were many parallels between Jesus' final entry into Jerusalem at the Passover and Paul's appearance there at the time of another feast day with gifts from the distant churches. Actually, he could hardly have chosen a worse time to come to Jerusalem but, willing to risk all in the service of him who had called him on the road to Damascus, this did not deter Paul. Nor was his zeal in any way diminished by the prophecy of a holy man, Agabus, when he paused at Caesarea to visit with

Philip. Binding Paul's hands and feet with his own girdle, the prophet had warned, "So shall the Jews at Jerusalem bind the man that owns this girdle, and shall deliver him into the hands of the Gentiles."

For years the object of a concerted attack by the temple authorities, Paul could not have hoped to remain long in Jerusalem without opposition from them. After turning over the money he had brought to the suffering church and reporting the great things that God had done among the Gentiles through his ministry, he was ready to go to Antioch. James and the elders begged him, however, to take time before leaving to combat the accusations of his enemies that he perverted the Law of Moses, and they persuaded him to join four men who had made a vow of purification, thus proving to his detractors that he still kept the Law.

Paul was not compromising his principles in following the advice of the elders. He was still a Jew; only in the question of accepting Gentiles into the church had he forthrightly refused to be bound by the customs followed by strict Jews. Brought up, by his own admission, a Pharisee of the Pharisees, Paul could undertake with good conscience the custom of purification as a proof that he did not consider himself other than a part of the whole body of the congregation of Israel. At the same time he no doubt hoped to diminish the attempts of some Jerusalem Christians to undermine his own work in bringing Gentiles into the church.

At first it seemed that Paul would succeed in removing much of the criticism which had been leveled against him. The period of seven days required for purification were almost ended and he was praying with the other four men in the temple, when some Jews from Asia recognized him and set up a commotion.

"Men of Israel, help!" they cried. "This is the man who teaches all men everywhere against the Law and the temple. Besides he has brought Greeks into the temple and polluted this holy place."

The reference was to one of the men who had come with Paul to Jerusalem, an Ephesian named Trophimus. And the accusation of defaming the temple was shrewdly calculated to arouse the ire of the mob, since it was strictly forbidden for any Gentile to ascend higher than the lower court. An angry crowd gathered quickly around Paul and was about to kill him upon the steps of the temple when the tribune of the Roman garrison stationed in the fortress of Antonia near-by heard the uproar. Running across the bridge connecting the Antonia with the temple, he and the Roman guard stationed there for just such an emergency took Paul, already badly beaten, into custody.

"May I speak to you?" Paul asked the tribune as he was being led into the fortress.

"Can you speak Greek?" the Roman officer asked in amazement.

"I am a Jew of Tarsus in Cilicia, a citizen of no mean city," Paul told him proudly. "I beg you to let me speak to the people."

The tribune gave Paul permission and, standing upon the stairs, he addressed the crowd in their own language: "Men, brethren and fathers, hear my defense which I now make to you. I am truly a man who is a Jew, born in Tarsus, a city in Cilicia, yet brought up in this city at the feet of Gamaliel, and taught according to the perfect manner of the Law of the fathers. I was zealous toward God as you all are this day, and I persecuted this way unto the death, binding and delivering into prison both men and women, as the High Priest will bear me witness, and the body of the elders from whom I received letters to the brethren and went to Damascus to bring them who were there bound to Jerusalem for punishment.

"As I made my journey and came near Damascus about noon," he continued, "suddenly a great light from heaven shone around me. I fell to the ground and heard a voice saying to me, 'Saul, Saul, why do you persecute me?' 'Who are you, Lord?' I answered, and he said to me, 'I am Jesus of Nazareth, whom you persecute.'

"They that were with me saw the light and were afraid, but they did not hear the voice of him that spoke to me," Paul added. "And I said, 'What shall I do, Lord?' And the Lord said to me, 'Arise, and go into Damascus, and there it shall be told you of all things which are appointed for you to do.' When I could not see for the glory of that light, being led by the hand of those that were with me, I came into Damascus, and one Ananias, a devout man according to the Law, came to me and said, 'Brother Saul, receive your sight. The God of our fathers has chosen you that you should know his will, and see the Just One, and should hear the voice of his mouth. For you shall be his witness to all men of what you have seen and heard.'

"When I came again to Jerusalem, while I prayed in the temple I was in a trance and saw him saying to me, 'Make haste, and get you quickly out of Jerusalem for they will not receive your testimony concerning me.' 'Lord,' I said, 'they know that I imprisoned and beat in every synagogue them that believed on you, and when the blood of your martyr Stephen was shed, I was standing by and consenting to his death, and kept the raiment of them that slew him.' But he said to me, 'Depart, for I will send you far hence to the Gentiles.'"

At this hated word, some of the Jews in the audience indignantly demanded that Paul be killed, but the tribune in charge of the soldiers took him into the castle and sent a centurion to examine him in the customary fashion, by scourging.

"Is it lawful for you to scourge a man who is a Roman and not yet condemned?" Paul asked the centurion as the torture instrument was being brought out.

"Are you a Roman?" the tribune demanded of Paul.

"Yes."

"I obtained this freedom with a great sum," the officer said, obviously doubting that an ordinary Jew could have afforded the cost.

"But I was freeborn," Paul told him proudly, and the officer removed his bonds at once.

The Jews who had tried to kill Paul were still clamoring for his blood, however, so the following morning he was brought before the Sanhedrin to make his defense. "I have lived in all good conscience before God until this day," Paul assured the council, but before he could go on, the High Priest ordered a guard to strike him in the mouth.

With blood trickling from a cut lip, Paul faced his accusers as had Jesus in this same chamber on the night he was arrested. "God shall strike you, you whited wall!" he told them. "For you sit to judge me according to the Law and yet you order me to be struck contrary to the Law. I am a Pharisee, the son of a Pharisee; it is because of the hope and resurrection of the dead that I am called in question."

This was a shrewd move on Paul's part, for on the question of life after death the Pharisees and Sadducees were at opposite poles. As he had hoped, the members of the council began to wrangle among themselves, and the disgusted tribune, fearing that a Roman citizen might be killed and he would be blamed, took Paul back to the Antonia.

During the night, a group of some forty Jews got together and agreed to ask the High Priest and the council to bring Paul before them for another hearing, planning to rush the Roman guard and kill the prisoner while he was outside the protection of the Antonia. The plot might have succeeded, if a nephew of Paul's had not learned of it and warned him. When he in turn told the tribune, the Roman officer sent the apostle to Caesarea the next morning under guard. Even then the Jews of Jerusalem brought charges against Paul, but when he exercised his right as a Roman citizen and demanded trial before the emperor, they could do nothing more except in the Roman court.

# 9. The Armor of God

*"Put on the whole armour of God,
that ye may be able to stand against
the wiles of the devil."*

EPHESIANS 6:11

A s HE STOOD upon the deck of the great merchant vessel, heavily laden with grain from Alexandria for sale in the markets of Rome, Paul could not find it in his heart to be bitter about his two years of imprisonment in Caesarea since the attack on him in the temple at Jerusalem. It was true that technically he had been in custody all the while, but the Romans had given him many privileges, for one who had appealed to the emperor was not treated as a common criminal. Guarded only by a centurion, he had been able to come and go largely as he wished. And since Luke and others of his companions had been with him, he had profitably used the time to dictate letters to the churches established on his missionary journeys, counseling and strengthening them as only he could.

When the temple authorities had failed in their first attempt to have Paul turned over to them, they had not prosecuted the case any further. As a matter of fact, if Paul had not appealed to Rome, he might have been freed by the governor at Caesarea. But an appeal once made could not be retracted and, since his enemies at Jerusalem troubled him no more, Paul could be fairly sure that they would not go to the expense of sending

337

witnesses to Rome, especially in view of the ruling by Gallio in
Athens that the charges made there against him were not
offenses against Roman law.

The great "round" ship—distinguished from the swifter
"long" military galleys—followed the coast very closely, since
the winds were notoriously fickle in the eastern end of the
Mediterranean, and it was comforting to have a port near-by in
case of a storm. The quay and magnificent buildings of Caesarea
were still in sight when the great square sail was hoisted to
take advantage of the strong offshore breeze and the slaves
sweating at the oars were allowed to relax. Paul's eager gaze
was set ahead toward Rome and the new ministry he would
assume once he was freed by imperial decree; there was nothing
to hold him now in Caesarea or in Jerusalem.

After Caesarea, the ship touched at Sidon, the old Phoenician
port, and then ran across to Cyprus and the coast of Pamphylia
in the neighborhood of Paul's old port of entry into Asia Minor.
At Myra, they found another vessel waiting to sail to Italy and
Rome and took passage on it, quickly reaching a port called
Fair Havens on the southern coast of Crete.

The outbreak of winter was nearing now, and with the almost
certain prospect of stormy weather before they could reach
Rome, the master of the ship and the centurion Julius, who was
in charge of Paul and several other prisoners, discussed whether
to go on or remain in port, as was the custom during the winter
season with these vessels. Even though he was anxious to reach
Rome, Paul, having had some experience with the weather in
this area during his frequent voyages to the Macedonian ports,
argued against continuing. But the master of the ship was
anxious to push on and they sailed, following closely along the
coast of the island of Crete.

Soon a great storm arose and they were forced to run before
the wind, seeking the shelter of an island called Clauda. The
ship was heavily buffeted by the storm and the panic-stricken
crew were afraid it would fall apart, although they had stretched
rope trusses above the decks to hold the stem and stern together and keep it from breaking in the middle. The tempest
showed no sign of abating and they began to throw out cargo,

but this gave only a small amount of relief. Finally, when it seemed that all was lost, Paul had a dream in which an angel said: "Fear not, Paul. You must be brought before Caesar, and God has given you all them that sail with you."

Buoyed up by this assurance, they sailed on through raging seas for many days and nights, but when the sound of breakers beating upon the shore was heard one night, it was obvious that they had come dangerously close to the beach. Soundings showed a shelving beach and they tossed out four anchors to hold the ship until daylight; meanwhile some of the crew tried to use a boat to escape.

"Unless they stay in the ship you cannot be saved," Paul warned the centurion, so the soldiers cut the rope and let the boat fall away before the sailors could use it. When dawn broke, a small creek was visible ahead, and the master decided to enter it and drive the ship up on the shore.

This desperate stratagem might have succeeded if the vessel had not been caught between two currents which seized it and ran it aground upon the beach. The front part was tightly wedged in the sand, but the stern was still in the raging breakers and was quickly broken up. The soldiers wished to kill the prisoners lest they escape, but the centurion in charge would not give the order. Using broken pieces of the ship and other parts of the cargo upon which to float, the crew, prisoners, and soldiers finally managed to reach shore safely.

When the storm subsided, the shipwrecked party learned that they were upon the island of Melita, or Malta, a short distance south of Sicily and not more than a week's sail from Rome itself. It was threee months before they were able to take another ship, but during the winter Paul ministered to the sick and preached the gospel on the island of Malta, making many converts. When spring came, he and his party went on to Syracuse, a large city in the easternmost part of Sicily, and thence to Rhegium and finally to Rome.

Under Roman law, Paul's appeal to Caesar could not be heard until the details of the charges against him were forwarded from Jerusalem and Caesarea. Months passed and still these were not forthcoming, perhaps because neither Porcius

Festus nor King Agrippa II, who had examined Paul at Caesarea, had found any reason to accuse him under Roman law. While he waited—free except for his centurion guard—the Apostle to the Gentiles was not idle.

As always, Paul went first to the Jewish synagogues in Rome and spoke there. Many were converted to the new faith by his preaching but, as had happened in almost all the cities he visited, some refused to receive his teachings, and a controversy soon developed. Having no wish to become embroiled while waiting for the charges against him to be dismissed, Paul washed his hands, so to speak, of the Roman Jews and turned to the Gentiles.

Though technically a prisoner, the years spent in Rome were among the most productive of Paul's entire career. His pen was as ready as his tongue, and while there he wrote the letters to the young churches which are among the most eloquent documents ever composed, explaining the new faith and the reason for its wide appeal, as well as setting down the way in which Christians should live and work. To the church at Philippi particularly, he wrote in the warmth of his love and gratitude to those stalwart Christians for continuing to spread the word, even though he was no longer with them.

While in Rome, Paul converted a former slave, named Onesimus, who had escaped from his master, Philemon, at Colossae, near Ephesus. Paul convinced the slave that he should return to his master, but he also gave him a letter to Philemon setting forth eloquently the way in which the love preached by Jesus frees slaves and removes the right of one human being to degrade another.

As usual, while Paul was imprisoned in Caesarea, proselyters had been at work in the churches he had established in Asia Minor and Macedonia, teaching false doctrines and trying to lead the people away from the simple gospel he had preached. To the Colossians and the Ephesians he now wrote in detail.

"Be you therefore followers of God as dear children," he exhorted these beloved Christians. "And walk in love, as Christ also has loved us and has given himself for us as an offering and a sacrifice to God. Put on the whole armor of God, that you may be able to stand against the wiles of the devil. For we wrestle not against flesh and blood but against principalities, against powers, against the rulers of the darkness of this world, against spiritual wickedness in high places. Stand therefore, having your loins girded about with truth, and having on the breastplate of righteousness, and your feet shod with the preparation of the gospel of peace. Above all, take the shield of faith, wherewith you shall be able to quench all the fiery darts of the wicked. And take the helmet of salvation, and the sword of the Spirit, which is the word of God."

Both Paul and Peter—who also came to Rome later—were to need that armor and to wear it with honor. Rome was ruled now by the dissolute and cruel Nero, already showing signs of the insanity which would culminate in an orgy of persecution, when thousands of Christians would be used as human torches to light the games or sent unarmed into the arena to be torn by beasts.

Paul and Peter gave their lives in this orgy of persecution, but the glowing, eloquent, warmly sincere letters which the Apostle to the Gentiles wrote to his beloved converts throughout the world were preserved and have been a beacon light to Christians down the centuries. Like the man of Nazareth he served so faithfully and so well, Paul achieved immortality in the hearts of men through the church which he, more than any other man after Christ himself, served to found.

For the millions who were to find in his epistles comfort, inspiration, and assurance of God's second covenant of salvation and eternal life through his own Son, Paul wrote this benediction:

"Now the God of peace, that brought again from the dead our Lord Jesus, that great shepherd of the sheep, through the blood of the everlasting covenant, make you perfect in every good work to do his will, working in you that which is well-pleasing in his sight, through Jesus Christ; to whom be glory forever and ever. A-men."

# ACKNOWLEDGMENTS

To list here each of the hundreds of references consulted in creating a picture of the ancient world and retelling the story of the Hebrew-Christian faith from its beginnings through the missionary journeys of St. Paul is, of course, quite impractical. Certain volumes, however, have been invaluable to me and I would like to acknowledge my particular indebtedness to: *Story of the Bible World* by Nelson Beecher Keyes, C. S. Hammond & Co.; *Abraham, His Heritage and Ours* by Dorothy B. Hill, Beacon Press; *The Westminster Historical Atlas to the Bible*, The Westminster Press; *Encylclopedia of Bible Life* by Madeleine S. and J. Lane Miller, Harper & Brothers; *Archeology and the Old Testament* by James B. Pritchard, Princeton University Press; *The Bible as History* by Werner Keller, William Morrow & Co.; *Light from the Ancient Past* by Jack Finegan, Princeton University Press; *Daily Life in Bible Times* by Albert E. Bailey, Charles Scribner's Sons.

As in the case of my own Life of Christ, *The Crown and the Cross*, I have chosen to use only the King James Version of the Bible published by The World Publishing Company. In converting Biblical phraseology to dialogue, however, it has been necessary to adapt slightly some portions of the King James text. The original meanings have not been changed in any way, and any resemblance to editions other than the King James Version is purely accidental.

FRANK G. SLAUGHTER

Jacksonville, Florida
*January 6, 1960*

ABOUT THE AUTHOR

Frank G. Slaughter was born in Washington D. C., in 1908. At the age of only fourteen he entered college and graduated from Duke University in 1926 with a Phi Beta Kappa key. Four years later he graduated from Johns Hopkins Medical School, an "M.D." at the age of twenty-two. For many years, both as a civilian and then as a major and lieutenant colonel during World War II, Dr. Slaughter devoted himself to the practice of medicine. During these years he also began to write, and upon his release from military service at the end of the war, he decided to devote himself full time to the career of an author. Since the publication of his first book in 1941, Dr. Slaughter has become one of the most prolific men of letters of any century. In less than nineteen years he has produced twenty-nine books, drawing his inspiration from fields as diverse as modern medicine, Renaissance history, and the timeless and unlimited sources of the Bible. In his own country and abroad, books such as *In a Dark Garden, The Road to Bithynia,* and *The Mapmaker* have given pleasure to more than 20,000,000 readers.

Dr. Slaughter is also well known as the author of novels dealing particularly with Bible times, such as *The Galileans, The Song of Ruth,* and *The Thorn of Arimathea.* His interest in spiritual affairs extends to on occasion filling a church pulpit in the pastor's absence. From this background of research and activity, both *The Land and The Promise* and his story of the life of Jesus, *The Crown and The Cross,* have been written.

Dr. Slaughter lives now with his wife and two sons in Florida.

This book was set in

Electra and Perpetua types

by The Haddon Craftsmen.

It was printed and bound at

the press of The World Publishing Company.